F UCATION

A Basic Course
in Statistics
With Sociological Applications

INTERNATIONAL SERIES IN DECISION PROCESSES

INGRAM OLKIN, *Consulting Editor*

A Basic Course in Statistics, T. R. ANDERSON and M. ZELDITCH, JR.

FORTHCOMING TITLES

Probability Theory, H. TEICHER and Y. S. CHOU

Introductory Statistics, R. HULTQUIST

Statistics Handbook, I. OLKIN, J. LIEBERMAN, L. GLASER, C. DERMAN,
    A. MANDANSKY, M. SOBEL, and G. GOLOB

Introductory Probability, I. OLKIN, J. LIEBERMAN, L. GLASER,
    C. DERMAN, A. MANDANSKY, M. SOBEL, and G. GOLOB

Statistics Methods, I. OLKIN, J. LIEBERMAN, L. GLASER, C. DERMAN,
    A. MANDANSKY, M. SOBOL, and G. GOLOB

Applied Probability, W. THOMPSON, JR.

Statistics for Business Administration, W. HAYS and R. WINKLER

Analysis and Design of Experiments, M. ZELEN

Statistics for Psychologists 2d ed., W. HAYS

Decision Theory for Business, D. FELDMAN and E. SEIDEN

Elementary Statistical Methods 3d Ed., H. WALKER and J. LEV

Statistical Inference 2d ed., H. WALKER and J. LEV

Reliability Handbook, B. A. KOSLOV and I. A. USHAKOV (translated by
    J. Rosenblatt)

A Basic Course in Statistics

With Sociological Applications

SECOND EDITION

Theodore R. Anderson
University of Oregon

Morris Zelditch, Jr.
Stanford University

HOLT, RINEHART & WINSTON
London · New York · Sydney · Toronto

This edition not for sale in the United States
of America, its dependencies, or Canada
A HOLT INTERNATIONAL EDITION
First printed in Great Britain May 1971
Copyright © 1958, 1968 by Holt, Rinehart and Winston, Inc.
All Rights Reserved
Library of Congress Catalog Card Number: 68-19664
SBN 03 910121 5
Printed by offset by Butler & Tanner Ltd, Frome and London

PREFACE
to the SECOND EDITION

This book has been designed strictly as a textbook. It is not a reference work. We have avoided certain topics and treated others only in a very introductory way. Our basic objective has been to create a textbook that would show the typical undergraduate major or the beginning graduate student how the statistician analyzes data and draws inferences from those data. In this specific revision we have attempted to preserve the basic character of the original text while at the same time giving it a detailed revision. The most extensive change involves placing the *Workbook* under a separate cover. Since the *Workbook* is designed to be used in handing in assignments (by tearing out the appropriate pages), it tended to destroy the text when they were combined. Now they are separate. The most extensively revised part of the book is Part III, where we have gone into greater detail about the logical structure of inference. We wish to take this opportunity to thank the various people who have read the preliminary draft of this edition. Their suggestions and comments have been most useful. They are: Professors Richard J. Hill, Don McTavish, Robert H. West, Ingram Olkin, and Norman Washburne. We also wish to thank Rosanne Polson, Helen Wiley, and Kay Winn who have contributed to the completion of the text in many ways, from typing to proofing to indexing. Finally, we want to thank Professor Robert A. Ellis who provided a place with many conveniences where the revision was written. In one way or another, all of these people have improved this edition. They are not, of course, responsible for any remaining errors or obscurities.

I am indebted to the Literary Executor of the late Sir Ronald A. Fisher, F. R. S., to Dr. Frank Yates, F. R. S., and to Oliver & Boyd, Ltd., Edinburgh, for permission to reprint Tables III and IV from their book *Statistical Tables for Biological, Agricultural, and Medical Research.*

Eugene, Oregon   T. R. A.

Stanford, California   M. Z., Jr.

March 1968

PREFACE

to the FIRST EDITION

This is probably among the most elementary of all elementary texts on statistics. The book is designed with the specific and pleasant intention of attracting the student who is frightened of mathematics. There is no mathematical derivations whatsoever in the text. We presume only some knowledge of arithmetic.

Yet the book is built around what appears to be a paradoxical conjunction of purposes. On the one hand we want to be elementary, but on the other hand, we want to be advanced. We intend to dispense with mathematical derivations; yet we want to say something about the mathematical theory underlying statistical techniques. Almost every serious student of the application of statistics recognizes the essential part that knowledge of this theory plays in the choice of appropriate techniques. Mood, we think, expresses it well:

> The use of statistical tools is not merely a matter of picking out the wrench that fits the bolt; it is more a matter of selecting the correct one of several wrenches which appear to fit the bolt about equally well, but none of which fit it exactly . . . there is nothing magic about the [algebraic] formula; it is merely a tool, and, moreover, a tool derived from some simple mathematical model which cannot possibly represent the actual situation with any great precision. In using the tool one must make a whole series of judgements relative to the nature and magnitude

of the various errors engendered by the discrepancy between the model and the actual experiment. [Mood, 1950, pp. 5–6.]

The central problem of the application of statistics is in the relation of model to practical circumstance. By "model" we mean the definitions and assumptions which the mathematician makes in order to create the statistical methods we use. It is from these definitions and assumptions that he is able to derive the principles of practical procedure, the formulas, the tables, etc., that make up the statistician's working tools. The model is prerequisite to precise conclusions. Nevertheless, it sometimes involves assumptions about the actual situation that are so far from being fulfilled that to apply methods based on the model is both pretentious and useless. This happens to be the case, for instance, in the application of some of the more rigorous and powerful techniques to sociological problems.

Statisticians themselves are well aware of this problem, and they are aware, furthermore, that they should communicate an understanding of it to others. Their usual form of communication, however, is mathematics; and the attractions of mathematics—elegance, power, precision—are not easily given up by those who have managed to perceive them. Thus the assumptions underlying a given mathematical model are frequently treated as part of its advanced mathematics. As descriptions of statistical techniques gradually filter down to those who have to apply them, somehow these assumptions begin to drop out of the discussion until at the most elementary level they disappear from sight. The really interested student is expected to master the mathematics of the subject in order to arrive at a more fundamental understanding of it.

In this book we take a different view. We may be wrong, of course. But the book was undertaken with the idea that even the most elementary and mathematically unprepared student can, and should, learn from the very beginning the conditions under which the more popular methods can and cannot be applied. Our entire interest, of course, is devoted to techniques appropriate to sociological data; this dominates to a large extent the choice of emphasis. In particular, this specific interest has led us to give a great deal of attention to attributes and orders. This is, clearly, a book for sociologists. But more important, it is a book in which we are concerned, throughout, that the student should learn how to recognize just when to apply a given technique and when not to, and to understand what kinds of assumptions are implied in the application.

I am indebted to Professor Sir Ronald A. Fisher, Cambridge, to Dr. Frank Yates, Harpenden, and to Messrs. Oliver & Boyd Ltd., Edinburgh, for permission to reprint in the appendix the chi-square and *t*-tables from their book, *Statistical Tables for Biological, Agricultural and Medical Research.*

I am more than usually indebted to those who have read and offered suggestions for the book, among them: W. J. Goode, Jiri Nehnevajsa, Hanan Selvin, Leda Burnshaw, and John Meyer.

Columbia University M. Z., Jr.

April 1958

ACKNOWLEDGMENTS

Grateful acknowledgment is made to the following authors and publishers for their permission to reproduce material from their publications.

Reprinted from *Voting* by B. R. Berelson, P. E. Lazarfeld, and W. N. McPhee by permission of The University of Chicago Press. Copyright 1954 by the University of Chicago.

Reprinted with permission of the Macmillan Company from *Social Statistics* by H. M. Blalock. © The Free Press, a Corporation 1956.

Reprinted from *Dynamics of Bureaucracy* by P. M. Blau by permission of The University of Chicago Press. Copyright 1955 by the University of Chicago.

Blau, P. M., W. W. Heydebrand, and R. E. Stauffer, "The Structure of Small Bureaucracies," *American Sociological Review,* XXXI (1966), 179–191.

Reprinted from "Marital Selection and Occupational Strata" by R. Centers by permission of The University of Chicago Press. Copyright 1949 by the University of Chicago.

Edwards, A. L. *Statistical Methods for the Behavioral Sciences.* New York: Holt, Rinehart and Winston, Inc., 1955.

Fisher, R. A., and Yates, F. *Statistical Tables for Biological, Agricultural and Medical Research.* London: Oliver and Boyd, Ltd., 1948.

Gorden, R. L. "Interaction between Attitude and the Definition of the Situation in the Expression of Opinion," *American Sociological Review,* XVII (1952), 50–58.

Johnson, B. "Theology and Party Preference among Protestant Clergymen," *American Sociological Review,* XXXI (1966), 200–208.

Sewell, W. H., and J. M. Armer, "Neighborhood Context and College Plans," *American Sociological Review,* XXXI (1966), 159–168.

From *Nonparametric Statistics for the Behavioral Sciences* by S. Siegel. Copyright 1956 New York. Used by permission of McGraw-Hill Book Company.

U.S. Bureau of the Census. *Census of Population, 1950. U.S. Census of Population, 1960. Current Population Reports, 1967.* U.S. Government Printing Office, Washington, D.C.

U.S. Department of Health, Education and Welfare; Public Health Service, National Health Survey, Series B—No. 37.

Reprinted with permission of The Macmillan Company from *Statistics, A New Approach* by W. A. Wallis and H. V. Roberts. © The Free Press, a Corporation 1956.

The World Almanac, 1963. New York: New York World Telegram.

From pp. 182–192 of *Say It with Figures,* Rev. 4th Edition, by Hans Zeisel. Copyright 1947, 1950, 1957 by Harper & Row, Publishers, Incorporated. Used by permission of the publishers.

Zetterberg, H. L. "Cohesiveness as a Unitary Concept," 1952.

Zurcher, L. A., Jr., A. Meadow, and S. L. Zurcher, "Value Orientation, Role Conflict, and Alienation from Work: A Cross-Cultural Study," *American Sociological Review,* XXX (1965), 539–548.

CONTENTS

1

SOME BASIC CONCEPTS

It has proved troublesome to define the term "statistics" and so we shall not try to give a precise definition of the field here. In even the most elegant and advanced treatises only rather vague definitions are provided. Instead, we borrow a phrase from Mood: "The statistician is . . . engaged in producing tools for research workers." (1950, p. 4)* The purpose of this text is to convey as simply as possible some idea of how these tools are to be used.

1.1 A SIMPLE STATISTICAL INVESTIGATION

Assume for the moment that we are interested in finding out how many people in New York City belong to voluntary associations, what kinds of association are involved, and perhaps what motivated the people to join. Ordinarily, faced with this kind of problem, we would interview individual people and ask each one to give us the relevant information about himself. However, we would *not* think of interviewing each and every person in New York City. Instead we would plan to question, say, 2000 people. We call these 2000 persons a *sample* and we call the eight million or so residents of the city a *population* or *universe*. (We shall use the term "population" throughout this text.)

A *population* is any total collection of persons, or objects, or events in

* We shall follow the practice of citing sources by giving name of author, date, and page or table number. The full citation will be found in the section on "Bibliography and References" at the end of the text.

which we are interested. Since we are going to observe these entities, we also refer to the collection of all of the observations in which we are interested as a population of observations.

A *sample* is any subset of persons, objects, or events selected from the population or any subset of the relevant observations.

By following certain rules in selecting the sample it is possible to make some general statements about the eight million in the population on the basis of the 2000 persons who were chosen to represent them. Of course, statements derived from the sample of 2000 persons will not be exactly correct for the population. There will be some degree of error or uncertainty in our conclusions. However, when the sample is selected properly, we will be able to state very exactly just how precise each of our statements is and just how certain our conclusions are. (How to select a sample in a proper manner will be considered in Chapter 10. Unless these or similar procedures are followed, little or nothing can be said reliably about the population.)

Suppose that we ask each member of our sample the following questions:
> In what year and month were you born?
> What was your total income from all sources last year?
> Do you own a television set?
> To what voluntary associations do you belong? (Please list them individually.)
> (After respondent stops) Are there any others?

The answers to these questions are called a set of observations. Statistical analysis ordinarily begins with such a set. The crucial property of these observations is that they can be converted into numbers of some sort. Some observations, such as ages and incomes, are numerical because they are *measurements*. Other observations are numerical because we *count* the number of times that something occurred. For example, we might count the voluntary associations on each respondent's list and record the *number* of associations to which he belongs. Since we ask the same questions of every respondent, we can also meaningfully count the number of times that each answer occurs in our sample. The result of such a count is called a *frequency*. Thus, we can count the number of times that the response "Yes" occurred in answer to the question on television ownership. This counting operation generates the frequency of television ownership in the sample.

In sociological research it is often the case that most observations can only be counted. Sometimes this statement is true even when the original observations appear to be numerical. A house address, for example, is usually expressed as a number (such as 2605 Riverside Drive). To add such numbers or to compute the "average" address would, of course, be meaning-less. However, we can convert an address into "distance from city center" through the use of a map and this number can be treated meaningfully by statistical procedures. The researcher's first problem, then, may be to transform observations into quantitative form either through measurement or counting and, thereby, to permit statistical analysis.

Let us suppose that we have gathered a set of observations. The problem now is, what shall we do with these data? It is with this kind of problem that statistics is directly concerned. The researcher who uses statistics usually goes through at least two steps: he summarizes the data and he draws inferences from his summary statements. Let us consider these two steps in greater detail.

The first step is to *summarize* the set of observations into some simple and convenient form. The principles behind this act of summarization (or data reduction as it is sometimes called) are customarily referred to as the principles of *descriptive* statistics. These principles are developed out of the concept of a *characteristic*. A characteristic is one single *kind* of information. For example, the answers to the birthday question mentioned earlier can be used to identify the *age* of each respondent. Age is a single kind of information and is, therefore, a characteristic. Similarly, the answers to the question "Do you own a television set?" all refer to the same thing and hence represent a single characteristic.

In summarizing observations we first divide them into the various characteristics that they represent. When we are concerned with only one characteristic, such as age, we say that we have *univariate* data or univariate observations. When we are concerned with two characteristics, such as age and television ownership, we say that we have *bivariate* data or bivariate observations. When we are concerned with more than two characteristics, such as age, television ownership, and voluntary association memberships, we say that we have *multivariate* data or multivariate observations. Descriptive statistics is concerned with summarizing the information that we have about characteristics no matter how many characteristics there are.

The general summarization problem is solved through working with what is called the *distribution* of the characteristic in the sample or population. A distribution contains two elements. First, it contains a list of the particular observations that can be made on each characteristic. If the characteristic is *age,* for example, the list simply contains the various ages that can occur in the population. If the characteristic is television ownership the list is the set of responses to the question on ownership, such as "Yes" and "No." Second, the distribution contains the frequency with which each and every response occurred in the sample or population. In the case of age these frequencies would identify the number of people in the sample who are 21 years old, the number who are 22 years old, and so on. In the case of television ownership, the frequencies would refer to the number of owners and the number of nonowners in the sample. In short, then, the distribution describes the frequency with which each different observation (or response category) occurs in the sample or population. In the pages that follow we shall go into much greater detail on the subject of distributions and how to work with them. Virtually all of the concepts of descriptive statistics represent ways of summarizing the information contained in distributions, whether those distributions be univariate, bivariate, or multivariate in form.

The second step in statistical analysis is to draw inferences from our observations or summaries. Usually we want information not only about the particular sample that we have actually observed (such as the 2000 respondents to our interviews) but also about the population from which the sample was drawn (such as the more than eight million residents of New York City). The principles that permit us to use our sample to say something about the population from which it was drawn are called the principles of *statistical inference*. These principles are based upon the theory of probability and can tell us how much error there is in generalizing from the sample to the population. The process of generalization is technically referred to as statistical *estimation*. As we shall see later, however, we can determine errors of this type only if we have drawn the sample in a certain way.

Statistical inference is also used to solve another kind of problem. We may think that we already know something about the population and want to *test* our ideas to see if they are really sensible. In the language of statistics this operation is called *hypothesis testing*. In statistical analysis hypotheses are tested by drawing a sample and determining whether or not the observations in the sample are consistent with the hypotheses about what exists in the population. It turns out that the same probability theory that permits us to make estimates of population values also permits us to test ideas or hypotheses about those population values.

1.2 HOW THE BOOK IS ORGANIZED

In relation to the above ideas this book is organized as follows. The remaining sections of this chapter show how to classify characteristics and how to present simple distributions in the form of tables. Part I of the book (Chapters 2 through 5) presents the principles of descriptive statistics as applied to observations of a single characteristic. In the language of statistics this part is concerned with describing univariate distributions. Part II (Chapters 6 through 9) contains the principles of descriptive statistics as applied to observations of more than one kind, which is to say, as applied to bivariate and multivariate distributions. When observations are made on more than one kind of information, we are usually interested in identifying how the various characteristics are *related* to each other. Part II can be interpreted, using this phraseology, as discussing the principles used to describe relationships among characteristics. As this book is introductory in nature, most of our attention will be directed to the bivariate distribution. Only in Chapter 9, the final chapter of this part, will basic multivariate problems be presented. Extensive and detailed discussions of multivariate problems lie in the province of more advanced texts. Part III of this book (Chapters 10 through 13) will consider various elementary problems in statistical inference. Since sociologists use statistical inference more commonly to test hypotheses than to make population estimates we shall stress hypothesis testing in this, the final, part of the book.

1.3 A NOTE ON THE NEXT SECTION

The next section is crucial for anyone who wants to get beyond the most elementary stage of statistics. Unfortunately, however, the information contained in that section is easily lost or overlooked by the beginner. The only purpose of the present section is to comment on why the next section is emphasized.

Theoretical or mathematical statistics consists of a number of precisely formulated mathematical models. The central problem of application is to understand the relation of these models to the given practical research situation. Ordinarily there are several models that *might* help in solving the practical or applied problem. One of the most important things for the student of applied statistics to learn is how to select the most appropriate method or model from among those that are available. Computational procedures can be filed away and pulled out when they are needed but it is of immediate importance to learn to ask, as well as to answer, the question: What statistical models or designs can I use in attempting to solve this problem and what assumptions must I make in using each one?

The next section is decisive in getting off to the right start by answering this question. It identifies what the student must know about his characteristics or kinds of information in order to determine what methods can appropriately be used to analyze them. Unfortunately, a method that is appropriate for one kind of observation may not be appropriate for another.

1.4 TYPES OF CHARACTERISTICS AND SIMPLE TABLES

Characteristics are usually classified in two ways: (1) according to the number of different observations that can be or have been made and

(2) according to the level of measurement used in making the observations. We shall discuss each of these in turn.

The different observations of a single characteristic are called its *classes,* its *categories,* or its *values.* In this way we refer to "Yes" and "No" as response *categories* and to particular ages, such as "21 years of age" and "73 years of age," as *values* of the characteristic, age. To classify the number of *different* observations of a characteristic is to classify the number of its categories or values. When a characteristic has only two categories or values it is called a *dichotomy.* When it has more than two it is called a *polytomy* or a *manifold classification.* Since a person either owns or does not own a television set, that characteristic is a dichotomy. On the other hand, since an individual may be any one of many ages we say that age is, potentially at least, a polytomy. What is usually important, however, is not how many categories or values there might be, but rather how many *are actually being used* by the researcher in recording his observations. If we classify age into categories such as "0 to 10 years old," "10 to 20 years old," "20 to 30 years old," and "30 or more years old," we are using a manifold classification because we are using four categories to record our observations; whereas, if we specify the categories "under 21" and "21 or over" we are using a dichotomy because only two categories are being recorded. When we take a characteristic (such as age) that potentially has many categories or values and divide all the observations into only two categories, we say that we have dichotomized the characteristic. This operation is reasonably common in sociological research.

With respect to levels of measurement, characteristics are usually divided into three general classes: (1) nominal characteristics or attributes, (2) ordinal characteristics (sometimes called quasivariables), and (3) interval characteristics (sometimes simply called variables). An attribute is a characteristic whose categories differ according to *what* is possessed, whereas an ordinal or interval variable is a characteristic whose categories differ according to *how much* of some one thing is possessed.

Attributes

The simplest kind of attribute is called an *all-or-none* attribute. It is a classification of all members of the sample or population into two and only two classes, on the basis of whether some one thing is possessed or not possessed. It is, therefore, a dichotomy. An individual is either blind or not blind, either owns a television set or does not own one, either is married or is not married. These characteristics are, therefore, all-or-none attributes. On the other hand, it is common to work with dichotomies that are *not* attributes. For instance, we might classify people by education (a variable) into two categories, "less than 12 years of education" and "12 or more years of education." Here we clearly have a dichotomy, since there are only two classes, but we are *not* dealing with an attribute, since both classes involve some education, but the second class involves more than the first.

An interesting problem occurs in the case of an attribute such as sex, with its categories "male" and "female." Clearly, a female is something other than just a "not-male," although it turns out that practically all people who are not males are, in fact, females. Sex is ordinarily treated as a dichotomy because only two categories or classes are normal, although other classes do occur occasionally, even in human populations; for example, the biological phenomenon of the hermaphrodite and the social phenomenon of the eunuch or castrated male. Furthermore, sex is clearly an attribute since there is no question about the quantity of any one thing that is possessed. Technically, however, if this characteristic is treated as a true all-or-none attribute, its classes should be either "male" and "not-male" or "female" and "not-female," whichever the individual prefers. When the categories "male" and "female" are both used each category possesses something not possessed by the other. In this case the attribute is a compound one, which just happens to possess only two classes in most relevant populations. The general point is that in a true all-or-none attribute the members of one class possess some particular thing not possessed by members of the other class.

The distribution of an all-or-none attribute in a population (or sample) is usually presented in the form of a table. The central part of such a table lists, first, each class or category and, second, the frequency with which each class occurs in the population. The main part looks like this (note that the table in this form is still incomplete—see below):

Class	Frequency
A	n_A
not-A	$n_{\text{not-}A}$
Total	N

In this representation of the distribution:

(1) the words "class" and "frequency" are column *headings,*

(2) A and *not-A* identify the two classes,

(3) n_A and $n_{\text{not-}A}$ identify the number of individuals in each class, and

(4) N stands for the total number of individuals in the population.

Notice that N is the sum of n_A and $n_{\text{not-}A}$.

As an example, we might be interested in the information contained in the following table:

Table 1.1   Employment status of the civilian labor
force of the United States, July 1962

Status	Frequency
Employed	69,564,000
Unemployed	4,018,000
Total	73,582,000

SOURCE: *The World Almanac,*
1963, New York, New York
World Telegram, p. 251.

Notice that the full table contains a *table number*, a *title*, and the *source* of
the information in addition to the classes and frequencies. The title should
identify the population (or sample) as well as the characteristic whose
distribution is reported.

Two or more all-or-none attributes may sometimes be combined into a
single classification system, which we shall call a *compound attribute*. This
combination is legitimate whenever the phenomena that are present in the
all-or-none attributes are *mutually exclusive*. Two classes are mutually exclusive (or exclusive of each other) if they cannot occur simultaneously in
the same object, event, or observation. For example, religious beliefs and
preferences are exclusive of each other or mutually exclusive. To be a
Lutheran implies that you are not a Catholic. To be a Jew implies that you
are not a Christian or a Buddhist. Because they are mutually exclusive, such
a set of all-or-none attributes may be combined into a single characteristic
called religion or religious preference. Thus, a classification of religions into
five categories (say, Protestant, Catholic, Jew, Other, and None) is equivalent to a classification using four all-or-none attributes, namely:

Protestant versus Non-Protestant
Catholic   versus Non-Catholic
Jew   versus Non-Jew
Other   versus Non-other

Notice that the number of all-or-none attributes is one less than the number
of categories in the compound attribute. The reason is that the final category
in the compound attribute (namely, "none") is contained in the negation
of all of the four all-or-none attributes.

The compound attribute is an example of what is called a manifold
classification or polytomy. Attributes of this type are quite common in

sociology; familiar examples include classifications of religions, occupations, and countries (or regions within a country).

The table of the distribution of a compound attribute (or any other manifold classification) looks much like the table of the distribution of an all-or-none attribute. In general, the symbols A_1, A_2, A_3, . . . ,A_k stand for the various categories and n_1, n_2, n_3, . . . ,n_k for the corresponding frequencies. The number of categories is symbolized by the letter k. The numbers 1, 2, 3, . . . k are called *subscripts* and identify the particular categories. Thus, A_k is the last category in the list. A typical example of a compound attribute is shown in Table 1.2.

Table 1.2   Arrests in 1961 in urban places of the
United States* by offense charged

Offense charged	Number of arrests
Criminal homicide	6,243
Forcible rape	7,143
Robbery	33,175
Aggravated assault	55,355
Other assaults	143,784
Burglary and theft	413,091
Embezzlement and fraud	34,286
Drunkenness	1,399,293
All other offenses	1,597,839
Suspicion	125,616
Total	3,815,825

SOURCE: *The World Almanac, 1963.* Adapted from
table on page 311.
* In 2776 cities with over 2500 population. Total
population in these reporting cities is 85,158,360.

The offenses along the stub (the names of the classes or categories listed in a table are called its stub) of this table form a compound attribute.

Ordinal Characteristics

The term "ordinal" in statistics is used to refer to sets of categories or classes that differ from each other in the amount of some one element possessed but where the amounts have *not* been measured with what is called an equal interval scale. When we discuss interval scales in the next section the distinction between ordinal and interval measurement will become clear. In this section, however, we shall concentrate on the distinction between ordinal characteristics and attributes. One common way in which ordinal measurement is utilized is when the amounts possessed are measured through subjective judgments. No ruler or thermometer can measure happiness, for example, though it is usually possible to judge which of two persons is the happier. When such judgments are made throughout a sample, the individuals might be classified as being "very happy," "happy," "of average happiness," "unhappy," and "very unhappy." These categories form an ordinal characteristic or variable that can be called happiness.

The key feature that distinguishes the ordinal characteristic from the compound attribute is that all of the categories of the ordinal characteristic represent different quantities or magnitudes of the same thing. The categories of an ordinal characteristic, therefore, can always be arranged *in order of magnitude* (hence the term "ordinal"). Furthermore, these categories can always be designated by some abstract terms referring to different quantities, such as

> small, medium, large
> poor, fair, good, excellent
> few, many

In each of these series a word at the right represents a greater quantity than any word to its left. Thus, "medium" represents a greater quantity than "small" and, of course, "large" represents a greater quantity than either "medium" or "small."

The method of distinguishing between compound attributes and ordinal characteristics or variables should now be clear. Remember that the categories of any compound attribute can be visualized as a series of *all-or-none* attributes. On the other hand, the categories of any ordinal variable can be visualized abstractly as a series of different quantities. To determine whether any given classification scheme represents a compound attribute or an ordinal characteristic, then, simply determine which image is appropriate. In effect, this procedure involves asking: (1) "Do these categories represent different quantities of the same thing?" (If "Yes," the classification is of an ordinal variable.) (2) "Do these categories each represent the presence of some different thing?" (If "Yes," then the classification is a compound attribute.)

Let us consider a few examples. Consider a classification often referred to as "education" or "level of education" with these categories: grade school, high school, college. We identify this classification as an ordinal characteristic because the categories differ in the *quantity* of education or the number of years of schooling possessed. Then consider a classification of specific occupations, such as: grocer, banker, farmer, or welder. This classification refers to a compound attribute because each category refers to a different role, which is either performed or not performed by an individual. Hence the classification could meaningfully be broken down into a series of *all-or-none* attributes.

At this point it is necessary to call attention to a semantic problem that is often confusing to the beginning student. *Any* classification system can be dichotomized. Further, the two resulting categories can always be referred to as *A* and *not-A*. To distinguish between an attribute and an ordinal variable, then, it is necessary to probe more deeply to determine whether the phrase "not-A" refers to the absence of *A* or to a different quantity of *A*. For example, we can dichotomize level of education in any one of several ways, one of which is "grade school" and "not grade school." Superficially it would appear that we have an all-or-none dichotomy here. However, a more careful analysis reveals that the phrase "not grade school" means *more* education than a grade school education and, therefore, refers to a difference in quantity rather than true presence or absence. (There is, of course, one all-or-none attribute that can be formed with respect to education, namely: "some formal education" and "no formal education.") The important thing to remember is that the categories of an ordinal variable all refer to different quantities of the same element whereas the categories of a compound attribute refer to the presence or absence of a series of different things.

The distribution of an ordinal variable is presented in tabular form in much the same way as is a compound attribute. In particular, the table still contains two columns; one names the categories and the other identifies the frequency of occurrence of each category in some population or sample. The only restriction on this form of presentation is that the categories of the ordinal characteristic *must be listed in order with respect to quantity.* (In contrast, the categories of a compound attribute may be listed in any order whatever.) For example, consider the following two lists of categories:

grade school	high school
high school	grade school
college	graduate school
graduate school	college

The list on the left is in order, whereas the list on the right is out of order and, therefore, is an incorrect listing. Notice that the list can proceed either from low to high or from high to low. Thus, another correct listing of these categories would be

graduate school
college
high school
grade school

Both of these correct arrangements will be found in the sociological literature.

Interval Characteristics

When quantities are measured through the use of some instrument or scale possessing a constant interval (such as a ruler, a clock, or a counting procedure in which identical objects are counted), it is possible to identify both the order among the observations and the *distance* between each pair of observations. Characteristics measured in this way are called *interval variables* and observations resulting from the use of such measuring instruments are collectively referred to as *interval data*. The term "interval" is used to describe these data because a given interval means the same thing wherever it occurs. For example, a mile involves precisely the same distance whether it is the first mile on a trip or the hundredth mile. Similarly, $10 is the same quantity of money whether it is added to $50 or to $75,000. Put slightly differently, the difference or interval between $75,010 and $75,000 is precisely the same as the difference or interval between $60 and $50. In both of these cases (miles and dollars) a given interval (or difference between observations) means the same thing at any point along the scale. The reason is that a measuring instrument with a single basic interval has been used to take the measurements or observations. Thus, a ruler has a single basic interval called an inch, which is repeated over and over to form the total scale. Similarly, a single unit called a dollar is used over and over to form a monetary scale.

The most important property of interval observations is that we can perform simple arithmetic operations such as addition and subtraction upon them. Consider, for example, the observations: $100 $300 $400. We can add $100 to $300 and get $400. We can do this operation because a dollar between 100 and 300 is the same as a dollar between 300 and 400.

Notice that we cannot add observations to each other when all we have is ordinal information. Thus, it is essentially meaningless to say that *poor* plus *fair* equals *good*. We can only compare ordinal observations as to size or quantity but we can add interval observations.

Interval observations are not too common in sociology. They occur typically in one of the following two ways:

1. We count something and assume that each unit counted is the same quantity as each other unit counted. We count dollars, for example, and arrive at a measure of *income*. We count people in a family and arrive at a measure of the *size* of the family. We count the number of people in a city and arrive at a measure of the population size or simply the *population* of the city.

2. We measure something using either a clock or a ruler, or any other instrument that possesses a basic constant unit which is repeated throughout the scale. For example, we measure the number of miles that a house is from the center of a city and arrive at a measure of *distance*. We ask a person to tell us how old he is and arrive at a measure of the time that has passed since he was born, which we call his *age*.

There are two important types of interval variable—*discrete* variables and *continuous* variables.

Discrete variables possess an elementary interval that cannot itself be subdivided. For example, when we measure the size of a family by counting the number of individuals in it, the elementary interval is a single person. This interval cannot be subdivided; there is no such thing as half a person. Observations of discrete variables can only be integer multiples of this elementary unit. Thus, a great many real numbers (such as fractions) cannot appear as observations.

Continuous variables are variables such that any interval can itself be subdivided. Therefore, any real number is a possible observation. Time and distance are examples of such indefinitely subdivisible measurements, and there are many others, such as weight, temperature, amount of energy expended in a given activity, and electric potential.

Concluding Comments on Characteristics

It should be noted that there is a certain order among the three main types of characteristic. An attribute identifies whether or not each of several mutually exclusive phenomena is present in an individual. An ordinal variable identifies the relative quantity of some one phenomenon present in an individual. An interval variable identifies relative quantity and also the *amount* by which one quantity is greater than another. This hierarchy is important primarily for one reason; a characteristic can always be reduced to a lower level on the hierarchy but it cannot automatically be raised to a higher level. In this sense we refer to the three types of characteristic as three levels of measurement. One important application of this hierarchical principle will become clear in the next few chapters, which are concerned with summarizing distributions at each of these three levels. As we shall see, any technique that summarizes the distribution of a characteristic on a lower level of the hierarchy will also summarize the distribution of a characteristic on a higher level, but not the converse. Thus, if a technique is suitable for the distribution of an attribute, it will also be suitable for the distribution of an ordinal variable and an interval variable. However, the techniques that are especially suited to interval observations cannot be used either with orders or attributes.

One final point is in order concerning nomenclature. The word "variable" is used in different senses in different books. On the one hand, a variable is any characteristic whose value changes from one individual to another within the population being studied (as opposed to a constant, which remains the same throughout the population). On the other hand, a variable is sometimes restricted to ordinal and interval characteristics as distinct from attributes. In the first sense we speak of variables versus constants and in the second sense we speak of variables versus attributes. Both meanings are sensible and they will both be used in this text. In the earlier portions of the text we use the term "variable" in the second sense and will, therefore, refer to attributes as distinct from variables. In the later portions of the text (after the distinction between attributes and ordinal or interval variables is clear) we shall use the term in the first sense.

When we use the term "variable" in its more general sense of any characteristic whose values vary within the population or sample we are studying, then we can treat an attribute in a slightly different way. In particular, an all-or-none attribute can be called a *dummy variable* in which the presence of the phenomenon is represented by the quantity "1" and the absence of it by the quantity "0." For example, if the attribute's categories are Protestant and Non-Protestant, we record the value "1" whenever we observe a Protestant and the value "0" whenever we observe a Non-Protestant. When we use this convention, a compound attribute must be represented as a series of all-or-none attributes. We would then refer to dummy variables, ordinal variables, and interval variables as the three levels in the hierarchy of characteristics.

1.5 WHERE WE STAND

Let us briefly review this chapter. Statistics is concerned with the distribution of one or more characteristics in a population. Usually we observe only a *sample* of that population. One basic problem in statistics is to summarize or describe in a succinct manner the information contained in our observations of the sample or population. Another basic problem, when only a sample is available, is to make inferences from that sample to the population. In sociology we generally use the principles of statistical inference to test hypotheses about what the population is like.

The kinds of statistics or summary measures that we use will depend primarily upon (1) how many characteristics we are considering at once and (2) at what level these characteristics have been identified or measured. When our interest centers on a single characteristic we say that we have a univariate distribution. When our interest concerns two characteristics we say that we have a bivariate distribution and we are very likely to be interested primarily in how the two characteristics are related to each other. When our interest concerns more than two characteristics we have a multivariate distribution in mind. The first two parts of this book show how to describe univariate and bivariate distributions and also provide some elementary information about multivariate distributions. The third part of the book is concerned with the problem of statistical inference.

We have seen that there are three major types of characteristic: the attribute (or dummy variable), the ordinal variable, and the interval variable. Each type refers to a way in which observations have been recorded or measured. It is very important that the student be familiar with the ways of distinguishing among these types because the kinds of description that can be used to summarize a distribution depend upon the type of characteristic being studied. What is appropriate for one type may be very inappropriate for another.

part I

Summarizing and Describing Univariate Distributions

2

MEASURES ESPECIALLY
APPROPRIATE
TO ATTRIBUTES

The first step in dealing with observations is to assemble and organize them. The next step is to summarize or condense the information contained in them. Even with the simplest set of observations we have to do something in order to make use of the set. Procedures for organizing and summarizing data are called descriptive statistics. We shall consider the description of univariate data in this part of the book.

In Chapter 1 we divided characteristics into three main types: attributes, ordinal variables, and interval variables. We also noted that these types form a hierarchy which may be visualized in terms of level of measurement. Attributes stand at the lowest level since they involve only the identification of whether or not a given property is present in an individual. This level of measurement is sometimes also called the *nominal* level since the classes are described in terms of the name of the property. Ordinal variables stand at the next level since they involve knowledge of the *relative* quantity of the property present in each individual who is observed. Finally, interval variables stand at the highest level since they involve knowledge of *how much* more of a given property is possessed by one individual than another.

This hierarchy is very important because the level of measurement of a variable can always be reduced by ignoring the extra knowledge implied by the given level. On the other hand, the level of measurement can never be increased—except by major scientific innovation or discovery. What these statements mean in practice is that any method appropriate to the description of attributes may also be used for ordinal variables and interval variables. Similarly, any method appropriate to the description of ordinal variables may also be used for interval variables. However, these statements cannot be reversed. Some techniques that are very useful in describing

19

interval data *cannot* be applied to either ordinal data or to attributes. And some techniques that are very useful in describing ordinal data *cannot* be applied to attributes.

In this chapter we shall see how statisticians organize and summarize the information contained in the distribution of an attribute. These techniques are the most elementary ways of describing any univariate distribution. In general, the procedures involve only the simplest actions on the part of the researcher; he need be able to perform only the following two operations:

1. He must be able, for each and every individual member of his sample or population, to distinguish between the presence and the absence of each property in which he is interested.

2. He must be able to *count*; in particular, to count the number of times that he observed each property to be present and the number of times that he observed it to be absent.

2.1 UNGROUPED OR RAW DATA

When observations are first reported they ordinarily are recorded individually. The resulting set of observations is called an *ungrouped* set. In the case of attributes it is convenient to let the letter A stand for an observation of the property and A' (read *not-A*) stand for an observation of its absence. A listing of the individual observations as they occur is called a set of *raw data*. Such a set might look like this:

$$A, A', A, A, A', A, A', A', A', A', A, A, A, A', A, A$$

This list means that the first observation was an A, the second one was not an A (or was a *not-A*), and so on. Ordinarily, the raw observations would not be listed across a page as was done here but would be recorded on individual questionnaire forms or on IBM cards. When the observations are recorded on IBM cards, the presence of the property may be symbolized by the 1-punch and the absence of the property by the 0-punch. In that case, this same set of observations would look like this:

$$1, 0, 1, 1, 0, 1, 0, 0, 0, 0, 1, 1, 1, 0, 1, 1$$

(Any pair of numbers would be used for this purpose but the numbers "0" and "1" are the simplest and most convenient.)

When data have been recorded in ungrouped form the first operation has been completed; that is, the presence or absence of the property has been listed for each and every case in the sample or population. The observations have been assembled, at least in a preliminary way.

2.2 GROUPING THE OBSERVATIONS

Ungrouped observations are hard to interpret. Lists of symbols or numbers such as the above are very difficult to read in any meaningful sense. To bring out the important aspects of a distribution, the researcher ordinarily *counts the number of times that each symbol appears on the list* and records the results of his counts in the form of a table. This operation is called *grouping* the data. As we saw in Chapter 1, the table contains a number, a title, a column listing the different categories of the characteristic, another column listing the frequency of occurrence of each category, and (unless clear from the context) the source of the information.

Tables of this type are usually constructed in two stages. In the first stage the raw observations are *tallied,* that is, recorded on a tally sheet. In the second stage the tallies are converted into the frequencies of the table itself. Tallying involves, first, listing the various different observations that can occur and, second, recording each observation that *did* occur as a tally mark to the right of the appropriate symbol on the list. For example, the raw data presented above would produce the following tally sheet:

Category	Tallies
A	ⅢⅣ ⅢⅠ
A'	ⅢⅣ ⅠⅠ

This tally sheet is easily converted into a table by counting the number of tally marks and recording the count as a frequency. In this way we might generate Table 2.1. Note that in this table we did not list a source since

Table 2.1 Hypothetical distribution of A

Categories	f
A	9
A'	7
Total	16

the source of the "observations" is clear from the context. In this table the symbol f stands for the word "frequency."

There are several options in preparing a table of this type. First, we might list the categories as 1 and 0 instead of A and A' as above. Second, we might use the symbol n to stand for a frequency rather than the symbol f.

Third, we might list the categories and frequencies in rows rather than in columns. By making all of these modifications, we produce Table 2.2.

Table 2.2   Hypothetical distribution of A

Categories	0	1	Total
n	7	9	16

When the characteristic being studied contains several categories or classes, as in a compound attribute or with most variables, the process of grouping may be carried even further. The individual categories themselves may be combined into more inclusive categories for the purpose of presenting the distribution in a simple form. For example, if respondents are asked, "What is your religious preference?" the answers will ordinarily contain many faiths, denominations, and sects. One person may answer "Lutheran," another "Unitarian," and a third "Catholic." These individual categories may be combined when presenting the table. Thus, the responses "Lutheran," "Methodist," and "Congregationalist" might be grouped into the single category "Protestant." Alternatively, the responses might be grouped according to how the particular faiths are organized, as into "Denominations" and "Sects." There are, generally, many ways of combining the categories of a compound attribute. When the characteristic is a variable, particularly an interval variable, there are also many ways of grouping the individual responses. This problem will be considered in Chapter 3.

2.3   THE PROBLEM OF NONRESPONSE
OR MISSING OBSERVATIONS

In most practical research situations it is difficult or even impossible to determine the presence or absence of a characteristic for every individual studied. When people are interviewed they will occasionally refuse to answer a question or will not remember some piece of information. An interviewer will occasionally forget to record the response or will make an obvious mistake in writing it down. Some interviews will be terminated before all of the questions have been asked and the respondent will not be home when the interviewer returns later to finish the interview. In these and many other ways, observations may be missing from the raw data. Obviously, the researcher should make every effort to keep these missing observations to a minimum but even the most careful scholar faces the problem of nonresponse.

Missing observations are difficult to handle at all levels of statistical analysis. Although some account must be taken of them, just *how* this should be done is another question. When one is preparing a table or grouping data it is ordinarily sound practice to list the nonresponses as a separate category. The result would look like Table 2.3.

An alternative that is also legitimate is to discard all missing observations or nonresponses and thereby reduce the size of the sample. When this alternative is adopted some reference to the missing observations should be made through a footnote, as shown in Table 2.4.

Sometimes the missing observations will really be ambiguous responses or responses that are very hard to classify for some other reason. In such cases it is often legitimate to change the *not-A* category into what is called a *residual* category, meaning that it is to contain all responses other than response *A*. When this alternative is adopted the residual character of the other category should be clearly indicated, perhaps as shown in Table 2.5.

Hypothetical frequency distribution

Table 2.3		**Table 2.4**		**Table 2.5**	
Category	*n*	*Category*	*n*	*Category*	*n*
A	37	A	37	A	37
A'	52	A'	52	Any other response	55
No answer	3	Total	89*	Total	92
Total	92				

* Three cases for which no information is available have been omitted from table 2.4.

This last alternative is also commonly employed when most responses are concentrated in a few categories but there are many infrequent, but scattered, additional responses. There are only a few major religions in the United States, for example, but there are some representatives here of virtually every religion extant on earth. It is conventional and entirely proper to collect such infrequent, scattered responses into a single residual category, usually labeled "other" or "other or none," or something similar. (For an extensive discussion of nonresponse and related problems see Kish, 1965.)

2.4 THE SIZE OF A TABLE

In statistics we often want to refer to the size of a table, by which we mean how many individual frequencies are contained in it or, more conventionally, how many "cells" (that is, locations for frequencies) it contains. This size is usually determined by first noting the number of rows of frequencies (r) and the number of columns of frequencies (c) that it contains. The total number of cells is the number of rows times the number of columns, or $r \cdot c$.

Consider a general table of a single characteristic, such as represented in Table 2.6. This table contains a single row of frequencies so $r = 1$. Ignoring

Table 2.6   General univariate distribution

Categories	A	B	C	D	Total
f	n_A	n_B	n_C	n_D	N

N (see below), the table contains four columns of frequencies, each column with but a single entry. The first column contains the frequency n_A, the second column, the frequency n_B, and so on. Here, then, $c = 4$ and the table as a whole is referred to as a 1×4 table. In this calculation, the "total" column was ignored. In a table, a frequency which is itself a sum of other frequencies in the table is called a *marginal* frequency or marginal total. In general, marginal frequencies are not included in determining the size of a table because they contribute no new information. The "total" column in Table 2.6 is an example of such a marginal frequency.

This same table could be written with the categories listed vertically rather than horizontally, as in Table 2.7. The table now has four rows and only a single column of frequencies so it would be called a 4×1 table. Of course, in either representation the size of the table is the same since $4 \times 1 = 1 \times 4 = 4$. In other words, either way there are four locations where individual frequencies appear or there are four *cells* in the table.

Table 2.7   General univariate distribution

Category	f
A	n_A
B	n_B
C	n_C
D	n_D
Total	N

2.5 RATIOS, PROPORTIONS AND PERCENTAGES, AND RATES

Condensing raw data into the form of a table with categories and frequencies makes it much easier to visualize and work with the distribution represented by these observations. However, the process must be carried one step further before the distribution is really easy to handle. An absolute number, such as any one of the frequencies in a table, is very difficult to interpret *by itself*. In order to interpret a number we usually need to *compare* it to another number. Suppose, for example, that you are told that college girls have poor morals because in University X it was found that 200 girls were heavy drinkers. Disregarding the problem of how to decide what we mean when we say that a person is a heavy drinker (which, in its general form, is often a fundamental research problem), the number "200" is essentially meaningless until we compare it with something—such as the number of girls at the university, or the number of girls *not* at the university who are heavy drinkers, or the number of boys at the university who are heavy drinkers. (Choosing an appropriate number for comparison is another fundamental research problem, one which will be discussed extensively throughout this book, although the discussion will often be implicit.)

Before considering what number to use for a given comparison, let us pause a moment and see just what it means to "compare" two numbers. Generally speaking, comparison means either (1) subtracting one number from the other or (2) dividing one number by the other. When we subtract one number from another we are able to tell which of the two is larger, and by how much. When we divide one number by another we generate what is called the *relative* size of the number. It tells us the quantity in one number relative to (or *per*) some standard quantity of the other number. Both methods of comparison are frequently used in sociology. When we consider frequencies, division is generally preferred because the absolute size of a frequency, or even the absolute difference between two frequencies, depends so much upon how many observations we happened to make. It is essentially impossible to compare, by subtraction, information gathered from the United States Census (involving perhaps 180,000,000 respondents) with information gathered from a sample survey (involving perhaps 1200 respondents) because of the vast difference in the sheer number of respondents. This problem largely disappears when frequencies are compared through division. In this section we discuss three different concepts built upon the idea of comparing numbers through division, namely, *ratios, proportions* and percents, and *rates*.

The fundamental problem in comparing one frequency with another is to make a sensible choice of the other frequency. Ratios, proportions, and rates represent three different solutions to this problem. The second frequency, the one with which our frequency is to be compared, will be the denominator of the comparison fraction. Therefore, it is called the *base*. The comparison of numbers with each other often proceeds by first comparing each one with a common *base*.

Consider a simple 1×2 table, such as Table 2.8, which presents a hypothetical distribution of people classified by sex. We might want to

Table 2.8   Distribution of people in a group, by sex

Category	Male	Female	Total
n	150	250	400

compare the number of males in this group with the number of males in some other group. If the other group possessed a different total size, however, such a comparison would not mean very much. Suppose, for example, that the other group contained 2000 people of whom 400 were male. We would note that there are many more males in the other group—but this statement, although technically correct, could be quite misleading. Actually, there are many more *people* in the other group and this is probably the reason that there are many more males. Or, put differently, there are also many more females in the second group so we have not said much by stating that there are many more males. The proper thing to do in this case would be to make a preliminary comparison. We might begin by comparing the number of males in each group either with the number of females there or with the total number of people there. These two types of simple comparison will now be considered in more detail.

Ratios

If the number of males is compared with the number of females we generate what is called a ratio (in this case, the sex ratio). Letting the word "males" stand for the phrase "number of males" and treating females in the same way, we have

$$\text{Sex ratio} = \frac{\text{males}}{\text{females}} = \frac{150}{250} = 0.60$$

Such a ratio expresses the number of males *per* female. In this case there were six-tenths of a male per female. Since it is a bit confusing to try to think of a fraction of a person, it is conventional to express this ratio as males per 100 females by multiplying the above ratio by 100. We then have

$$\text{Sex ratio} = (100) \frac{\text{males}}{\text{females}} = \frac{100 \times 150}{250} = 60$$

This number tells us that there are 60 males in this group for every 100 females.

The general form of a ratio is n_A / n_B where the n values are frequencies associated with individual categories in the population or sample; that is, they are both cell frequencies, to use the language introduced in Section 2.4. Ratios once were quite common in social science but there has been a marked diminution in their use in recent years because they are quite unstable when the base is small. In a population containing very few women, for example, the sex ratio could be a number like 12,470 males per 100 females. This very large number proves to be rather difficult to compare with other numbers in a meaningful way.

Proportions and Percents

The number of males may also be compared with the total size of the group. In this case we have what is called a proportion and we write:

$$\text{Proportion male} = \frac{\text{males}}{\text{total people}} = \frac{150}{400} = 0.375$$

This fraction is also often multiplied by 100 so that we can speak of so many males *per 100 people*. A proportion multiplied by 100 is called a *percent*—a very common and useful figure. Proportions and percents have come to be used more and more because they solve the problem of the ratio. In particular, the base or denominator of a proportion cannot be too small since it includes the numerator frequency. For example, total people = males + females. Clearly, then,

$$\text{Proportion male} = \frac{\text{males}}{\text{people}} = \frac{\text{males}}{\text{males} + \text{females}}$$

From this form we can see at once that the denominator cannot be smaller than the numerator. Usually, of course, it will be considerably larger.

The kind of comparison with which we started this discussion is easily accomplished once each number is expressed as a percentage. Proportions and percentages are sometimes referred to as relative numbers or relative frequencies. We can easily compare the relative number of males in our group (namely, 37.5 percent) with the relative number in the group containing 2000 members (namely, $(100)(400)/(2,000) = 20.0$ percent.) If we compare 37.5 percent and 20 percent, we can say, for instance, that males were almost twice as common as females in our group. The percentage also makes it easier to visualize the number of males relative to the number of females. In our group 38 percent were male and 62 percent female. It is a simple matter to compare these numbers. (Notice that the percentages were "rounded" in this last comparison so that 37.5 percent became 38 percent and 62.5 percent became 62 percent. This is a very common practice when working with percentages.)

Summarizing these measures we have

A ratio is   *A proportion is*   *A percent is*

$$\frac{n_A}{n_B} \qquad \frac{n_A}{N} = \frac{n_A}{n_A + n_B} \qquad (100)\,\frac{n_A}{N}$$

In these formulas n_A and n_B are cell frequencies and $N = n_A + n_B$ is the total or marginal frequency.

The proportion or percent is such an important figure that we give it a special symbol. Just as we let n and f stand for frequencies, we let p stand for a proportion. Proportions or percentages are often included routinely in tables, either in addition to frequencies or instead of them. The typical table of a univariate distribution will have three columns, headed "categories," "frequencies," and "percentages." The distribution by sex presented in Table 2.8 would be presented as in Table 2.9 using these columns.

Table 2.9   Distribution of people in a group, by sex

Category	n	$(100)p$ = percent
Male	150	37.5
Female	250	62.5
Total	400	100.0 percent

Rates and Percent Change

One other kind of elementary comparison is quite useful in many statistical descriptions. Social scientists often observe *events*. An event is a happening, an action, a motion, or a change. It occurs and then is gone. Typical of the events that we study are births, divorces, and acts of crime or delinquency. When dealing with events such as these we face the same kind of problem that was bothersome before. The number of events that occur during some time period will depend primarily upon the number of *potential* actors or the number of objects that *might* change. This latter number is referred to as the number of individuals *exposed to the risk of the event*. Births occur only among sexually mature females, for example, so the number of births will depend upon the number of such females as well as upon the underlying process that leads them to have babies. Similarly, divorces can only occur to couples who are married. The number of divorces in a population, then, will depend upon the number of married couples there as well as upon whatever process leads such couples to seek divorce.

The solution to this problem is to compare the number of events with the number of potential events, that is, with the number of individuals exposed to the risk of the event. The comparison is accomplished by dividing the number of occurrences by the number of individuals exposed. This fraction is called a *rate* or a rate of occurrence. Often the fraction is multiplied by some standard number such as 1000 and we speak of the number of occurrences per 1000 exposures. Since the events always occur during some time period, we ordinarily refer to this time period in identifying the rate. Thus, we might refer to a rate as the number of occurrences per 1000 exposures per year.

Table 2.10 illustrates how the calculation of rates can simplify the comparison of counts of the number of times that events occur.

Table 2.10   Persons injured in the United States in 1960, and annual rate by age

Age	Total injuries	Injury rate per 1000 population
ALL AGES	44,994,000	255.2
0–5	7,067,000	293.7
6–16	11,916,000	314.9
17–24	4,903,000	277.9
25–44	10,346,000	227.8
45–64	7,856,000	218.3
65+	2,906,000	189.5

SOURCE: U.S. Department of Health, Education, and Welfare; Public Health Service, National Health Survey. Series B—No. 37, Tables 8 and 9.

This table reports the number of injuries occurring to Americans both for the total population ("all ages") and for various specific age groups. Look first at the frequency column headed "total injuries." The numbers in this column are very difficult to compare with each other in any meaningful way. No particular pattern among them can be found. Now look at the rates in the next column. This column shows clearly that the rate at which people become injured decreases steadily from childhood through old age. The risk is greatest in the age range 6–16. The reason that the column of frequencies is hard to interpret is that the number of people in each age category varies a great deal from category to category. By expressing each frequency as a rate, we adjust for this difference in the total number of people exposed. Notice that in this situation the total population in the age group is the number who are exposed to injury since each and every person might possibly become injured during the course of a year.

In many cases it is difficult to determine just who is and who is not exposed to a given risk. Furthermore, the extent of exposure may well vary from person to person. For this reason it is usually possible to compute many different rates, depending upon how we define the population of exposed individuals. These rates are usually defined as either *crude* or *refined* rates. A crude rate uses as the denominator a total population without concern for whether or not each individual in the population is actually exposed. A refined rate uses as the denominator some more carefully defined population relative to exposure. For example, the crude divorce rate is the number of divorces occurring during a year divided by the total population alive at the middle of the year. This population, of course, includes children, single adults, and others who are not at all exposed to the risk of divorce. A refined divorce rate is the number of divorces occurring during a year divided by the number of married couples existing at the middle of the year. Obviously, refined rates are more accurate than crude rates although, in practice, it is usually much easier to calculate the crude rate.

There are two main reasons for computing rates. One reason is that we wish to compare *different populations* with respect to the relative frequency of the event in question; the other is that we wish to compare *the same population* at different times. For example, suppose that we are interested in the frequency of automobile accidents. We might be interested in whether or not the risk of automobile accidents varies by age, in which case we would compute rates in the manner of Table 2.10. We might also be interested in whether or not the risk of automobile accidents has been changing as the years pass, in which case we might compare the rate in 1940 with the rate in 1950 with the rate in 1960. In general, the study of trends through time is greatly facilitated by the use of rates.

Another way to examine change over time is to compute what is called the *percentage change* in some frequency from the beginning to the end of a given period. The procedure is a simple one. Let n_1 be the original or beginning frequency and n_2 be the final or terminal frequency. We have

$$\text{Percent change} = (100)\,\frac{n_2 - n_1}{n_1}$$

As an example let us compare the number of farm laborers in the United States in 1870 and in 1950. In 1870 there were 2,885,996 farm laborers here (Sogge, 1954), and in 1950 there were 2,497,637. Using the percent change concept to make the comparison more meaningful, we then have

$$\text{Percent change} = \frac{(100)(2,497,637 - 2,885,996)}{2,885,996}$$

$$= \frac{(100)(-388,359)}{2,885,996}$$

$$= -13 \text{ percent}$$

In other words, there was a decrease of 13 percent in the number of farm laborers in the United States during this time period.

To make a percent change such as this one even more meaningful, we carry the process of comparison one step further. In particular, we may compare one percent change with another. For example, the decline of 13 percent in farm labor from 1870 to 1950 might be compared with a rise of about 360 percent in total employment in the United States during this same 80-year period. Here we see again one of the principal advantages of the simple fractions that we have discussed in this chapter. By converting frequencies into these fractions—to generate ratios, percentages, rates, and the like—we find it much easier to make further comparisons.

2.6   ANOTHER KIND OF SUMMARY: THE MODAL CATEGORY

In summarizing the distribution of an attribute, particularly a compound attribute, it is often useful to determine the category that appears *most often* in the population or sample. To find this category we examine the frequency column and identify the largest frequency. We then look at the category that corresponds to this frequency. This category is called the *modal category* or the mode of the distribution. Often a knowledge of the mode or modal category will be sufficient to characterize a distribution in a general way. Refer back to Table 1.2, for example. We may summarize the information in this table by noting the most frequent offense. Excluding the category "all other offenses," which is a residual category that presumably contains many different offenses, the most frequently occurring offense is "drunkenness." Drunkenness is, therefore, the modal category. To summarize the distribution using this information we might say, "In the United States the offense for which people are most commonly arrested is drunkenness."

Looking for the modal category and identifying it is a very sound way to summarize a distribution, particularly when you want a quick picture of that distribution. At the same time, however, it should be recognized that there will be occasions when such a procedure may be misleading. This situation arises whenever the categories are of unequal "breadth" or scope. It is important to check the categories to be sure that they are all about equally broad before we rely upon the mode as a summary. In the case of Table 1.2, for example, we eliminated the category "all other offenses" on the grounds that it was much broader or more inclusive than the other listed categories. In other cases, the problem may arise even when there are no residual categories. In occupational classifications we usually consider the terms *professional* and *businessman* as being comparably broad. A classification that listed specific professions such as architect, dentist, and professor, as well as the category businessman, would be mixed in breadth. Unfortunately, there are no general rules that can be applied to determine the breadth of a nominal category. About all that the reader or researcher can do is examine the particular categories with which he is concerned and judge their relative breadth. Only when they appear to be comparable as to breadth should the modal category be used as a summarizing device.

2.7 WHERE WE STAND

In this chapter we have developed some fundamental tools for statistical description, tools that can be used for all kinds of characteristics but are most appropriately applied to the distribution of an attribute. The first tool is the univariate frequency *table,* which is a way of describing the number of times that each of several categories appears in a population or sample. The second tool is the idea of *comparison,* either through subtraction or division. When we divide one frequency by another we further condense the information in a distribution. Often all of the important information in a distribution can be expressed in a single percentage (or rate or ratio). We saw that there are several ways of comparing numbers through division. These ways differ primarily in how the *base* or denominator is selected. The major methods include ratios, proportions, percentages, rates, and percentage change figures. Finally, we mentioned the most frequent or modal category as a useful tool. Already we have learned a good deal about how to summarize quantitative information. (See Yule and Kendall, 1950, for a classic discussion of attributes and their analysis.)

3

MEASURES ESPECIALLY
APPROPRIATE
TO ORDINAL VARIABLES

We saw in the last chapter that the distribution of an attribute can best be described in terms of fractions developed from the frequency of occurrence of the various categories. The most important and common of these fractions is called a proportion (or a percent when it is multiplied by 100). A proportion is a cell frequency divided by the total frequency in the table. In the case of attributes, the various proportions associated with the categories must be treated separately. They cannot be combined except by the device of combining the categories themselves. This inability to combine the proportions creates a certain clumsiness in conceptualizing the distribution when there are several categories because there are as many proportions as there are categories. Another way to make this same point is to note that there is no way to relate observations of an attribute to each other except by determining whether or not the two observations are the same. This problem can be solved in the case of ordinal variables. Since the various categories of an ordinal variable possess an intrinsic order, their frequencies or proportions may be combined by a process called *cumulation*. As a result some very elegant statistical descriptions can be generated. The researcher's ability to cumulate is the principal advantage he gains when working with ordinal data rather than with attributes. It is our purpose in this chapter to show just why this statement is true and what kinds of description can be achieved using cumulation.

3.1 HOW ORDINAL VARIABLES ARISE

It is useful to begin by considering just how ordinal variables arise in a field such as sociology. In a very elementary sense, of course, ordinal variables arise when we think quantitatively about some concept *without* having any measuring instrument by which to identify *just how much* of the concept is present in any one member of our population or sample. As an example, consider a concept such as "maturity." As ordinarily used, we assume that there is some degree of maturity present in all people. However, we also assume that people differ in the amount of maturity that they possess at any one time. In general, for instance, we assume that people who have had more experience in an area are more mature in that area than are persons with less experience. Thus a senior in college is presumably more mature in his handling of classroom situations than is a freshman, because the senior has had more experience in the classroom and has learned to cope with many situations that are still a mystery to the freshman, or that cause the freshman to stumble.

This line of thought establishes maturity as a variable rather than an attribute because the issue is not its presence or absence but rather the degree to which it is present. Having established that maturity is a variable, then, we search for some way to measure it. Now we are somewhat stopped. What is a *unit* of maturity? No matter where we look we will not find such a unit—at least we will not find one that will apply equally well (that is, generate equal intervals) at all levels of maturity. Differences in maturity among children who are, say, three to five years old simply cannot be measured in a way that is commensurate with differences in maturity among college students. In fact, there is no existing measure of a *unit* of maturity at all. If we are to measure the quantity of the phenomenon present in a given individual we must do so by some means that does not require the presence of a standard unit. Can this other kind of measurement be done? The answer is "yes," under certain conditions, at least, and the manifestation of this answer is what gives rise to ordinal measurement.

Actually, there is not just one but three major ways of generating measurement up to an ordinal level. None of these ways require a knowledge of a standard unit. All of them are used very commonly in social science research.

Ordinal Measurement Through Judgment

The first way in which we can achieve ordinal measurement is to use a judge who is familiar with the general concept that we are trying to measure. Such a knowledgeable judge can ordinarily decide which of two objects or events possesses more of the quantity in question. A man who is familiar with the concept of weight can, for example, ordinarily judge which of two other men is the heavier even though he has no scale. Similarly, an interviewer who is familiar with houses and their condition can ordinarily tell which of two houses is the more deteriorated.

There are two limitations, of course, upon judgments of this sort. In the first place, there is some degree of similarity between the objects beyond which it is very difficult to make reliable judgments. It would be very hard for a man to judge correctly which of two men was heavier if one weighed 180 pounds and the other 183 pounds. This difficulty is intrinsic to the judgment process and is a necessary limitation on ordinal measurement. Ordinal measurement is unreliable when differences are very small. In the second place, it may be difficult to acquire the knowledge, if such exists, by which to render a judgment. This problem can be solved by using more than one judge and using only concepts that can be reliably measured from one judge to another. (We might want several judges to agree before we claim to have a measure of a complicated concept such as "maturity," for example.) Given these two limitations, however, ordinal measurement can often be achieved through the use of judges. This kind of measurement is very common in connection with mental phenomena and represents one way of approaching the problem of scaling. Essentially all that is involved is the ability of the judge to tell which of two objects possesses more of the quantity in question.

Ordinal Measurement Through Counting Unequal Elements

The second way in which we can achieve ordinal measurement is to count a number of things that are unequal (or whose equality cannot be determined) and treat the resulting frequency as a measure of the quantity possessed. This method is almost universally used by educators in tests, for instance. A true–false test is a simple example. Knowledge of the subject is measured by counting the number of correct responses. The unit of count is a single question. However, we do not know that each question correctly answered represents the same amount of knowledge possessed. Indeed, we know in general that there are some easy questions and some difficult ones, that there may be three questions dealing with one area of knowledge and only one dealing with another area, and so on. The individual questions, in other words, are unequal with respect to a *unit of knowledge*. Despite that inequality, however, we assume that by asking enough questions we get a fairly sound *relative* picture of the knowledge of a student by counting the number of correct responses. To say that the picture is relative is simply to say that we can presume that a person who gets a higher score knows more than a person who gets a lower score (the paired comparison again), *but* we *cannot* know how much more knowledge is involved. Again, this method of achieving ordinal measurement tends to break down when the differences are small but it is sound in situations in which differences are relatively large.

Ordinal Measurement Through Frequency of Occurrence

There are certain situations in which it is possible to reach a decision about relative quantity by comparing the frequencies with which various events occur. For example, consider asking a group of people the following set of questions:

  (a) Are you at least four feet tall?
  (b) Are you at least five feet tall?
  (c) Are you at least six feet tall?
  (d) Are you at least seven feet tall?

In general, more people will answer "Yes" to the first question than to the second, more will answer "Yes" to the second question than to the third, and so on. Only a very small proportion of people will answer "Yes" to the last question. This small proportion of positive responses suggests that this last question is very extreme with respect to height and hence that a "Yes" man here must be very tall. In the case of height, of course, we can tell at once that this is the case because we are using an interval measurement in the questions. The same logic, however, can be applied (sometimes) to sets of questions that do not contain obvious implied direct measurement. If a series of questions can be presumed all to deal with the same concept or quantity, then the questions that are answered one way (say, "Yes") less frequently can be assumed to represent more extreme quantities than questions that are more commonly answered that way. This idea forms the basis of what is called Guttman scaling. The interested student may consult any one of many methodology texts for a further discussion of this procedure. Here we note only that this approach can also lead to measurement up to an ordinal level.

3.2 NUMBERS AND ORDINAL OBSERVATIONS

We have seen that the basic operation in ordinal measurement is the comparison of two objects (or events) to determine which possesses more of the phenomenon in question. In this way, quantities are compared with each other and ranked. This operation differs quite sharply from that of measurement at an interval level. Interval measurement (see Chapter 4 for more details) is achieved by comparing a given object's quantity with a standard scale, rather than with another object's quantity. Thus, with interval measurement, all of the objects can be located on the scale, but with ordinal measurement they can only be ranked with respect to each other. (See below for a further discussion and qualification of this point.)

The question arises as to how to represent these ranked or relative positions. Here a certain amount of confusion exists of which the student should be aware. Let us consider three observations, say, X_1, X_2, and X_3. Let us suppose further that X_2 is the smallest of the three, X_3 is the middle quantity, and X_1 is the largest. The direct and exact way to represent these relations involves the use of inequalities ($>$ means "greater than" and $<$ means "less than"). Using these symbols, we could write the above relations in the following way:

$$X_2 < X_3 < X_1$$

or

$$X_1 > X_3 > X_2$$

This direct symbolization is correct, but cumbersome, particularly if there are several hundred observations. It has become conventional, therefore, to place the observations on a *scale* even though the scale itself is arbitrary except for the relative ranks that are implied. This operation may be done by using the integers, that is, "1," "2," "3," and so on. Here we agree beforehand that the integer "1" stands for the smallest observation, the integer "2" for the next larger, and so on. Now the inequalities are represented indirectly by assigning these integers, or ranks, to the various observations. We write:

$$X_2 \text{ has rank } 1$$
$$X_3 \text{ has rank } 2$$
$$X_1 \text{ has rank } 3$$

This operation is known as assigning rank orders to the observations and presents exactly the same information as was presented above through the use of inequalities.

The scale consisting of the integers is the one most commonly used for expressing quantities measured in an ordinal way but it is not the only one. Any set of symbols with a conventional order may be used. For instance, in testing and grading in schools and colleges it is conventional to use the alphabet for ranks, since the letters in the alphabet occur in a conventional order, namely, $A, B, C, D, E, \ldots$. By mutual agreement the letter A is assigned for the best relative performances, B for performances that are somewhat better than most but not as strong as A performances, and so on.

Using this convention, we might write our rank order in the following way:

$X_2 = C$ (it is the lowest of the three quantities)

$X_3 = B$

$X_1 = A$

Notice that the performance of a student in a classroom situation is always measured relative to the performance of other students rather than relative to a standard scale. Thus, a given performance might be worth an A in a high school class, but the very same performance might be worth only a D in a college class, and would almost certainly be a flat F in a Ph.D. comprehensive examination. This kind of variation is quite realistic because we are *not* measuring any absolute quantity of performance or knowledge but only relative performance or knowledge.

A final scale that is frequently used is the system of real numbers. When we score a test by counting the number of correct answers we are assigning a real number to the quantity possessed. If each correct answer represents the same quantity of knowledge as each other correct answer, the measure is interval. (See Chapter 4.) Ordinarily, however, we cannot tell whether the quantity is constant or not. Nor can we ordinarily tell whether or not two correct answers are twice the quantity represented by one correct answer. When we do not have this knowledge it is prudent to treat the achieved score as an arbitrary scale to be used in assigning ranks. In our illustration, using this convention, we might represent the quantities as:

X_2 scores 80

X_3 scores 85

X_1 scores 95

Actually, of course, we could use any real numbers for these scores as long as their quantities generate the same inequalities. One word of caution here, however. When the real numbers are used as an arbitrary scale it is very easy to forget that the scale actually is arbitrary. In the above list it would appear that X_1 is twice as far from X_3 as X_3 is from X_2. At least, $X_1 - X_3 = 95 - 85 = 10$, whereas $X_3 - X_2 = 85 - 80 = 5$. The first difference appears to be 10 units and the second difference only half as much or 5 units. This analysis makes no sense, however, because there is no unit involved in the measurement activity. The numbers are arbitrary except for their order. We could just as well have written

X_2 scores 80

X_3 scores 85

X_1 scores 86

As long as the measurement is ordinal, the two representations are identical.

This issue occurs, for example, when teachers grade essay examinations numerically, perhaps using a scale from 50 to 100. Such grades are basically ranks (relative either to other students in the same class or to former students of that teacher) even though real numbers have been used to indicate relative position.

3.3 CUMULATED FREQUENCIES OR PROPORTIONS

The basic table describing the distribution of a single characteristic contains one column that identifies the various categories and another column that identifies the frequency with which each category appears in the sample or population. The frequencies of an ordinal or interval variable are conventionally symbolized by the letter f. Thus, f_i stands for the frequency in the ith category. When categories possess an intrinsic order it is possible to introduce a third column of information called the *cumulated frequency column*. Cumulated frequencies are symbolized by the capital letter F.

At this point it is useful to pause a moment and consider a possible source of confusion for the beginning student. In the table of a variable both the categories and the frequencies represent quantities. We need some way to keep these two quantities separate. Symbolically, we use the letter X to stand for the quantity of the variable in a category and the letter f for a frequency. Verbally, we will always refer to the quantity of the variable by qualifying the word "category." For example, the phrase "smallest category" will always refer to that category which represents the least quantity of the variable. Whenever we want to refer to the category containing the smallest frequency we will refer to that category that occurs "least often" in the sample or population. To avoid confusion this point should be understood before proceeding further.

Returning to the main theme, a cumulated frequency is the frequency with which a given category *or any smaller category* occurred. A simple numerical example will illustrate this point. Suppose we have the following three categories with the indicated frequencies:

$$X_1 \text{ occurred } 15 \text{ times}$$
$$X_2 \text{ occurred } 13 \text{ times}$$
$$X_3 \text{ occurred } 9 \text{ times}$$

Suppose further that the subscripts indicate the ranks of the categories, that is, X_1 is smaller than X_2, which, in turn, is smaller than X_3. The *cumulated frequency* in X_2 is the number of times that that category occurred (namely, 13) *plus* the number of times that any smaller category occurred. The only smaller category is X_1, which occurred 15 times. Therefore, the cumulated frequency in $X_2 = 13 + 15 = 28$. Similarly, the cumulated frequency in X_3 is $9 + 13 + 15 = 37$. Technically, there are two ways that cumulation can proceed and when we start with the smallest category we should call the results "less than" cumulated frequencies. Since that phrase is quite pedantic we shall simply refer to them as cumulated frequencies. The student should, of course, remember that cumulation can be done in the other direction too.

The general pattern of cumulation is illustrated by Table 3.1, in which A, B, C, and D stand for the various ranked categories, such that D represents the smallest quantity of the variable.

Table 3.1   General pattern of cumulation

Category	$f = Frequency$	$F = Cumulated\ frequency$
D	f_D	$F_D = f_D$
C	f_C	$F_C = f_D + f_C$
B	f_B	$F_B = f_D + f_C + f_B$
A	f_A	$F_A = f_D + f_C + f_B + f_A$

The cumulation is from the smallest category up. If the categories had been listed in the opposite order (that is, with D at the bottom and A at the top), the cumulation would still be from D up. In other words, cumulation has *nothing to do* with position on the list. It may occur down the column or up the column. The key point to remember is that it is always done from the category containing the least quantity toward the larger categories. A cumulated frequency in a category is the number of observations that were smaller than or equal to the indicated category. In the scheme of Table 3.1, for example, categories C and D are both smaller than category B. The cumulated frequency in category B is, therefore, $F_B = f_D + f_C + f_B$.

A Note on Computation

Throughout statistical analysis you will face an interesting, but sometimes confusing, fact. A great deal of computation is required to summarize and describe observations and distributions of observations. The computations are based upon concepts such as the concept of a cumulated frequency. The concept, in turn, is defined in terms of mathematical operations such as addition, subtraction, and so on. We say that the concept is defined in *operational* terms, meaning in terms of the operations that are necessary to produce it. But here is the somewhat confusing fact: The operations in terms of which a concept is defined are not always the simplest operations to use when actually making calculations. Therefore, two basic things must be learned about each concept: (1) how to define and use it and (2) how to compute it in an efficient way. In this book we shall try to separate these two problems as much as possible by discussing the computational routines in separate sections. The habit of keeping definitions and computational routines separate is a useful one to acquire.

We can illustrate the distinction between definition and computation by considering cumulated frequencies. We defined a cumulated frequency as the sum of the frequencies in all categories of lower or equal rank to the indicated category, such as $F_B = f_D + f_C + f_B$ in our illustration. It turns out, however, that this definition does not indicate the best way actually to compute cumulated frequencies, because, using the definition only, we would make the same individual additions over and over again. For example, notice that the sum $f_D + f_C$ occurs in both of the following cumulated frequencies:

$$F_B = f_D + f_C + f_B$$

and

$$F_C = f_D + f_C$$

There is no reason to find that particular sum twice. Once we have calculated the cumulated sum F_C we have found the value of $f_D + f_C$ and do not need to do that computation over again for F_B. Instead, we can compute

$$F_B = F_C + f_B$$

In a similar way we can see that

$$F_A = F_B + f_A$$

and

$$F_C = F_D + f_C$$

In general, these facts may be summarized in the following formula, which provides the best way to compute cumulated frequencies:

$$F_i = F_{i-1} + f_i$$

which should be read "the cumulated frequency in the ith category is equal to the cumulated frequency in the next smaller category plus the frequency in the ith category." In this statement the first category ($i = 1$) is assumed to be the smallest (that is, the one with the least quantity of X).

Let us see how this formula works. Consider the following hypothetical distribution of grades in a college class (see Table 3.2). We want to compute the cumulated frequencies. We start with grade F because that category represents the least quantity of knowledge. The rule is: take the cumulated frequency up to that class and add to it the frequency in the class. For grade F there are no frequencies below it and two frequencies in it, so we have $0 + 2 = 2$ for the cumulated frequency.

Now we look at the D category. Applying the same rule we see that there are two cumulated frequencies below D and six frequencies in D, so we have $F_D = 2 + 6 = 8$. In the same way we look at category C. Now there are 8 cumulated frequencies below it and 20 in the category, so we get $F_C = 8 + 20 = 28$ (see the arrowed line in Table 3.3 for this computation). Our final table looks like Table 3.3.

Hypothetical distribution of grades in a college class

Table 3.2			Table 3.3		
Grade	f		Grade	f	F
A	6		A	6	48
B	14		B	14	42
C	20		C	20 ⟶	28
D	6		D	6 ⟵	8
F	2		F	2	2

3.4 CUMULATED PERCENTAGES: THE PERCENTILE

In the chapter on attributes we noted that a frequency, by itself, is rather hard to interpret or use. This problem was solved by comparing it with another frequency (through division). We suggested that the most common and also most useful base or denominator in this comparison is the total number of observations in the table, that is, N. We defined the proportion, p_i, as the fraction, f_i/N, and noted that it is conventional to multiply the proportion by 100 when talking about it. A proportion multiplied by 100 is, of course, called a percent.

The same kind of problem and the same solution exist in the case of cumulated frequencies. We take a cumulated frequency, say F_i, and divide it by the sum of all the frequencies, N, to generate the cumulated proportion. Now we multiply that proportion by 100 and create the cumulated percent or, as it is usually referred to, the percentile. In a formula we have

$$\text{Percentile in } i\text{th category} = (100) \frac{F_i}{N}$$

Look back at Table 3.3 (on grades). Notice that the number of observations in the table is $N = 48$ and that this number appears at the very top of the cumulated frequency column. The cumulated frequency in the highest ranking category will always equal N because all of the observations are necessarily in categories that are less than or equal to this highest ranking category. Using the formula for a percentile we see that an A is in the 100th percentile since $(100)(48)/(48) = 100$. Similarly, since there were 42 students who received grades of B or less, a B puts a student in the $(100)(42)/(48) = 88$th percentile.

It is important to note that we have defined the percentile on a "less than or equal" basis. A B was in the 88th percentile because 88 percent of the observed grades were less than or *equal to B*. It is also possible to consider percentiles that are only "less than" figures. Such a percentile indicates what percent of the scores are less than the indicated score. This convention is adopted, for example, when the highest grade that can be achieved is reported as in the 99th percentile—meaning that 99 percent of the grades are lower. Students who work extensively with percentiles should be aware of this option.

The percentile is a very valuable tool, particularly in psychology and education, where ordinal measurements in the form of tests are common. Many test scores are reported as percentiles. There is a great advantage in this practice. With the percentile we create a *relative* measuring instrument that allows us to tell at a glance just where any one person stands relative to a comparison group. A person who receives a score that puts him in the 25th percentile, for instance, knows that 25 percent of other students did at least as poorly as he did, but that 75 percent did better. In this way we create a sound and sensible measurement where none appeared to exist before. Furthermore, we did it just by being able to tell which of a pair of objects possessed more of whatever it was that we were looking for. Intellectually, then, this conversion of ranked scores into percentiles is quite an achievement.

3.5 ORDINAL MEASUREMENT AND CONVENTIONAL SCALES

The procedures that we discussed in this chapter for summarizing the distribution of an ordinal variable (namely, cumulation and the percentile) are based upon the elementary way that ordinal measurement arises. This way is through the comparison of each pair of objects to determine, for each pair, which (if either) is the larger, that is, possesses the greater quantity being measured. By making these comparisons for every possible pair of objects we can place those objects in a rank order and, from this rank order, compute cumulated frequencies and percentiles. In actual fact, however, we rarely proceed in just this way when making ordinal measurements. Instead, we proceed through the use of what we shall call *conventional scales,* which will be defined in the next paragraph. When conventional scales are used to accomplish the measurement we still use cumulation as the basic summarizing device. In addition, however, we can relate the cumulated frequencies or percentiles to the scale that we are using. We shall present these additional procedures in the next chapter, since they are also appropriate to interval scales. In this section we shall explain what is meant by a conventional scale and show how it can be used to generate other ways of summarizing distributions.

The labor involved in making every possible paired comparison among a set of objects is very great, indeed. With a sample of 500 objects we would have to examine well over 100,000 separate pairs. To reduce this labor we usually proceed in a slightly different way; namely, we create a conventional scale and then compare each object with the points on this scale. Each point on the conventional scale represents some relative quantity of the variable being measured. It is identified by a description of the typical kind of object that would possess this quantity. Notice that the quantity itself is *not* identified. To use such a scale we compare each object in our sample with the points as described and assign to it the point that is most similar.

The usual way that tests and papers are graded provides an illustration of this process. The letter grades, *A* through *F*, form a conventional scale. Each teacher who uses this scale to grade students has a picture of what performance is typical of the grade *A*, what performance is typical of the grade *B*, and so on. In grading actual papers the teacher compares each one with these typical ones and assigns that grade that seems most appropriate. Precisely the same idea is involved when the teacher uses numerical grades as a conventional scale.

There are many conventional scales in use in sociology. Familiar examples include scales of socioeconomic status (from lower class to upper class, where each class is identified by typical members) and scales of mental states, such as happiness (very unhappy to very happy, where each state is identified by an image of how a person acts when in that state).

The use of a conventional scale greatly reduces the work involved in rank ordering a series of objects or events. To the extent that there is general agreement as to how the points on the scale are described, it also is useful in summarizing the distribution. For example, the middle of a rank order is the 50th percentile since half of the observations are at least as large as this percentile and half are at least as small. Unfortunately, however, it does us little if any good to know this fact if all we have is the rank order because we do not know what the 50th percentile represents. If we have a conventional scale, though, then we can identify the point on this scale where the 50th percentile falls. This point is called the *median*. The median helps us locate the distribution on the scale by telling us where the middle of the distribution is located. We will discuss the median and other similar concepts in the next chapter. As we shall see, these concepts are also useful in summarizing distributions of interval variables. Our primary objective here is to illustrate how a conventional scale is useful both in facilitating ordinal measurement and in summarizing the resulting distribution.

It is very important to remember that the conventional scale does *not* in any way identify the quantity of the variable at any point or the difference in quantity between any two points. Only interval scales identify these quantities. What the conventional scale does is provide a hypothetical set of observations that are themselves in rank order and with which the actual observations may be compared.

3.6 WHERE WE STAND

In this chapter we have introduced the idea of cumulation and have shown how it can be used to describe the distribution of an ordinal variable. In considering ordinal measurement it is important to remember that there is no scale *of quantity* against which to compare an observation. We never know *how much* of the variable is present in any object or event that we examine. Ordinal measurement involves the comparison of observations with respect to quantity. From this comparison we judge which object or event (if either) possesses more of the quantity in question. We may make comparisons directly on pairs of observations. In this case we achieve a rank ordering of the observations. This rank order, in turn, can be summarized through the use of percentiles. We may also make comparisons by comparing each object or event being studied with a hypothetical set of ranked observations; this set is called a conventional scale. Through the use of such a scale we achieve a rank ordering of the observations. In addition we can relate the rank order to the scale in certain ways (which will be discussed more extensively in Chapter 4). We have also noted that there are three major ways in which ordinal comparisons occur in sociology: through judgment, through counting unequal elements, and through observing the frequency of occurrence of various responses.

4

MEASURES ESPECIALLY
APPROPRIATE
TO INTERVAL DATA

We now consider, for the first time, observations that can be directly expressed as numbers. When an observation can be compared with some standard unit of quantity, its *position* on a scale (such as a straight line) can be identified. For example, an age, such as 18 years, can be placed on a line that represents all ages, thus

18 years of age

| 0 | 10 | 20 | 30 | 40 | 50 | 60 | . . . .

Age in years

If the numeric location of a single observation can be visualized in this way, then so can the location of a set of observations, such as the *distribution* of a variable in a population. The ability to use numbers to describe observations permits us to develop many interesting and important ways of summarizing the distribution of an interval variable. These summaries will be considered in this and the following chapter. There are three main ways to summarize a univariate distribution; namely, descriptions of the *form, central tendency,* and *dispersion* of a distribution. Since there are several new ideas to consider, it is important that we begin right at the beginning and see just how we locate a distribution or a set of observations on an interval scale.

4.1 THE ARRAY

The first step in describing and summarizing quantitative observations is to organize them conveniently. As we saw in Chapter 2, the original form in which observations ordinarily come to us is in the form of raw data, somewhat as illustrated here.

2, 2, 1, 1, 3, 5, 7, 8, 3, 0, 2, 0, 0, 1, 3, 2, 3, 4, 5, 6, 3, 2, 6, 1

These numbers come from an actual investigation (Gorden, 1952) and represent the number of times each of 24 members in a cooperative living project agreed in his private opinion with what he perceived to be the opinion of his group on 12 questionnaire items. The set of observations is in order by the interview number of the individual case (that is, case no. 1 is first, case no. 2 is second, and so on). Examination of even this simple set of observations is facilitated by arranging them in a somewhat different order. We may, for instance, arrange them as follows:

0, 0, 0, 1, 1, 1, 1, 2, 2, 2, 2, 2, 3, 3, 3, 3, 3, 4, 5, 5, 6, 6, 7, 8

This listing is called an *array*. The observations are in order from the lowest to the highest value. We can see readily from this array, for instance, that the observations tend to fall largely in the 0, 1, 2, 3 values. The observations are still ungrouped; all we have done is to rearrange them. An array, therefore, can be defined as *an ordered set of observations*.

4.2 THE TABLE: GROUPING INTERVAL DATA

With ungrouped data we are given, and preserve, each observation's exact value. When we group these data and present them in the form of a table we replace the individual observations with two columns of information, just as we did when making a table of the distribution of an attribute. Now, however, each of the columns will contain numbers. The first column is a list of the different values that the variable takes on and the second column lists the frequency with which each value occurs. Table 4.1 provides an example, using the data from the array presented above.

Table 4.1 is a frequency distribution, in which the variable is called X. The letter X is used to signify two things. First, it is a general name of a *variable*. Second, it stands for any *value* of that variable. Sometimes the particular values will be represented through the subscript i. Thus X_i may be read "the ith value of X." Often, however, X by itself stands for "an observation of X" or "a value of the variable X."

At first it may be a bit confusing to see a table in which both the categories and the frequencies are numbers, perhaps even both "frequencies." It is very important to distinguish them. Any column labeled X or any other *name* for a variable will contain the values of that variable. On the other hand, the listing of the number of times that each value occurred in a set of observations (that is, its frequency) will be labeled f or "frequency."

Table 4.1 Number of agreements among people living in a cooperative housing project

X	f
9	0
8	1
7	1
6	2
5	2
4	1
3	5
2	5
1	4
0	3
	$N = 24$

These are the same data as before, but now they are grouped. The symbol X stands for the variable (number of agreements in this case); f stands for frequency of occurrence, as before.*

* Throughout the text we shall comment on formulas, examples, figures, and so on, in material set off from the text and placed with the features that we desire to emphasize. These comments will serve several purposes: frequently they will summarize text material, sometimes they will simply emphasize text material, and very infrequently they will add to text material. They are not to be regarded as text material in themselves and are of more importance in reviewing than during the first reading.

Ordinarily it is a good idea to create a table from raw data in two steps, as we saw in Chapter 2. First we tally the observations and then we prepare the table from the tallies. The tally sheet for these observations might look like this:

X	Tallies
9	
8	/
7	/
6	//
5	//
4	/
3	////
2	////
1	////
0	///

This tally sheet is easily converted into the table. Tallying is a useful computational aid because it saves time and also reduces error. To convert raw data into tallies we need scan the data only once. If you try to count the frequencies directly from the raw data you must keep going back over the figures each time you shift to a new value. There is another advantage to the tally sheet, which will become clear in the next few pages. It gives us a preliminary picture of what the distribution looks like. Because of this fact it is a useful aid if we should want to group the observations into more inclusive classes or categories.

Table 4.2 Distribution of census tracts in the Birmingham, Ala. SMSA, by percent housing units which are owner-occupied, 1960

X	f
PERCENT OF THE HOUSING UNITS WHICH ARE OWNER-OCCUPIED	
90–100	0
80–90	10
70–80	26
60–70	22
50–60	10
40–50	13
30–40	10
20–30	5
10–20	1
0–10	9
Total	106

SOURCE: U.S. Bureau of the Census. *U.S. Census of Population and Housing: 1960. Census Tracts*. Final Report PHC(1)–17. U.S. Government Printing Office, Washington, D.C., 1961. Percents calculated from frequencies in this source.

4.3 INTERVALS, LIMITS, AND MIDPOINTS

Now look at Table 4.2. Here we have the table of another frequency distribution. Look carefully at the variable. Each observation is a percent that has been calculated from another table. In sociology, where we deal with groups and aggregates, it is very common to develop characteristics of the group from distributions within the group. This variable is an example. The aggregate is something called a census tract, which is, in effect, a kind of urban neighborhood usually containing about 30 to 40 blocks. The entire census tract is the "object" being observed. The particular observation made in each tract is the percent of the housing located there that is owner-occupied. This percent is, of course, itself the summary of another distribution, namely, the distribution of houses by type of occupancy within a tract.

Table 4.2 looks about the same as Table 4.1, but there is an important difference. In Table 4.2 each "value" of the variable is really a series of values. The first category, for example, is "90–100," meaning that any percent between these limits would be tallied in this category. A category of this type is called a *class interval*. It is really a collection of individual values. When we group quantitative data into a table we ordinarily collect the values of the variable into class intervals. Indeed, when the variable is continuous (see Chapter 1) we have no other choice for it is literally impossible to list separately each and every value of a continuous variable. Individual observations are grouped into class intervals to keep the table small and easy to read. Generally speaking, it is a good idea to use 10 to 12 class intervals when further calculations will be made from the data in the table. However, as few as five or six class intervals will often suffice when the table is intended only to be read.

The use of class intervals creates certain problems that must be understood and solved. These problems will be discussed in the next several paragraphs. The first problem concerns defining the boundaries of the class interval. These boundaries are usually called the upper and lower *limits* of the class interval. It is sometimes surprisingly difficult to identify these limits exactly. The second problem concerns the slight loss of information that results from shifting from individual values to class intervals containing more than one value.

The class intervals of a variable must be defined in such a way that *all possible* values of the variable in the range of the observations are included in one interval or another and such that any given observation appears in one interval only. These conditions are sometimes referred to by saying that the class intervals must be *exhaustive* and *mutually exclusive,* respectively. To achieve these results what is called the *true upper* limit of one interval is identical to the *true lower* limit of the next higher interval. Table 4.2 lists these true limits. Notice, for example, that the interval representing the smallest percents is "0–10" and the next higher interval is "10–20." The number "10" is the upper limit of the first and the lower limit of the second of these intervals. In this way we make sure that all possible observations are included in at least one class interval.

There is obviously a problem in the use of intervals such as these, however, because there appears to be overlap between each adjacent pair of intervals. It is not clear, for example, where to put a tract that has exactly 10 percent of its housing owner-occupied. Does this tract belong in the "0–10" category or in the "10–20" category? A similar problem occurs in many other contexts. In order to resolve the problem of overlap we distinguish between what are called *open* and *closed* intervals. An interval is open when it does *not* contain its limit and it is closed when it does include the limit. By a very widely accepted convention, statisticians have agreed to use the following rule for continuous variables: *Intervals are closed at the bottom and open on top.*

This rule means that the true lower limit is included in the interval but the true upper limit is not included in it. A tract that had 10 percent owner-occupied housing would, according to this rule, always be placed in the interval 10–20, since 10 is the lower limit of this interval and is included in it. The 10 percent observation would *never* be placed in the 0–10 interval because 10 is the upper limit of this interval and, therefore, is not included within it. Remember, this rule applies only to continuous variables.

Unfortunately, however, we need to know a little more than just this rule because observations, particularly of continuous variables, are themselves *intervals* even though we do not ordinarily think of them in this way. When a person tells us that he is 22 years old, for example, he does not really mean *exactly* 22, but rather that he has lived at least 22 years, but less than 23 years. Similarly, when we say that 10 percent of the houses in a given tract are owner-occupied we do not mean exactly 10 percent (that is, 10.0000000000000 percent) but rather approximately 10 percent. If the calculated percent happened to be 10.003 percent we would probably round it to 10 percent. The observation, as reported, is usually what is called the *midpoint* of the interval in which it falls. The midpoint of an interval is defined as that point which is halfway between the true lower limit and the true upper limit of the interval. Thus, when a man says, "We stayed in Europe about *one month* on our last vacation," we usually assume that he means anything from a few days less than exactly a month to a few days more than exactly a month. That is, we assume that "one month" is the midpoint of some interval that includes exactly how long he actually stayed in Europe.

In scientific work the interval represented by a given observation may be very small. In fact, in what are called the exact sciences the observation may be correct to the third, fourth, fifth, or even sixth decimal place. Even in those cases, however, the observation, as reported, is really the midpoint of an interval. The width of the interval involved in a particular observation is sometimes called the maximum measurement error or the maximum rounding error.

When we combine individual observations into class intervals, then, we are really just substituting larger intervals for smaller ones. In this process, however, we *always assume* that the individual observation is correct. In this way we always know in what interval it belongs. Whenever this assumption is seriously in doubt, the researcher is best advised to modify the *limits* he is using for his intervals. For example, people often round incomes to the nearest $1,000, or even to the nearest $5,000. Therefore, when a man says that he earns $20,000 a year we should be careful. If we create a class interval from, say, $20,000–$25,000, we will probably be falsely classifying many people because $20,000 is the lower limit of our interval, but is probably a midpoint when people report their incomes. Therefore, it would be better in this case to use an interval from, say, $17,500–$22,500 to report incomes, since this interval makes $20,000 a midpoint. Another way to solve this problem is to show the respondent a card listing various income class intervals and ask him in which one he belongs.

There are various ways of representing the limits of class intervals in statistics, some of which are quite confusing. In this book we shall always represent a class interval for continuous data either by reporting the true upper and lower limits or by reporting the midpoint of the interval. To avoid ambiguity when tallying observations, the student should always remember the rule that an interval is closed on the bottom and open on top. To avoid possible confusion, alternative representations will not be presented in this text. The interested student should consult other elementary texts for these alternatives.

So far, we have only discussed continuous variables. It is also important to consider intervals involving discrete observations, that is, observations where there are gaps between possible individual observations. As noted earlier, family size is one example. This variable is discrete when we measure it by counting the number of people in the family. Intervals built out of discrete observations are handled by the following rules, which are quite different from the rule for continuous variables. For discrete variables we have:

1. The limits that are written down are the smallest and largest actual values appearing in the interval. For example, if an interval of family size is to contain one, two, or three members, then we write it as extending from 1–3. We would also write the next interval as beginning at 4.

2. The *true* lower and upper limits are defined as falling halfway between each interval and its nearest neighbors. Thus, for family sizes, the *true* upper and lower limits of the interval 1–3 are 0.5 and 3.5 respectively.

Refer back to Table 4.1, which is a distribution of the number of agreements. Here each "interval" is a discrete specific observation such as "0," "1," and so on. If we interpret these numbers as representing intervals, we can find their true lower and upper limits from the above rules. The gap between numbers is one unit. The true limits lie halfway through the gaps, or one half unit each way. Thus, the true limits of the smallest value ("0") are −0.5 and 0.5 and the true limits of the largest value ("9") are 8.5 and 9.5.

Now that we see clearly how to identify the true limits of an interval in both the continuous and discrete situations it is a simple matter to locate the midpoint of the interval as well. In fact the midpoint of an interval is

$$\text{Midpoint} = \frac{L + U}{2}$$

where $L =$ the true lower limit, and $U =$ the true upper limit of the interval.

In a similar manner we define the *width* of an interval to be

$$\text{Width} = w = U - L$$

These computations are illustrated in Table 4.3, which presents the same distribution as Table 4.2.

The midpoint of an interval is equivalent to an observation. Indeed, it *is* an observation. In Table 4.3, for instance, there are ten observations be-

Table 4.3 Table 4.2 Repeated to illustrate computation of midpoints and interval width

X	X	f	
(CLASS INTERVALS)	(MIDPOINTS)		
90–100	95	0	The first midpoint is 95, which is
80–90	85	10	$\frac{90 + 100}{2}$.
70–80	75	26	The second midpoint is
60–70	65	22	$85 = \frac{80 + 90}{2}$.
50–60	55	10	
40–50	45	13	Note that the upper limit of each
30–40	35	10	interval is ten units higher than the
20–30	25	5	lower limit. That is, each interval is
10–20	15	1	ten units wide.
0–10	5	9	
Total		106	

tween 80 and 90. The midpoint of this interval is 85. Whenever we need to know what specific value these ten. observations possess, we say that each one was an 85. That is, we assign each of them the midpoint value. Of course, there may be a slight amount of error in this practice. However, remember that all observations of continuous variables are midpoints of some interval so there is always some error in the observing process anyway. If we are careful to keep the width of each interval relatively small the amount of error introduced by grouping is also relatively small.

Look again at Table 4.3. The symbol X stands for the variable and also for the different values of the variable. In this table we see that there are two ways of representing these values, namely, the class intervals and the midpoints. Each of these columns has been headed X because each column is a list of the possible values of the variable. Since these two columns contain essentially the same information it is more conventional to include just one of them in a table. When we want to present a table we usually report the class intervals of X and when we want to make calculations from a table we usually put the midpoints in the table.

4.4 TYPES OF DISTRIBUTIONS

One of the first steps in examining a distribution is to identify its general form. The form is important for two reasons. In the first place, the information is intrinsically interesting and is useful in discussing and presenting the data. In the second place, many statistical techniques depend on what we call "distribution assumptions," or the answer to the question: "What is the shape of this distribution?" In the next chapter, for example, we shall present several different measures of what is called the central tendency of a distribution. The choice among these measures will depend, in part at least, on the shape of the distribution.

We may distinguish between a verbal description of the form of a distribution and a relatively precise mathematical description. In this chapter we are concerned mostly with verbal descriptions. The easiest way to begin is to convert a frequency distribution into a picture or visual representation. There are several ways to draw such a picture but we shall describe only the two most common types, *histograms* and *frequency polygons*.

The histogram represents the frequencies in each class interval by a rectangular bar, the *area* of which is proportional to the frequency. A histogram of Table 4.2 is shown in Figure 4.1. To make a histogram the class intervals are marked off along the baseline (the X axis, or "abscissa," in geometry) and frequencies are marked off along the side of the figure (the Y axis, or "ordinate," in geometry). A rectangular bar is constructed for

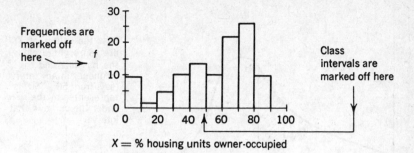

Figure 4.1.   Histogram of the distribution of census tracts in the Birmingham, Ala. SMSA by percent housing units which are owner-occupied, 1960.

each interval. When the class intervals are all equally wide, the height of the bar is determined by the frequency in the interval and the width of the bar by the width of the interval. (See Figure 4.1.) Further instructions are contained in some "computation designs," which will be presented and explained subsequently.

The second common visual representation of a distribution is the *frequency polygon*. The frequency polygon represents each frequency by a dot, or point, placed above the midpoint of the class interval. When the intervals are all equally wide, the height of this dot indicates the frequency. A frequency polygon of Table 4.2 is shown in Figure 4.2. In the frequency polygon the points are connected by straight lines.

When looking at a histogram or a frequency polygon it is often convenient to "smooth" the curve. We imagine that the curve has a simple or smooth shape approximately the same as the shape given in the graph. (Technically, such smooth curves result from fitting some mathematical function to the distribution. We shall not go into the curve fitter's art in this text, but we shall discuss the elementary forms of distributions in terms of smooth curves.) An example of a smooth curve (drawn freehand) is given

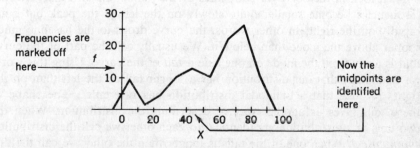

Figure 4.2.   Frequency polygon of data presented in Table 4.2.

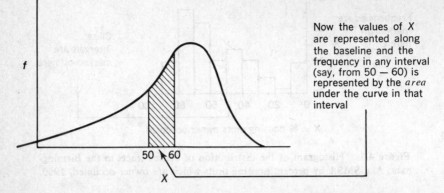

Now the values of X are represented along the baseline and the frequency in any interval (say, from 50 — 60) is represented by the *area* under the curve in that interval

Figure 4.3. A smooth curve fitted to data of Table 4.2.

in Figure 4.3; it represents the same distribution as in the other illustrations in this chapter. Notice that even when the distribution is smoothed, we still think of frequency (visually) as area under the curve in some interval. It is very important to acquire the habit of visualizing frequency in this way. Notice that in smoothing the curve we left out some of the individual humps but we preserved the general form of the distribution.

Now let us try to describe this frequency distribution in a rough but serviceable fashion. Notice, first, that the curve has a single peak, or hump. This peak is called the maximum of the curve. If we drop a line straight down from the maximum to the baseline the value of X at that point is called the *mode* of the distribution. The mode in our distribution is approximately 75 percent. When a curve has just one peak we refer to it as a *unimodal* distribution. When it has two peaks we call it *bimodal*. Technically, a curve is bimodal only if both peaks are exactly the same height, although in practice the term is used for any distribution that has two obvious peaks. There is one curve that is the same height for all values of X. This curve has no maximum or peak. It is called a *uniform* distribution.

Next look at the curve on both sides of the maximum. In Figure 4.3 the frequencies become smaller quite slowly on the left of the peak but quite rapidly on the right. In other words, the curve drops to the baseline much sooner above the mode than below it. We usually call the part of the curve that is away from the mode on one side a *tail* of the curve. Using this word, we would say that our distribution has a longer tail on the left than on the right. (Notice that a unimodal distribution has *two* tails.) The shape of these tails gives us another way of describing the distribution. When the two tails of a distribution are identical to each other we call the distribution *symmetrical*. When one of the tails is longer than the other we call the dis-

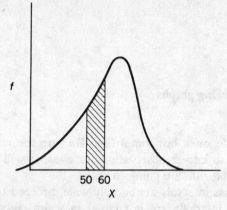

Figure 4.4. Distribution of Figure 4.3 drawn to a different scale.

tribution *skewed*. We usually identify a skewed distribution according to which tail is the longer. When the long tail extends out to the left (that is, occurs with low values of X) we say that the curve is *negatively skewed*. When the long tail extends out to the right we say that the curve is *positively skewed*. The distribution represented by Figure 4.3 is, then, negatively skewed.

It is important to understand that the form of the distribution remains the same (is *invariant*) regardless of the scale used for the frequencies or the X values. Curves drawn to different scales may *look* different but the crucial issue is what proportion of the total area lies between any two points under the curve. Figure 4.4, for example, is another smooth curve of the distribution in Figure 4.3. The scale of X has been shortened considerably, making the distribution look taller and narrower. However, the distribution is the same, which means that the shaded area is the *same proportion of the total area* in both figures.

4.5 USE OF THE COMPUTATION DESIGNS

On the following pages you will find the first in a series of what we call "computation designs." These designs are intended to serve two purposes. They summarize the steps in some operational or computational procedure and they show the most useful way to lay out a problem for computation. These designs will be provided in most of the remaining chapters. At this point we introduce a design that should be helpful in drawing graphs.

Useful hints in drawing graphs

GENERAL STEPS

1. Mark off a scale on a horizontal line. Be sure the entire range of the table (smallest to largest observations or classes) will fit on your page.
2. Examine the table you are going to graph.
   a. If all the class intervals are equally wide, proceed to step 3.
   b. If the class intervals are *not* equal in width, subdivide them until they are. Assign frequencies uniformly to the subdivided parts. For example, if one interval is three times as large as the others, divide it into three intervals and assign one third of its frequency to each of these three smaller intervals. When you have a table in which all intervals are equally wide proceed to step 3.
3. Mark off the intervals on the horizontal line.
4. Make a vertical scale of frequencies to the left on the page.

FOR A HISTOGRAM

5. Draw in the rectangles that represent the distribution.

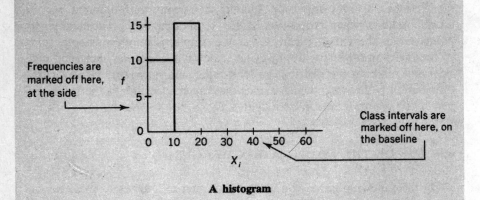

A histogram

FOR A FREQUENCY POLYGON

6. Mark the *midpoint* of each class interval and draw a small circle or dot above this midpoint at the appropriate height on the frequency scale.

7. Imagine an *extra* class interval on each side of the intervals in the table (one below and one above). Record the frequency in these extra intervals as *zero* by the same circle or dot.

8. Connect all circles or dots. Your polygon line now begins at the baseline (or *X* axis), extends up and then back down to the baseline again. It must touch the baseline on both ends.

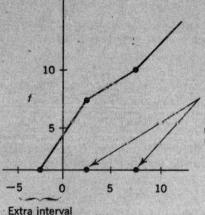

Midpoints are marked on the baseline. Actually, the class boundaries are not necessary except to find the midpoints

Extra interval

A frequency polygon

4.6 THE NORMAL DISTRIBUTION

One type of symmetrical, unimodal curve has played a very important part in the development of theoretical statistics. It is called the *normal* curve. This distribution is approximated by many *observed* distributions. In the study of errors of measurement in physics; in the study of biometric distributions (height, length of arm); and in the study of intelligence, this curve turned up sufficiently often to earn the name "normal." A normal curve is shown in Figure 4.5. Without a technical mathematical description little can be said about this curve except that it is symmetrical and unimodal. These characteristics have caused it to be called a bell-shaped curve. (There are unimodal, symmetrical curves that are *not* normal but they are relatively unimportant in elementary statistics.)

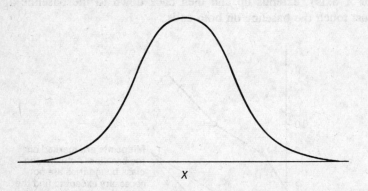

X

Figure 4.5. A normal distribution (the normal curve is very important in statistical analysis; a more precise description of it is given in Chapter 5).

All normal distributions, regardless of the scale to which they are drawn or their location on the X axis, have the same mathematical form. That is, a single mathematical formula describes how frequencies are related to values of a variable when the distribution of those frequencies is normal. Technically, only continuous variables can be normally distributed. The distribution of a *discrete* variable is said to *approximate* the normal curve, however, if it is symmetrical and unimodal, and also contains many individual values of the variable. As we shall see in Chapter 5, there is a table of the normal curve which is very convenient to use. One advantage then of a distribution that is approximately normal is that we can utilize this table.

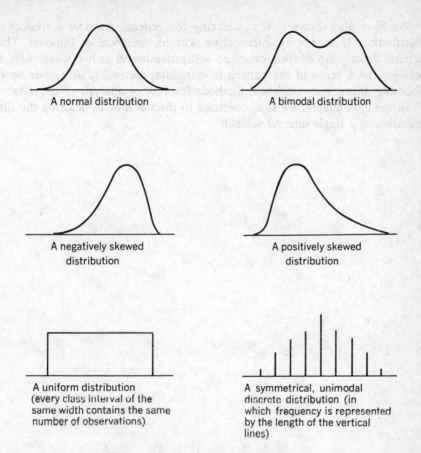

A normal distribution

A bimodal distribution

A negatively skewed
distribution

A positively skewed
distribution

A uniform distribution
(every class interval of the
same width contains the same
number of observations)

A symmetrical, unimodal
discrete distribution (in
which frequency is represented
by the length of the vertical
lines)

Figure 4.6. Some types of distribution.

4.7 WHERE WE STAND

We are now in a position to do two things: we can organize our observations into a table or a graph, and we can describe, at least roughly, the shape of their distribution. With a small number of observations an *array* is useful as a tool of organization. In an array we arrange the observations in order from the lowest to the highest value. With a large number of observations *grouping* becomes useful. Through grouping we create *class intervals*. When we tally observations into class intervals we treat them as if they all had the value of the midpoint of the interval in which they fall. After we have tallied observations we may present them in the form of a table or a graph.

We have also shown how to describe the general shape of a frequency distribution. It may be symmetrical or skewed, unimodal or bimodal. This general description of form or shape will prove useful in two ways: first, it will give us a sense of the pattern in our data; second, it will guide us in choosing appropriate statistical methods for further analysis of the data.

In the next chapter we shall continue to discuss how to describe the distribution of a single interval variable.

5

MEASURES OF CENTRAL
TENDENCY
AND DISPERSION

We have seen, in the last chapter, that an interval variable can be represented as a straight line such that points on the line correspond to individual values of the variable. We have also seen that the frequency with which these values occur can be represented by area under a curve drawn above this line. This ability to give a geometric interpretation of the distribution permits us to discuss its "location" with respect to the line or scale, in addition to discussing its form or shape as in the preceding chapter. Location ordinarily is discussed in terms of two key concepts: *central tendency* and *dispersion*. A measure of central tendency tells us where, in relation to the scale, the middle or center of the distribution is located. A measure of dispersion tells us how spread out or dispersed are the observations relative to the scale. In this chapter we shall show how statisticians define and compute measures of these two concepts.

5.1 MEASURES OF CENTRAL TENDENCY

A measure of central tendency is designed to describe a set of data in terms of a single representative or typical number. The three most commonly used measures, the *mean,* the *median,* and the *mode,* are all based on the idea that one way to describe a set of observations is to choose the most typically occurring or central value in the set. These measures, however, differ in how the word "typical" is defined and in the kind of information that is lost in accomplishing the summarization.

The Mean

The *mean* (sometimes called the arithmetic mean) is defined as the *sum* of a set of observations divided by the *number* of observations in the set. We use the symbol $\bar{X}$ (read "X-bar") to signify the mean of the distribution of X. In terms of a formula we define the mean as

$$\bar{X} = \frac{\Sigma X_i}{N}$$

(A mathematical formula is simply a set of instructions. In this case you are instructed to carry out two operations: (1) *add up* the observations (ΣX_i), and (2) *divide* the result by the number of observations (N). The result is called the *mean*. Using a formula rather than a verbal statement to define the mean is more economical and precise.)

In this formula: X_i is any observation in the set, namely, the i_{th} observation. Σ means "add up" or "sum" and is called the summation sign. This symbol—a capital Greek sigma—will be used many times in the following, so learn it now. The instruction is to "add up" whatever appears to the right of the sign, in this case, X_i or the individual observations. N is the total number of observations in the set.

To illustrate this computation suppose that we have the following set of nine observations: 8, 12, 14, 3, 4, 6, 8, 12, and 5. To find their mean we first add them up and get 72. Next we take this sum and divide it by 9, giving 8, which is the mean. Symbolically,

$$\bar{X} = \frac{72}{9} = 8$$

Computation of the Mean for Grouped Data

When the observations are available in raw form the mean may be computed from the definition given above. However, when the data are grouped it is impossible to use this definition directly because the observations no longer are listed separately—and we cannot just add them up in a single step. The way in which we solve this problem involves the basic procedure for all computation based on grouped data. It is, therefore, quite important for us to understand it. As a start, let us consider a very simple table, such as Table 5.1, which contains the distribution of a discrete variable. In this table there are 16 observations in all ($N = \Sigma f = 16$). Three of these observations are in the interval 0–2. Recalling the discussion in the last chapter, we assume that each of these observations has the midpoint value,

Table 5.1   Hypothetical table illustrating computations based on grouped data

X	X	f	fX
(CLASS INTERVALS)	(MIDPOINTS)		(CALCULATIONS)
0–2	1	3	3
3–5	4	8	32
6–8	7	5	35
Total		16	70

namely, "1." Similarly, eight of the observations have the value "4," which is the midpoint of the second interval, and five observations have the value "7." Let us write out these observations in the form of an array.

$$\underbrace{1,\ 1,\ 1,}_{3\ \text{obs.}}\ \underbrace{4,\ 4,\ 4,\ 4,\ 4,\ 4,\ 4,\ 4,}_{8\ \text{obs.}}\ \underbrace{7,\ 7,\ 7,\ 7,\ 7}_{5\ \text{obs.}}$$

Now let us find the mean by adding up the individual values in this array and dividing the sum by N, as follows:

$$1+1+1+4+4+4+4+4+4+4+4+7+7+7+7+7 = 70$$

$$\bar{X} = \frac{70}{16} = 4.375 = 4.4$$

(Notice, incidentally, that we have rounded the fraction "4.375" to "4.4" in order to avoid the appearance of greater accuracy in the mean than existed in the original observations. It is conventional to express a summary measure as having one more significant figure than is present in each observation. Thus, since each observation is represented as a whole number we express the mean in tenths.) There is another, and simpler, way to carry out the summation necessary to calculating the mean. Notice that the number "1" is added to itself three times, the number "4" is added to itself eight times, and the number "7" is added to itself five times. The operation of adding a number to itself so many times, however, proves to be the definition of *multiplication*. For example, "1" added to itself three times is 3 times 1 or $(3)(1) = 3$. Similarly, "4" added to itself eight times is 8 times 4 or $(8)(4) = 32$ and "7" added to itself five times is 5 times 7 or $(5)(7) = 35$. Therefore, we can write

$$\Sigma X = (3)(1) + (8)(4) + (5)(7) = 70$$

These three products have been written as the last column in Table 5.1.

Symbolically, we have

The sum of the observations $= f_1X_1 + f_2X_2 + f_3X_3$

where f_1 is the frequency with which the first value (X_1) occurred; f_2 is the frequency with which the second value (X_2) occurred; and f_3 is the frequency with which the last value occurred.

More generally, we can say that the sum of the observations of X is equal to

$$\Sigma fX = \Sigma f_i X_i$$

when the observations are grouped. This fact is very convenient, for it is precisely this information which is in our table. Notice that we can write the formula either with or without the subscript "$_i$." There are two operations in this formula: addition and multiplication. When a summation sign is followed by a product or a quotient, always compute the products or quotients *first* and then add them up. This order is very important.

We can summarize this discussion by giving the general formula for computing the mean from grouped data. We have

$$\bar{X} = \frac{\Sigma fX}{N}$$

Computational Short Cuts and Coding

At this point it is useful to pause a moment to consider a special computational problem. In almost all statistical computations we must face the fact that we have to perform our operations on rather large numbers. This task is quite cumbersome. Even something as simple as a mean can be quite tedious to compute. If we have several hundred observations and use the ungrouped formula we must add up or sum a very long series of numbers. If we group the observations and compute the mean from the grouped formula we must form several products (namely, the product of each midpoint and the corresponding frequency). If the numbers involved in these products are large their calculation becomes tedious.

There are two ways to solve the problem. The first is to utilize some sort of machine as an aid in the calculations. For many years statisticians have used desk calculators for this purpose, and most statistical laboratories today are equipped with such calculators. In the last 15 years or so the use of what are called digital computers to make statistical calculations has become commonplace. Large computers can carry out many hundreds of thousands of calculations in a single second, which makes them very efficient, indeed. The second kind of solution is to reduce the numbers being used to smaller ones, make the calculations on these smaller numbers, and then enlarge the results back to the original size. To some extent the use of digital computers makes it less important to understand this second solution. When we work through a digital computer we often perform the calculations directly from the individual observations rather than from tables. However, the number of individual observations may be quite large, and it may be desirable to reduce their size if for no other reason than to keep them from occupying so much space on a punched card. In this text we shall present some aspects of the second solution. That is, we shall show how numbers can be reduced for computational purposes. Even in situations in which the researcher has access to a digital computer, it is useful to know these procedures, even though they will not be used in quite the same way under those circumstances.

The table of an interval variable's distribution contains two basic columns: the column of midpoints and the column of frequencies. We may simplify the computations by reducing the size of the numbers in either or both of these columns. To reduce the size of the frequencies, divide each frequency by some *constant*. In using the formulas, then, remember that the symbol N stands for the sum of the frequency column or its reduced equivalent. For example, when we find percentages we divide each frequency by (0.01) (N). [Dividing a frequency by (0.01) is the same as multiplying it by (100) as we did earlier in finding a percentage.] If we compute a mean from grouped data using percentages rather than frequencies, we must remember that the symbol N in the formula will stand for the sum of the percents. Symbolically, we have

$$\bar{X} = \frac{\Sigma fX}{N} - \frac{\Sigma fX}{\Sigma f} - \frac{\Sigma PX}{\Sigma P} - \frac{\Sigma PX}{100}$$

where P stands for a percent in a particular class interval. In general, we may reduce the size of the frequencies through division by a constant provided only that we also divide the total of the frequencies by the same amount.

We may also reduce the size of the numbers in the column of midpoints. We accomplish this objective through a process called *coding*. Coding itself becomes rather complicated when tables contain class intervals whose widths are unequal. This book is intended as a simple introduction to statistics. Accordingly, *we shall only consider calculation problems arising in tables where the intervals are equally wide*. The student should always remember that these procedures *cannot* be used directly on other tables.

Coding involves two steps. First, one of the midpoints is selected as what is called the "guessed mean" and is assigned a value of zero. Second, each successive interval away from this guessed mean is assigned an integer in succession, from "1" to however many intervals there are in that direction. Intervals whose midpoints are smaller than the guessed mean are assigned *negative* integers; intervals whose midpoints are larger than the guessed mean are assigned *positive* integers. Each of these assigned numbers is called a *"d"* value. The set of d values is written in a new column called "coded midpoints." Table 5.2 illustrates the process.

Table 5.2   Age distribution of the population of the United States, 1960

(X)	f	d	f · d	
AGE (IN YEARS)	FREQUENCY (IN MILLIONS)	CODED MIDPOINT	CODED CLASS SUMS	
0– 10	40.0	−3	−120.0	$\bar{X} = X_0 + \dfrac{(\Sigma fd)}{N}\, w$
10– 20	30.8	−2	−61.6	
20– 30	22.5	−1	−22.5	
30– 40	25.0	0	0	$= 35 + \dfrac{(-59.7)}{183.2}\, 10$
40– 50	22.8	1	22.8	
50– 60	18.2	2	36.4	$= 35 + (-.325)(10)$
60– 70	13.5	3	40.5	$= 35 - 3.25$
70– 80	7.9	4	31.6	$= 31.75$
80– 90*	2.0	5	10.0	$= 31.8$
90–100*	0.4	6	2.4	
100–110*	0.1	7	0.7	
	$N = 183.2$		$\Sigma fd = -59.7$	

SOURCE: Table 45, U.S. Bureau of the Census. *U.S. Census of Population: 1960. General Population Characteristics, United States Summary.* Final Report PC(1) -1B. U.S. Government Printing Office, Washington, D.C., 1961.
* Estimated from the census figures.

Once the d values have been inserted in the table it is easy to find the mean. The mean is

$$\bar{X} = X_0 + \frac{(\Sigma fd)w}{N}$$

where $X_0 = $ the actual midpoint of the "guessed mean" interval and $w = $ the width of each interval.

This formula looks a bit more complicated than the one given earlier but it is really much simpler to use in calculations because the numbers actually handled are much smaller. As noted before, we can also reduce the frequencies to smaller numbers provided that we make the same reduction in the total (N). Table 5.2 illustrates these calculations. In this table the frequencies have each been divided by 1,000,000 to reduce their size and the midpoints of X have been coded to reduce their size. A general computation design for the mean using coded data is presented following this table.

The mean carries most of the burden in standard statistical discussions, largely because of certain theoretically useful properties that it possesses. (See section 5.2 for more details.) In sociological research, however, the necessary data are often not available to compute it and sometimes it is actually inappropriate to use it as the summary measure of central tendency. Whenever a table contains what is called an "open-ended interval," the mean cannot be calculated directly because we cannot determine the midpoint of that interval. In an age classification, for example, an interval might be "65 or over." This interval is open-ended because no upper limit is specified. Aside from this technical problem, note that the mean takes into account each and every observation in proportion to the size of that observation. Ordinarily, this fact is an advantage; but if there happen to be a few very extreme observations, it may be a disadvantage and may make the mean an inappropriate or misleading measure of central tendency. We understand this fact easily when we consider income data. A few very large incomes can inflate the apparent "center" of the distribution of income in a population when this "center" is expressed as a mean, because the mean depends upon the numerical value of each observation. For example, if a star on a professional basketball team earns $100,000 annually and each of the other nine team members earns $10,000 annually the mean income is $19,000 per year. This figure does not represent the distribution very well.

The Median

If we do not want the extreme values to weigh so heavily, we must find a measure that does not depend so much on the *amounts* contributed by the extremes. The *median* (symbolized by *Md*) is the measure that serves this purpose. It is defined as the value that neither exceeds nor is exceeded by more than half the observations in an ordered set. The easiest way to become familiar with this concept is to see how we find it.

Computation of the Median for Ungrouped Data

To find the median for ungrouped data we arrange the observations in order of magnitude; that is, we form them into an array. Then,

1. If there is an odd number of observations we take the middle one as the median. Consider these observations:

$$1, 3, 4, 4, 4, \textcircled{7}, 7, 10, 88, 88, 150$$

Computation design for mean of grouped data, using coding short cuts, for interval variables having k class intervals

(1)	(2)	(3)	(4)
X_i	f_i	d_i	$f_i d_i$
INTERVAL	FREQUENCY	CODED MIDPOINT	CODED CLASS SUM
X_1	f_1	d_1	$f_1 d_1$
X_2	f_2	d_2	$f_2 d_2$
X_3	f_3	d_3	$f_3 d_3$
.	.	.	.
.	.	.	.
.	.	.	.
X_k	f_k	d_k	$f_k d_k$

1. $X_0 =$

2. $\Sigma f_i d_i =$

3. $\Sigma f_i d_i / N =$

4. $(\Sigma f_i d_i / N)(w) =$

5. $\bar{X} = X_0 + (\Sigma fd/N)(w)$

$\qquad =$

$N = \Sigma f_i =$

1. Choose some interval as the one provisionally containing the mean. The midpoint of this interval is X_0. Enter on line 1, at right of table. (Note: unlike d, this is not a coded value; the actual midpoint is used.)
2. Assign the coded midpoints by counting in each direction from X_0; the first interval in each direction is assigned 1, the second 2, the third 3, and so on. For the interval containing X_0, $d = 0$. The sign of d is negative for those intervals the midpoints of which are smaller than X_0; otherwise it is positive. Enter d in column 3 of the table.
3. Multiply the frequency of each class (column 2) by the coded midpoints (in column 3) giving fd. Enter in column 4 of the table.
4. Take the algebraic sum of the fd's (column 4); that is, add the positive values, then add the negative values and take the difference. If the negative fd's are larger, the sum of the fd's is negative, otherwise the sum is positive. Enter the result on line 2 at the right of the table.
5. Compute the value of the correction term (lines 3 and 4 on the right of the table). Divide Σfd (line 2) by N, then multiply by the width of the class interval, entering the result on line 4 at the right of the table.
6. Add the result to X_0, giving the true mean. Note that to add implies either addition or subtraction, depending on the sign of the correction term. If the sum of fd is negative, then the correction term will be negative and you will subtract it from X_0.

There are 11 observations. The sixth observation divides the set in half since five observations fall on either side of this sixth one. The median is, therefore, the value of this sixth observation, namely, $Md = 7$. (For the same set of observations, incidentally, the mean is 33.3.)

2. If there is an even number of observations the median is conventionally taken to be halfway between the two middle observations. For example:

$$\downarrow$$
$$4, 4, 7, 10$$

might be an array of observations. The median lies between the "4" and the "7." We call it the mean of these two numbers or $Md = (4 + 7)/2 = 5.5$.

The *location* of the median in an array can be found, in general, by counting up to the $(N + 1)/2^{nd}$ observation. The value of the observation in this position will be the median if N is odd and the mean of the two adjacent observations will be the median if N is even. For example, in our first series above, $N = 11$ so $(N + 1)/2 = 6$, which is why we counted up to the sixth observation to find the median.

Computation of the Median for Grouped Data

If the data are grouped we have to interpolate within the class interval that contains the middle value in order to give an exact figure for the median. The formula used is

$$Md = L_{md} + \left[\frac{N/2 - F_{-1}}{f_{md}} \right] (w)$$

where Md designates the median; L_{md} is the lower limit of the interval containing the median; N is the number of observations in the set; F_{-1} is the accumulated sum of the frequencies up to, but not including, the interval containing the median; f_{md} is the frequency in the interval containing the median; and w is the width of the class interval containing the median.

In this formula the term to the right of the plus sign is called the *interpolation* term. It serves to locate the value of the median within the interval that contains it. Note that the median uses only one width, namely, the width of the interval in which the median falls. Therefore, it is irrelevant in computing the median whether or not all of the class intervals are equally wide.

Table 5.3 illustrates the computation of the median. Notice that the categories in this table are of unequal width and the last category is open-ended. These facts make the median appropriate. For ungrouped data the first operation was to order the observations. For grouped data the equivalent step is to cumulate the frequencies. These cumulated frequencies are shown as column 3 in the table. As usual we start from the low values of the variable in cumulating the frequencies. Thus, the first frequency is 1,459,000, which is also the first cumulated frequency. The second frequency is 2,956,000, which, when added to the first frequency, generates a cumulated frequency of 4,415,000. We proceed in this manner to calculate all of the cumulated frequencies. (See Chapter 3 to refresh your memory on this point, if necessary.)

Now we wish to find the median. We proceed in two steps. First, we locate the interval that contains the median; second, we use the formula to estimate the exact value of the median within this interval. To find the median interval form $N/2 = 24,139,500$. Now locate this value in the cumulated frequencies. Each cumulated frequency tells us the number of families earning less than the upper limit of the indicated interval. We see that 24,666,000 families earned less than $7,000. Comparing this number with $N/2$ we conclude that the median is less than $7,000. On the other hand, only 20,189,000 earned less than $6,000. Since 20,189,000 is less than $N/2$ we know that the median is above $6,000. Therefore, the median interval is $6,000–$7,000.

Table 5.3   Distribution of total money income among families, United States, 1965

X	f	F	
TOTAL MONEY INCOME	FREQUENCY	CUMULATED FREQUENCY	$Md = L_{md} + \left[\dfrac{N/2 - F_{-1}}{f_{md}} \right] w$
0–$1,000	1,459,000	1,459,000	$N/2 = 24,139,500$. This observation falls in the class interval
1,000–2,000	2,956,000	4,415,000	$6,000–7,000. (The median interval is identified from the cumulated frequency column.)
2,000–3,000	3,583,000	7,998,000	
3,000–4,000	3,806,000	11,804,000	
4,000–5,000	3,883,000	15,687,000	
5,000–6,000	4,502,000	20,189,000	$Md = 6,000$
6,000–7,000	4,477,000	24,666,000	$+ \dfrac{24,139,500 - 20,189,000}{4,477,000} (1,000)$
7,000–8,000	4,683,000	29,349,000	
8,000–10,000	6,952,000	36,301,000	$= 6,000 + \dfrac{3,950,500}{4,477,000} (1,000)$
10,000–15,000	8,342,000	44,643,000	
15,000 and over	3,636,000	48,279,000	$= 6,000 + (0.882)(1,000)$
Total	48,279,000		$= \$6,882$

SOURCE: U.S. Bureau of the Census, *Current Population Reports*, Series P-60, No. 51, "Income in 1965 of Families and Persons in the United States," U.S. Government Printing Office, Washington, D.C., 1967. Adapted from Table A, page 1.

Now we must interpolate within this interval to find just what value the median possesses. To accomplish this task we assume that the frequencies in the median interval are *uniformly* distributed throughout it. With this assumption all we need to do is find what proportion of the frequencies in the interval must be counted to reach the median frequency (that is, $N/2$). For Table 5.3 this proportion is 0.882. Next we convert this proportion into a distance in the interval (by multiplying it by w). Finally, we add this distance to the lower limit to get the median. These steps are presented in Table 5.3 and also are shown in the accompanying computation design.

Note one convenient property of the median relative to the mean. Table 5.3 contains one open-ended interval. For all other intervals midpoints could be calculated directly but for this interval we would have to estimate the midpoint before we could calculate the mean. On the other hand, the fact that this interval is open-ended has no effect at all upon our ability to calculate the median. In situations such as this it is usually preferable to compute the median. This practice is followed in most tables prepared by government census bureaus and statistical abstracting services.

It should also be noted that the median can be used to summarize the distribution of an *ordinal* variable, provided that variable has been measured through the use of a conventional scale. In particular, we can identify the point on the scale that is the median. It turns out, of course, that this point corresponds to the 50th percentile. Thus, we can see that the median is essentially a way of relating the 50th percentile to a *scale* of possible values of the variable. This scale may be either ordinal or interval in character. The 50th percentile is the middle of a rank order. The median is the point on a scale that corresponds to that middle.

The Mode

The mode is another measure of central tendency which is occasionally useful; it will be symbolized by the letters *Mo*. By definition it is the value of X that occurs most frequently in the set of observations. If, for instance, we have the following set of ungrouped observations

$$6, 5, 7, 8, 10, 6, 6, 8, 6, 5$$

the mode is $Mo = 6$; that is, "6" is the number that occurred most often in the set.

The chief advantage of the mode (relative to the median and the mean) lies in the fact that it is very easy to identify. Unfortunately, even this advantage is lost in the case of grouped data, if an exact value for the mode is desired. If a rough estimate of the mode is sufficient you can simply identify the modal interval—that is, the class interval that contains the largest frequency. Otherwise you must interpolate, as with the median. (We do not show the interpolation formula here since it is seldom used.) The modal interval itself can only be identified easily if all of the class intervals are equally wide. When the widths of the various class intervals vary the modal interval is the interval that contains the largest of the ratios, f_i/w_i. For example, the modal interval in Table 5.3 is the interval "$7,000–8,000" rather than either of the other intervals that contain higher frequencies.

Perhaps the most useful purpose of the mode arises in the case in which more than one mode exists; that is, in bimodal or multimodal distributions as described in Chapter 4. Both the median and the mean usually conceal essential features of such distributions, which are revealed by identifying all of the modes or peaks. A good illustration of this use of the mode concerns the average age of death. In many countries people are very likely to die just after they are born, say, within one year of birth. In other words, one mode in the age distribution of deaths is below one year of age. Another mode occurs in later life, say around 50 to 60 years of age. The *mean* age at death is about 30 years in such a case—but this mean is somewhat misleading since people at age 30 are not very likely to die for many more years. An adequate description of this distribution involves identifying, at least roughly, both modes or peaks.

5.2 USES AND INTERPRETATIONS OF THE MODE, MEDIAN, AND MEAN

The choice among the mean, median, and mode depends primarily on the purpose the measure is to serve. Consider, first, the purpose of *describing the distribution* effectively. For this purpose the *mode* is the most useful measure to use when quickly reading or scanning a table in a book. Just find the interval containing the largest of the values, f_i/w_i. It is a good idea to get into the habit of automatically searching for this figure when you read a table. It quickly locates the center of a distribution and thus makes the table more meaningful. The mode is also useful, of course, in describing bimodal or multimodal distributions. The *median* is most useful in the case of highly skewed distributions. Tables of such distributions often contain at least one open-ended interval, in which case the mean cannot be computed unless the midpoint of that interval can be estimated. The median, however, can almost always be computed from such tables. Aside from this technical advantage, highly skewed distributions contain a few very extreme observations, which have a marked impact upon the mean but very little impact upon the median. The *mean* is most useful for this descriptive purpose when the distribution is relatively symmetrical. If a distribution is perfectly symmetrical and unimodal, incidentally, the three measures of central tendency will all be equal.

Computation design for the median of grouped data for interval variables having k class intervals

(1)	(2)	(3)	
X_i	f_i	F_i	
INTERVAL	FREQUENCY	CUMULATIVE FREQUENCY	
X_1	f_1	f_1	1. $N/2 =$
X_2	f_2	$f_2 + F_1$	2. $L_{md} =$
X_3	f_3	$f_3 + F_2$	3. $f_{md} =$
.	.	.	4. $F_{-1} =$
.	.	.	5. $Md = L_{md} + \left[\dfrac{N/2 - F_{-1}}{f_{md}}\right](w)$
.	.	.	$=$
X_k	f_k	$f_k + F_{k-1}$	
$N = \Sigma f_i =$			

STEPS IN COMPUTATION

1. Obtain the cumulative frequency distribution. Review Chapter 3 if unclear as to how. The last entry should equal N. Enter these cumulated frequencies in column 3 of the table.
2. Divide N by 2. Enter the result on line 1 at the right.
3. By inspecting the cumulative frequency column find which interval contains the middle observation. Enter on line 2 the lower limit of this interval and on line 3 the frequency in this interval.
4. Find the cumulative frequency up to (but not including) the median interval. Enter this number on line 4 at the right of the table.
5. Compute the median (Md) following the instructions in the formula on line 5.
   (a) Subtract F_{-1} from $N/2$.
   (b) Divide the result by f_{md}.
   (c) Multiply this result by w. This step gives the interpolation term.
   (d) Finally, add the result in (c) to L_{md} to yield the median.

The other major uses to which a distribution may be put are *inference* and *prediction*. Inference occurs when we want to use the distribution in a *sample* to say something about the distribution in the population from which the sample was drawn. Prediction occurs when we want to use the distribution to identify the value of some particular observation *before* we have actually observed it. *In either of these cases, the mean is definitely the preferred measure*. In inference it is preferred because it fluctuates less from sample to sample. In prediction it is preferred because it is what is called the "expected value" of the distribution. In particular, if you always predict (or "expect") that the mean will occur you will make less total error than if you always predict any other value. In making this statement we assume that error is measured by what is called the standard deviation, which will be discussed later in this chapter. Problems of estimation and prediction will be considered in the remaining chapters of this book.

5.3 MEASURES OF DISPERSION

The central tendency of a distribution is useful because it locates the distribution on the scale by identifying its single, most representative value. Of course, the actual observations are not all concentrated at this value but are spread out or "distributed" among many values (hence the word distribution, incidentally). In this section we shall discuss how to measure the extent to which the observations are spread out or dispersed. It turns out that the concept of dispersion is closely linked to the concept of central tendency. Corresponding to the three measures of central tendency are three principal ways of measuring dispersion: the *variance* (or its square root, the standard deviation), the *interquartile range,* and the *range.* These measures will be discussed in the paragraphs that follow.

The Standard Deviation and Variance

The most elegant measure of central tendency is the mean, which is computed by summing all of the observations and dividing the sum by the number of observations. In the same way the most elegant measure of dispersion involves a summation process, although it is a bit more difficult to describe this measure of dispersion than it was to describe the corresponding measure of central tendency.

To develop the appropriate measure, let us first note that dispersion can be visualized as *deviation from the mean*. If all of the observations were concentrated at the mean value there would be no dispersion. Dispersion exists when the individual values of the observations are not all identical to the mean value. The extent of dispersion, then, can be visualized as the extent to which the observations deviate from the mean. We begin by identifying just how far any particular observation is from the mean. If X is an observation and $\bar{X}$ is the mean, then $X - \bar{X}$ is the distance of the observation from the mean, which is called its deviation from the mean. This notion of deviation from the mean is so important in statistics that we use a special symbol for it, namely, x (read "little x"). We define

$$x = X - \bar{X}$$

and refer to x as the "mean deviate form of X."

Since x measures the deviation of any *individual* observation from the mean, it is reasonable to think of taking an average of these deviations to get the overall measure of dispersion in the distribution as a whole. The mean of any set of numbers is the sum of those numbers divided by how many there are. If we apply this idea directly to x, we are disappointed. Regardless of how near to or far from the mean the observations are, it is always true that

$$\frac{\Sigma x}{N} = 0$$

because $\Sigma x = 0$.

Consider, for example, a set of ten observations of family size:

$$2, 3, 3, 4, 5, 5, 5, 6, 6, 8$$

The mean of these observations is $X = \Sigma X/N = 47/10 = 4.7$. Let us now rewrite each observation as a mean deviate, as follows.

X	x $(X - \bar{X})$
2	−2.7
3	−1.7
3	−1.7
4	−0.7
5	0.3
5	0.3
5	0.3
6	1.3
6	1.3
8	3.3
	$\Sigma x = 0.0$

We see at once that the sum of the mean deviates is zero. (A simple exercise in algebra will show that this result is necessarily the case, given the definition of a mean. In actual computations, rounding errors in the mean may make Σx not quite equal to zero.) This example also shows why the sum of the mean deviates is zero. Some of the mean deviates are negative numbers; others are positive numbers. The negative numbers just balance the positive ones, producing the zero sum.

One way to solve this problem is just to ignore the negative signs and work with what is called the absolute value of the mean deviate. This solution was widely adopted 40 to 60 years ago but has since fallen into disuse. Another way to eliminate negative signs, which yields numbers that are more easily manipulated mathematically than are absolute values, is to *square* each number. Squared numbers are always positive. For example, $(3)^2 = (3)(3) = 9$ and $(-3)^2 = (-3)(-3) = 9$.

Today we ordinarily square each mean deviate and then find the average of these squared values to measure dispersion. This average of the squared deviations is called the *population variance* and is defined as

$$\text{Population variance} = \sigma^2 = \frac{\Sigma x^2}{N} = \frac{\Sigma(X - \bar{X})^2}{N}$$

Notice that the lower-case Greek sigma, or σ, is used to symbolize this measure. We write it as "σ^2" because each mean deviate was squared. Treating the ten observations listed earlier as a population of observations we can calculate their population variance as follows:

X	x	x^2
2	−2.7	7.29
3	−1.7	2.89
3	−1.7	2.89
4	−0.7	0.49
5	0.3	0.09
5	0.3	0.09
5	0.3	0.09
6	1.3	1.69
6	1.3	1.69
8	3.3	10.89

$$\Sigma x^2 = 28.10$$

$$\sigma^2 = \frac{28.10}{10} = 2.81$$

The variance has become the typical measure of dispersion and is used when the data permit its calculation. It has one minor drawback, however. Since it is based on the squares of the mean deviates, it is hard to relate it directly to a visual picture of the distribution (squaring distorts the X axis). For this reason when we want to visualize dispersion we work with the square root of the population variance, which is called the *population standard deviation*. We have

$$\text{Population standard deviation} = \sigma = \sqrt{\frac{\Sigma x^2}{N}}$$

There is one more important point to discuss. When we are working with a *sample* of observations (which is ordinarily the case) we do not use this exact formula because it would give us what is called a *biased* estimate of the population variance. In particular, we would systematically underestimate the population variance. This bias is corrected by dividing Σx^2 (called the "sum of squares") by $N - 1$ instead of N. The resulting measure is called the sample variance or simply the variance. It is symbolized by s^2. In this text whenever we use the term *variance* we mean the sample variance or s^2. To refer to the population variance we always use the phrase "population variance." Thus, we define the variance as

$$s^2 = \frac{\Sigma x^2}{N - 1}$$

In the same way, we define the standard deviation to be

$$s = \sqrt{s^2} = \sqrt{\frac{\Sigma x^2}{N - 1}}$$

Computing s and s^2 from Ungrouped Data

The definition of the variance is not the most convenient formula to use in calculating it, even though it gives exact instructions for computation (that is, it is an operational definition). We have encountered this problem before and shall again before the book has come to an end. The definition provides the best way *to think about* the concept but not the best way to compute it. In the next few paragraphs we shall present the best computational procedures, first for ungrouped and then for grouped data.

The following formula is the most useful for calculating the variance from ungrouped data, either by hand or with a desk calculator.

$$s^2 = \frac{\Sigma X^2 - \dfrac{(\Sigma X)^2}{N}}{N - 1}$$

[Note that this formula is in terms of the *original observations* (X) rather than the deviations (x). Using the original observations saves a great deal of labor in computation.]

The key to understanding this formula lies in being able to distinguish between the two summation operations that it contains. The first summation is written ΣX^2. These symbols tell us to square each X and then to sum the squares. The second summation is written $(\Sigma X)^2$. Here we first sum the X values and then square the sum. The clue to the difference in these directions lies in the parentheses. If this explanation is not clear, study it and the example that follows very carefully for it is very important in understanding computational formulas of many kinds in statistics.

In this formula we do *not* find $X - \bar{X}$ for each X, instead we square each X itself.* This substitution is what makes the calculations easier. For the same ten observations we have already used, these computations look like this:

X	X^2	
2	4	
3	9	
3	9	
4	16	
5	25	
5	25	
5	25	
6	36	
6	36	
8	64	
$\Sigma X = 47$	$249 = \Sigma X^2$	

$$s^2 = \frac{\Sigma X^2 - \dfrac{(\Sigma X)^2}{N}}{N - 1}$$

$$= \frac{249 - \dfrac{(47)^2}{10}}{10 - 1}$$

$$= \frac{249 - 220.9}{9}$$

$$= \frac{28.1}{9}$$

$$= 3.12$$

$$s = \sqrt{s^2} = 1.77 \text{ family members}$$

In these calculations we deal with the original observations in the first column and their squares in the second column. Each of these columns is summed to generate the two sums that will be used in the formula. We then

* A table of squares and square roots will be found in the Appendix.

count the number of observations to get N and we have all of the elements that enter into the formula. We square the sum of the X values and divide this result by N. Next we subtract this result from the sum of the squares of the X values. We now have what is called the sum of squares. Finally, we divide the sum of squares by $N - 1$ to get s^2 or the variance. If we prefer we can take its square root and work with s or the standard deviation. Finding the sum of squares by this formula is the same mathematically as adding the squared deviations. In other words,

$$\text{Sum of squares} = \Sigma x^2 = \Sigma(X - \bar{X})^2 = \Sigma X^2 - \frac{(\Sigma X)^2}{N}$$

Computing s and s^2 from Grouped Data

When dealing with grouped data we use the same type of short cuts that we used in finding the mean. In fact, usually $\bar{X}$, s^2, and s are computed at the same time. The formula that we use for s^2 involves coding as before. This formula is

$$s^2 = w^2 \left[\frac{\Sigma fd^2 - \dfrac{(\Sigma fd)^2}{N}}{N - 1} \right]$$

As usual, if we want the standard deviation instead we take the square root of s^2. In the formula for s^2 the various symbols are defined in the usual way. To refresh your memory: w is the width of a class interval and w^2 is its square; f is a frequency in a class interval; d is the coded midpoint of a class interval or its step deviation from the guessed mean; N is the total number of observations (the sum of the cell frequencies); and Σ is the summation sign. Table 5.4 illustrates the use of this formula to calculate s^2 for the age distribution with which we have already worked. In this table we have also reduced the frequencies to facilitate the calculations.

Up to a point our procedure is exactly the same as in the computation of the mean. A guessed mean is chosen and we assign d by counting, stepwise, up and down from the guessed mean (or X_0). Next, we multiply each f by the corresponding d and enter these products in column 4. Now, however, we include a new column of calculations—the column headed fd^2. Here it pays to look carefully at how we find these numbers. The formula tells us to take $(f)(d)(d) = fd^2$. Ordinarily, when you think about such a product you take the square first. In this case, however, we take advantage of the fact that we have already found $fd = (f)(d)$ for each class interval. To find fd^2 all we have to do is multiply each fd (in column 4) by the corresponding d (in column 3). Now we sum each of the columns headed f, fd, and fd^2, and enter the sums into the formula as shown in Table 5.4. The accompanying computation design reviews the procedure. Notice that in the computation design we have used the optional subscript i in identifying the cell frequencies and midpoints. You should be familiar with the computation formulas both with and without these subscripts.

Table 5.4   Age of population of United States, 1960 (Illustrating computation of the variance)

X	f	d	fd	$(d)(fd) = fd^2$
AGE (IN YEARS)	FREQUENCY (IN MILLIONS)	CODED MIDPOINTS	CODED CLASS SUMS	CODED SUM SQUARE
0 – 10	40.0	−3	− 120.0	360.0
10 – 20	30.8	−2	− 61.6	123.2
20 – 30	22.5	−1	− 22.5	22.5
30 – 40	25.0	0	0	0
40 – 50	22.8	1	22.8	22.8
50 – 60	18.2	2	36.4	72.8
60 – 70	13.5	3	40.5	121.5
70 – 80	7.9	4	31.6	126.4
80 – 90	2.0	5	10.0	50.0
90 –100	0.4	6	2.4	14.4
100 –110	0.1	7	0.7	4.9
$N = \Sigma f = 183.2$			$\Sigma fd = -59.7$	$918.5 = \Sigma fd^2$

$$s^2 = w^2 \left[\frac{\Sigma fd^2 - \dfrac{(\Sigma fd)^2}{N}}{N - 1} \right]$$

$$= 10.0 \left[\frac{918.5 - \dfrac{(-59.7)^2}{183.2}}{183.2*} \right]$$

$$= 10.0 \left[\frac{918.5 - \dfrac{3564.09}{183.2}}{183.2} \right]$$

$$= 10.0 \left[\frac{918.5 - 19.45}{183.2} \right]$$

$$= 10.0 \frac{(899.05)}{183.2}$$

$$= 49.07$$

$$s = 7.0 \text{ years}$$

* Subtracting one from 183,200,000 does not change the number as expressed.

Quartiles and the Interquartile Range

Another measure of dispersion can be used that is essentially analogous to the median. It is called the *interquartile range*. The interquartile range is the difference between what are called the third and the first *quartiles* of the distribution. The first quartile, or Q_1, is defined as that X value so selected that no more than 25 percent of the observations are smaller and no more than 75 percent of the observations are larger than it is. The second quartile, or Q_2, is the median. The third quartile, or Q_3, is defined as that X value so selected that no more than 75 percent of the observations are smaller and no more than 25 percent are larger than it is. In effect, the quartiles divide the distribution into fourths or quarters. The interquartile range, in turn, is a measure of the distance or difference between the upper quarter of the distribution and the lower quarter. Although it is important to understand the idea behind this measure it is also important to note that sociologists do not use the concept too often. When it is used, it is normally calculated from grouped data. We will present the formulas for these computations below. We shall not present a computational design because the method of calculation is so similar to that of the median. If you are in doubt as to how to accomplish these computations check the computation design for the median.

Computing the Quartiles from Grouped Data

We have the following formulas for Q_1 and Q_3:

$$Q_1 = L_1 + \left[\frac{N/4 - F_{-1}}{f_1}\right] w_1$$

$$Q_3 = L_3 + \left[\frac{3N/4 - F_{-1}}{f_3}\right] w_3$$

where

$Q_1 =$ the X value at the 25th percentile or the first quartile

$Q_3 =$ the X value at the 75th percentile or the third quartile

$L_1 =$ the lower limit of the interval containing Q_1

$L_3 =$ the lower limit of the interval containing Q_3

$f_1 =$ the frequency in the interval containing Q_1

$f_3 =$ the frequency in the interval containing Q_3

$w_1 =$ the width of the interval containing Q_1

$w_3 =$ the width of the interval containing Q_3

$F_{-1} =$ the cumulated frequency up to the interval specified by the quartile being calculated.

When discussing the median we introduced Table 5.3, which shows the distribution of total money income for families in the United States during 1965. We can now compute Q_1 and Q_3 from the same data. We have

$$Q_1 = 4,000 + \left[\frac{12,069,750 - 11,804,000}{3,803,000}\right] (1,000)$$

$$= \$4,070$$

$$Q_3 = 8,000 + \left[\frac{36,209,250 - 29,349,000}{6,952,000}\right] (2,000)$$

$$= \$9,974$$

These figures can be used in several ways in describing the distribution of income. For one thing, we can use them to compute the interquartile range, which is $Q_3 - Q_1 = \$9,974 - 4.070 = \$5,904$. This number tells us something about the dispersion of incomes in the United States. In particular, it tells us that there is almost a $6,000 spread (note that we have rounded the exact figure) between the income of a person at the first quartile and one at the third quartile. That is, the income spread in the *middle half* of the population of families is almost $6,000.

Another way to use these quartile figures is to compare them with the median. The median income was $6,882. There is, therefore, a spread of $2,812 between the median and Q_1 and a spread of $3,092 between the median and Q_3. Note that the spread in the upper tail is slightly greater. This difference means that the distribution is skewed to the right.

A third way to use the figures is by themselves. Q_3 tells us, for instance, that 25 percent of the families in the United States earned at least $9,974 in 1965. In the same way, Q_1 tells us that 25 percent of the families in the United States earned no more than $4,070 in 1965. Either of these figures is, in itself, a summary of the distribution of income.

The Range

One final measure of dispersion is worth mentioning. It is called the *range*. The range is the difference between the largest observation and the smallest observation in a set. If, for instance, we have these observations

$$5, 7, 8, 9, 11$$

the range is

$$11 - 5 = 6$$

The range is a relatively crude measure of dispersion because it takes into account only two specific observations—the largest and the smallest—and thus is obviously quite subject to the occurrence of one extreme observation in a set. Despite this crudeness, the range may be quite useful when we are reading tables or quickly scanning data. In a table, the smallest and largest class intervals containing any frequencies give us a rough picture of the range of the observations and, hence, their tendency to be dispersed.

5.4 THE NORMAL CURVE

There is one important curve which is completely characterized by its mean and standard deviation. This curve is called the *normal curve*. It is important because there is every reason to believe that *error* is actually distributed normally. Since statistical inference, which will be considered in Part III of this book, is largely concerned with the study of error, the normal curve looms large in many statistical analyses. This point will be elaborated more fully in Part III. In this section we discuss the normal curve in a very preliminary way because it provides us with a sensible way to interpret the standard deviation.

We can visualize the standard deviation in a normal curve by looking at Figure 5.1. The area under the curve is interpreted as the proportion of

Computation design for the variance and standard deviation for grouped, interval observations with k class intervals, using coding short cuts

(1)	(2)	(3)	(4)	(5)
X_i	f_i	d_i	$f_i d_i$	$f_i d_i^2$
		CODED MIDPOINT	CODED CLASS SUM	CODED SQUARES
X_1	f_1	d_1	$f_1 d_1$	$(f_1 d_1)(d_1)$
X_2	f_2	d_2	$f_2 d_2$	$(f_2 d_2)(d_2)$
X_3	f_3	d_3	$f_3 d_3$	$(f_3 d_3)(d_3)$
.	.	.	.	.
.	.	.	.	.
.	.	.	.	.
X_k	f_k	d_k	$f_k d_k$	$(f_k d_k)(d_k)$
$N = \Sigma f_i$			$\Sigma f_i d_i$	$\Sigma f_i d_i^2$

1. $f_i d_i =$

2. $f_i d_i^2 =$

3. $(f_i d_i)^2 =$

4. $(f_i d_i)^2 / N =$

5. $s^2 = w^2 \left[\dfrac{\Sigma f_i d_i^2 - \dfrac{(\Sigma f_i d_i)^2}{N}}{N-1} \right]$

6. $s = \sqrt{s^2}$

1. Choose X_0, the guessed mean, and count off the step deviations d, entering the results in column 3. You will not need the guessed mean itself in computing the variance.
2. Multiply the frequency in each class (column 2) by the coded midpoints (the d_i values of column 3) giving $f_i d_i$. Record these products as column 4.
3. Multiply each $f_i d_i$ by d_i (multiply each number in column 4 by the corresponding number in column 3 and enter the results in column 5).
4. Sum the $f_i d_i$ products in column 4 and enter the result on line 1 at the right.
5. Sum the $f_i d_i^2$ products in column 5 and enter the result on line 2 at the right.
6. Square the sum of the $f_i d_i$ values (line 1) and enter the result on line 3.
7. Find N by summing the frequencies.
8. Divide the quantity in line 3 by N and enter the result on line 4.
9. Find the width of the intervals (w) by inspection of column 1.
10. Compute the variance using the formula in line 5. Be sure you *square w*. You will find the other terms that you need on lines 2 and 4.
11. Find the standard deviation by taking the square root of the variance (line 5). Record the result on line 6.

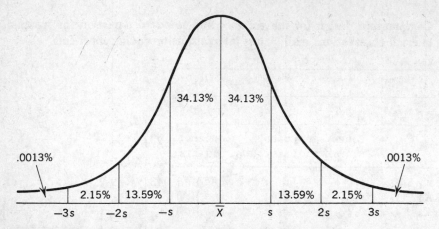

Figure 5.1. Area under the normal curve.
The area under the curve is interpreted as the proportion of observations in the
distribution, the total adding to 1.00, or 100 percent. Between $\bar{X} \pm s$ lie about
68 percent of the observations (or area) in a normal distribution. Between
$\bar{X} \pm 2s$ lie about 95 percent and between $\bar{X} \pm 3s$ lie over 99 percent of the
observations.

observations in the distribution, the total adding to 1.00, or 100%. Between
$\bar{X} \pm s$ lie about 68% of the observations (or area) in a normal distribution. Between $\bar{X} \pm 2s$ lie about 95%, and between $\bar{X} \pm 3s$ lie over 99%
of the observations.

The mean of a normal distribution divides the distribution exactly in half.
If we go one standard deviation to the right of the mean, we will include
approximately 34 percent of the observations between lines marked off at
the two points. If we go one standard deviation to the left, we include another 34 percent of the observations. Altogether, a little more than two
thirds of our distribution is included within $\bar{X} \pm s$. Within $2s$ on either side
of the mean, about 95 percent of the distribution is contained; *almost* all
the observations lie within $\bar{X} \pm 3s$. This information is useful in many ways,
if (and only if) a distribution actually approximates a normal curve.

Reading the Normal Curve Table

In the discussion above, certain specific areas under the normal curve
were presented. Because this curve is so important in statistics, it is very
useful for the student to learn how to find these areas (that is, proportions
of cases) for any interval. To make it easier to accomplish this objective, a
special table has been constructed from which it is relatively easy to figure
the area in any interval. The following paragraphs show how to read

and use this table. (In this book, most of our uses of the normal curve table will involve the points and areas already presented in Figure 5.1. Therefore, this section is somewhat optional.)

First the values of X are converted to *standard deviation units,* sometimes called *standard scores,* or *standard normal variables.* This means that we express each X in terms of the number of standard deviations it departs from the mean. We use the letter z to designate this transformed value of X.

$$z = \frac{X - \bar{X}}{s}$$

(The numerator is simply x again, so that the formula can also be read $z = x/s$.)

In this formula, X is some value of the variable that we wish to convert to a standard score so that we can use the table of the normal curve, which is in standard form; $\bar{X}$ is the mean of the distribution of X in a very large sample of observations; and s is the standard deviation of the distribution of X in that very large sample.

Class frequencies are represented by an area under the curve and expressed as a proportion of the total area. The total area equals 1.00.

The table of the normal curve, which comes in several different versions, will show the areas under the curve in one or more of these three ways:

1. It may show the area from $\bar{X}$ to z (area a in Figure 5.2). If $z = 1.00$, for instance—that is, you go out one standard deviation from the mean—the table shows 0.3413. In other words, about 34 percent of the total area is between $\bar{X}$ and an ordinate erected at a point one standard deviation out from $\bar{X}$.

2. It may show the area in the smaller portion of the curve cut off by z (area b). This is the case, for instance, with Table 2 in the Appendix to this

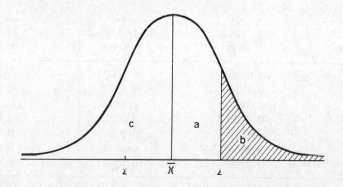

Figure 5.2. Areas under the normal curve.

book. If $z = 1.00$ the area to the right of z is 0.1587, or about 16 percent of the total area. If $z = -1.00$ instead of 1.00, the area in the smaller portion is again 0.1587, although it is the tail on the left side of the curve that is involved. The area to the right of z_i will equal the area to the left of $-z_i$ since the curve is perfectly symmetrical.

3. A complete table may also show the area in the larger portion of the curve cut off by z. (This would be area c in Figure 5.2, plus area a.) If z is 1.00, for instance, the area to the left of z would be 0.8413. If z is -1.00, the area in the larger portion is now to the right of z, but is still 84 percent of the total area. If the table does not give the area in the larger portion, you can find it simply by taking $1 -$ the area in b, since the area as a whole is equal to 1.00. You can also find it by taking 0.5000 plus the area in a. (Do you see why?)

Now look at Table 5.5, a portion of a table of the normal curve. The only other information you might want from the table is the area *between* two values of z. Suppose, for instance, that we want the area between z_1 and z_2 where z_2 is the larger of the two scores. We find this area with the aid of column 4. First, find the area beyond z_1. Second, subtract from this area beyond z_2. We can visualize this process as in Figure 5.3.

Table 5.5   Portion of table of the normal curve

(1)	(2)	(3)	(4)
$z_i = x_i/s$	AREA FROM $\bar{X}$ TO z_i	AREA IN LARGER PORTION	AREA IN SMALLER PORTION
0.00	0.0000	0.5000	0.5000
0.50	0.1915	0.6915	0.3085
1.00	0.3413	0.8413	0.1587
1.96	0.4750	0.9750	0.0250
2.00	0.4772	0.9772	0.0228
2.58	0.4951	0.9951	0.0049
3.00	0.4987	0.9987	0.0013

SOURCE: Adapted from Edwards, 1955, Appendix, Table III. The full table shows, of course, many more values of z.

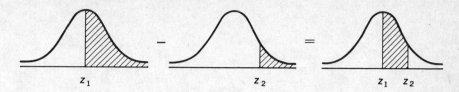

Figure 5.3 Process of finding area between two orders of z. Area between z_1 and z_2, z_2, $> z_1$.

For example, to find the area between the second and third standard deviations from the mean in Figure 5.1 (this area is not given in the table itself) we take the area out from $z = 2.00$, which is 0.0228, and subtract from it the area out from $z = 3.00$, which is 0.0013, giving 0.0215.

5.5 WHERE WE STAND

We have now surveyed the major concepts used by statisticians in summarizing the information contained in the distribution of a single interval variable. For most purposes, this information can be condensed to three items: a name, and two numbers. The name describes the form of the distribution—symmetric, skewed, bimodal, and so on. The numbers describe, respectively, the location of the "center" of the distribution and the amount of dispersion or variation present among the observations. With regard to these numbers we have three major choices:

1. The mode and the range. This choice is best when *reading* tables since both figures can be quickly estimated without any actual calculations.

2. The median and interquartile range. This choice is best when distributions are highly skewed, or when data are presented in a form that makes the computation of other measures impossible.

3. The mean and standard deviation (or variance). This choice is generally best, except under the conditions mentioned above. The mean and standard deviation are particularly appropriate in connection with a distribution known as the normal distribution.

part II

The Relationship between Two or More Characteristics

Introductory Comments

We have now reviewed the various ways that are available for describing the distribution of a single variable in a single population. The choice among the fundamental descriptive concepts depends upon the type of characteristic being studied. There are five major descriptive concepts and three primary levels of measurement. The descriptive concepts are a *proportion* (or percent), a *percentile*, the *form* of the distribution, its *central tendency*, and its *dispersion*. The three levels of measurement are the *nominal*, *ordinal*, and *interval* levels. Throughout the remaining chapters of this book we shall be using these ideas as building blocks in the study of more complicated structures. Before turning to the subject matter of this part of the book it is important to stress one point about which concepts to use in a given situation.

We have already noted that we cannot treat data as though they were measured at any higher level than the actual level at which they have been measured. That is, for example, we cannot use the concept of the mean to summarize data measured at the nominal level. This concept does not apply to such data. We have also noted that we *can* treat data as though they were measured at some lower level than that actually used in assembling the data. For example, if we ask each respondent to identify the last year in school that he completed we have accomplished interval measurement. It is possible, in such a situation, to treat the observations as though they were ordinal by ranking the respondents according to amount of education. It is also possible to treat the observations as though they were nominal.

The point that needs stressing here, however, is that although it is possible to reduce the level of measurement it is usually poor policy to do so. Generally speaking, if the raw data have been assembled in a way that involves interval measurement then those data should be analyzed using concepts appropriate to the interval level. Similarly, if the raw data involve ordinal measurement then their analysis should make use of ordinal concepts. In other words, the choice of level of measurement for description and analysis should depend primarily upon the level of measurement that was used in making the raw or original observations. For example, in analyzing data on years of school completed we should ordinarily think in terms of central tendency and dispersion rather than in terms of a proportion or percent. The reason for this principle is clear. Whenever we reduce the level of measurement we throw away information. Generally speaking, we have gone to a good deal of trouble to collect that information. It does not make much sense to throw some of it away when we start analyzing the data.

Now that we know how to summarize the information in a single distribution, the next problem is to learn how to *compare* distributions with each other. In this part of the book we shall consider such comparisons at each of the three basic levels of measurement. To compare univariate distributions we create what is called the *bivariate distribution*. As we shall see, the bivariate distribution can be visualized as a collection of univariate distributions that describe the distribution of a single variable under various conditions. In Chapter 6 we shall consider how to present the bivariate distribution in the form of a table; in Chapter 7, how to summarize the distribution of two interval variables; and in Chapter 8 we shall do the same for attributes and ordinal variables. Finally, Chapter 9 will discuss, in an introductory way, how to describe multivariate distributions, which are distributions containing three or more variables.

6

THE BIVARIATE TABLE

Bivariate distributions, usually presented in the form of tables, are the basic ingredients of most quantitative papers and monographs in social science. It is, therefore, important to understand clearly just what information these distributions contain and how this information may be extracted and used. Accordingly, this chapter is devoted entirely to the structure of the bivariate table. The basic form of this table remains the same for all levels of measurement. Here, then, we shall concentrate upon those general principles involved in reading and interpreting bivariate tables that apply regardless of how the variables have been measured.

6.1 THE ORIGIN OF A BIVARIATE FREQUENCY DISTRIBUTION

Any bivariate distribution can be visualized as arising in either of two different ways. The first way involves observing two different characteristics on each member of a population. The second way involves looking at the distribution of a single variable in two or more populations. It is important to understand each of these ways but it is also important to recognize that they are just different ways of visualizing the *same* thing, namely, the bivariate distribution.

A. A bivariate distribution arises whenever we observe two different characteristics of each individual in a population (or in a sample from the population). For example, it is very common in surveys and censuses to identify both the *age* and the *sex* of each respondent. In such a survey our raw data would look something like the table on page 96.

	Age	Sex
1st respondent	36	Male
2nd respondent	24	Male
3rd respondent	52	Female
. . .	. . .	. . .
. . .	. . .	. . .
Last or Nth respondent	17	Female

This bivariate information may be assembled into a table in much the same manner as in the case of univariate information. Of course, the bivariate table will contain two sets of categories or class intervals, one for each variable. It is conventional to list one of these sets of categories across the top of the table and the other down its left-hand side. In this way we create several *cells* in which we record the frequencies. The frequency in each cell identifies how many times the category in its row and the category in its column occurred in the same individual. Table 6.1 presents the distribution of age and sex in the population of the United States as of 1960. (The frequencies in this table have been rounded to the nearest million.) The first frequency is 36,000,000. It refers to the number of people in the population who are *both* under 20 years of age *and* male. We say that this frequency refers to the *joint* occurrence of a particular age category and a particular sex category. In this table there are six of these joint frequencies. In addition, several frequencies are written around the edge of the table that are sums of the individual joint or cell frequencies. We shall show how we identify and name the various parts of this table after we consider the other way in which it can arise.

B. A bivariate distribution also arises whenever we compare the distribu-

**Table 6.1   Distribution of residents of the United States
by age and sex, 1960**

	Sex		
AGE	MALE	FEMALE	TOTAL
Under 20	36,000,000	35,000,000	71,000,000
20–65	47,000,000	49,000,000	96,000,000
65 and over	8,000,000	9,000,000	17,000,000
Total	91,000,000	93,000,000	184,000,000

**Table 6.2   Univariate and bivariate distributions of age and sex
of United States residents, 1960**

A. *Age distribution of males*			B. *Age distribution of females*	
AGE	*f**		AGE	*f**
Under 20	36		Under 20	35
20–65	47		20–65	49
65 and over	8		65 and over	9
Total	91		Total	93

AGE	MALE	FEMALE
Under 20	36	35
20–65	47	49
65 and over	8	9
Total	91	93

C. Distribution of residents by age and sex

* Each frequency represents 1,000,000 people.

tion of a variable in one population with the distribution of the same
variable in another population. For example, we can create the above
distribution of *age* and *sex* in the following way. First, we define a population as consisting of *all male residents* of the United States in 1960 and look
at the age distribution in this population. Second, we define another population as consisting of *all female residents* of the United States in 1960 and
look at the age distribution in this population. Finally, we compare these
two distributions with each other by placing them next to each other in the
form of a bivariate table. Table 6.2 illustrates this process. (In this table
each frequency refers to 1,000,000 people, which gives just the same information as would the rounding off of each frequency to the nearest million,
as was done in Table 6.1.)

Notice that in Table 6.2 the categories of sex (male and female) were
used in the definitions of the univariate populations. This fact illustrates an
important point about characteristics and their categories. In general, populations are defined in terms of categories of characteristics that *must be
present in each and every member*. Such categories are referred to as
constants or *conditions*. Within each population so defined there are other
characteristics whose value or category varies from individual to individual.
These characteristics are referred to as *variables*. (Note here the two senses

in which the term variable is used—as something that varies and as something whose *quantity* varies. The former sense includes attributes whereas the latter sense excludes them.) In Table 6.2, section *A*, for example, three characteristics of people have been used to define the population. The population consists of *males* (a category of the characteristic "sex"), who are *residents of the United States* (a category of the characteristic "country of residence") in *1960* (a category of the characteristic "time"). These three categories are *constants* or *conditions*. We say, in particular, that we are looking at the age distribution *under these conditions* or in this population. In Table 6.2, section *C*, sex is now treated as a *variable* because in this population the observed category of sex will vary from individual to individual. The basic point to remember is that a characteristic and its categories can appear either as a variable whose distribution is being studied or as a constant that contributes to the definition of the population.

6.2   THE GENERAL FORM OF A BIVARIATE TABLE

A bivariate table describes the joint distribution of two variables. The table is laid out in the form of a rectangle containing a certain number of rows and a certain number of columns. Each position in the table is called a "cell" and is identified by two subscripts, i and j. The first subscript, i, identifies the *row* in which the cell is located and the second subscript, j, identifies the *column* in which the cell is located. The rows are listed from the top of the table down so the first row ($i = 1$) is the row at the top. Similarly, the columns are listed from left to right, so the first column ($j = 1$) is the column on the left of the table. In this way we can identify $cell_{11}$ as the cell in the first row and the first column. In general, $cell_{ij}$ is the cell in the ith row and jth column of the table. Using this notation for Table 6.1, for example, we would have this general form:

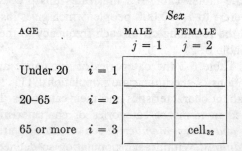

This structure can be generalized a bit more. The bivariate table contains two variables and a list of the categories of each. We use the letter X to refer to the variable whose categories are listed across the top and the letter Y to refer to the variable whose categories are listed down the left side of the table. In Table 6.1, for example, we have $X =$ sex and $Y =$ age. Each category or class interval of these variables is usually identified just by noting the row or column in which it appears. Thus, the category "female" is called X_2 because it is in the second column and the class interval "65 or more" is called Y_3 because it is in the third row. Using these conventions, we have as the general structure of a bivariate table:

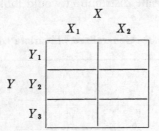

The entries that would appear in each cell are, of course, frequencies. In Table 6.1, for instance, the entry in cell$_{32}$ is 9,000,000, meaning that there were (approximately) 9,000,000 people in the United States in 1960 who were *both* 65 or over and female. In general the frequency in cell$_{ij}$ tells us the number of times we observed individuals who were both Y_i and X_j. Such frequencies are called *joint* frequencies. They are also called *conditional* frequencies because each one describes the number of times that a value of one of the variables occurred given that a particular value of the other variable also occurred. These cell frequencies are symbolized either by f or n as before. Thus, our table would take this general form with the cell frequencies inserted:

	X					X	
	X_1	X_2				X_1	X_2
Y_1	n_{11}	n_{12}			Y_1	f_{11}	f_{12}
Y Y_2	n_{21}	n_{22}	or	Y	Y_2	f_{21}	f_{22}
Y_3	n_{31}	n_{32}			Y_3	f_{31}	f_{32}

Fundamentally, a bivariate distribution contains the information presented above. It is a description of the frequency with which each pair of values (one from each variable) occurs in the population or sample. A complete table of such a distribution, of course, contains more information. In particular, as is illustrated in Table 6.1, it contains the usual table number and title, as well as various subtotal and total frequencies written around the margins of the cell frequencies. These subtotals and totals are called *marginal* frequencies. Each one is designated by the letter n, followed by a subscript and a period. For example, the sum of the cell frequencies in the first row of a table is symbolized by $n_1.$, where the "1" indicates that $i = 1$ and the "." indicates that it is a sum over all the columns. Similarly, $n_{.1}$ symbolizes the total of the first column, the "." before the "1" indicating that we have summed over the rows and the "1" indicating that we are considering the first column. Using these conventions, the complete generalized table of a bivariate distribution would look like Table 6.3.

Table 6.3 Generalized bivariate distribution

		X		
		X_1	X_2	TOTAL
	Y_1	f_{11}	f_{12}	$n_1.$
Y	Y_2	f_{21}	f_{22}	$n_2.$
	Y_3	f_{31}	f_{32}	$n_3.$
	Total	$n_{.1}$	$n_{.2}$	N

Of course, actual tables may contain more rows or more columns than are indicated in this table. The number of *rows* in a table is the number of class intervals of the variable Y, and is usually represented by the letter r. Similarly, the number of *columns* in the table is the number of class intervals or categories of the variable X, and is represented by the letter c. In this table, for example, there are three rows and two columns so $r = 3$ and $c = 2$. Remember, when using a bivariate distribution table to specify the source if it is not obvious.)

6.3 SUMMARIZING THE INFORMATION IN A BIVARIATE TABLE

With this general scheme in mind, let us now look carefully at how we can summarize the information contained in the bivariate distribution. Actually, we have already discussed all of the tools that we need to examine and summarize this table. The examination proceeds through three steps:

1. We visualize the table as a set of univariate distributions (each of which is called a conditional distribution).

2. We summarize each of these univariate distributions using measures appropriate to the level of measurement.

3. We *compare* the conditional distributions to each other by comparing these summary measures.

To make this process more meaningful let us examine a particular table and see how we summarize its information through these steps. Table 6.4 shows the distribution of male public high school seniors in Milwaukee, Wis., in 1957 classified according to whether or not each plans to attend college and to the socioeconomic status of each student's family. The data are from a study by Sewell and Armer (1966).

Table 6.4   Distribution of male public high school seniors classified by college plans and socioeconomic status (SES), Milwaukee, 1957

PLAN TO ATTEND COLLEGE?	SES			
	LOW	MEDIUM	HIGH	TOTAL
Yes	138	251	388	777
No	423	359	195	977
Total	561	610	583	1754

SOURCE: Sewell and Armer, 1966.

The first step in analyzing this table is to visualize it as a set of univariate distributions or conditional distributions. Table 6.2 showed us how to accomplish this visualization. Each column of frequencies is the frequency column in a univariate distribution in which the column heading identifies the condition. For example, the first column of Table 6.4 describes the college plans of high school seniors all of whom are from low socioeconomic status backgrounds. This distribution is represented by the frequencies in the column combined with the categories on the left. The condition is "low SES." Similarly, the next column describes the conditional distribution of high school seniors by college plans under the condition of medium SES background. The third and last column does the same for high SES background students.

Our main problem at this step is to decide whether we want to break the table up into univariate distributions by columns or by rows. We can do it either way. For example, we can consider the distribution of socioeconomic status under different conditions of college plans. In this case we would look at each *row* of frequencies coupled with the headings at the top of the table as identifying the conditional distributions. In elementary analysis, then, there are *two* sets of conditional distributions that might be selected. We must decide which one we want. This decision is up to the researcher and depends upon his interests and objectives. Sewell and Armer were interested in studying the college plans of high school seniors. Thus, the distribution in which they were most interested was the distribution of answers to the question "Do you plan to attend college?".

The variable in which the researcher is most interested is called the *dependent* variable. It is this variable whose distribution is compared under various conditions. The other variable is called the *independent* variable. Its categories become the conditions under which the distribution of the dependent variable is examined. In this example, college plans is the variable being studied under various conditions of socioeconomic status. This analysis permits us to decide which set of conditional distributions to study. In particular, we want to examine the distributions represented by the *columns* of the table. There are three of these columns, so there are three conditional distributions to be studied.

Table 6.4 has been set up in the conventional way with respect to this decision. By widespread (but not universal) agreement, the dependent variable is at the left of the table and the independent variable at the top of the table. That is, the letter Y is used to identify the dependent variable and the letter X the independent variable. When this convention is followed, the conditional distributions to be examined will always be found within the columns of the table. This convention is followed in the present text.

Once we have identified the conditional distributions that we want to study (that is, once we have selected the dependent variable) the second step is to summarize each of these distributions. To accomplish this task we use whatever summary measures seem to be most appropriate. In Part I of this text we studied how to make this decision. In general, we identify the level of measurement of the dependent variable and use a measure appropriate to that level. In our example here we note that college plans is a dichotomy and an attribute, with the categories "Yes" and "No." One sensible way to summarize the distribution, then, would be to express the frequencies as *percentages*. In particular, it would be sensible to find the percent of students answering "Yes, I plan to attend college" under each of the three SES conditions; that is, in each of the three conditional distributions. (Notice that we use the same percent to summarize each conditional distribution—namely, the percent answering "Yes.")

To calculate these percents we work entirely within each column. For example, to find the percent of "Yes" answers among the low SES students we take the number of "Yes" responses in that column and divide it by the total number of students in that column (and then multiply the result by 100). In other words, we calculate $(138/561)(100) = 25$ percent. Similarly, to find the percent in the "medium SES" column we calculate $(251/610)\ 100 = 41$ percent. Finally, to find the percent in the "high SES" column we take $(388/583)(100) = 67$ percent. These summary figures may be presented in the form of a table, as in Table 6.5. In a summary table such as this one it is important to show the denominator upon which each percent is based as well as the percents themselves. The creation of this table or its equivalent completes the second step.

Table 6.5   Percent of male high school seniors planning to attend college, by socioeconomic status, Milwaukee, 1957

		SES	
	LOW	MEDIUM	HIGH
Percent	25	41	67
n	561	610	583

The third, and final, step is to compare the conditional distributions with each other by comparing the summary measures we have computed for each one. In this case we simply compare the three percents reported in Table 6.5. We note, for example, that the percent is largest (67 percent) among high-status students and lowest (25 percent) among low-status students. In other words, only about one in every four low-status students in this population planned to attend college as compared with two out of three high-status students. The medium-status students also were in the middle with respect to college plans. This verbal description accomplishes the comparison of the conditional distributions with each other. In later chapters in this part we will see that there are more formal ways to represent the results of this comparison but the general idea will always remain as presented here.

Notice that in carrying out these three steps we always compute our percentages in one direction and make our comparisons in the other direction. If we percent within columns, for instance, then we compare within a row. Similarly, if we were to percent within each row we would compare within a column. We always compare in the other direction to that used in making the percentages. Table 6.6 illustrates this point.

6.4   THE CONCEPT OF RELATIONSHIP

The final step in analyzing a bivariate distribution involves comparing the conditional distributions, as we have just seen. We can summarize the result of this comparison in a very simple way. If each conditional disis identical to each other conditional distribution, either in terms percentages or in terms of measures of central tendency, then we say that the two variables involved are *independent* of each other or are *not related* to each other. If the conditional distributions differ in either of these ways then the two variables are said to be *related* to each other. Table 6.5, for example, shows that socioeconomic status and plans with respect to college are *related* to each other. In this case we decided that they were related by comparing the conditional percentages. These percentages were quite different, as we just saw. This fact establishes the existence of the relationship between the variables. In the application of statistical reasoning to sociology there is probably no more important concept than the concept of relationship between variables. Nothing more is involved in this concept, basically, than noting whether or not the various conditional distributions are identical to each other with respect to percentages in corresponding locations or measures of central tendency. A word of caution is appropriate at this point, however. When working with a sample of data (see Part III) we must remember that some differences between conditional distributions may be just sampling fluctuations.

6.5 THE BASIC RULES FOR PERCENTAGING TABLES

Certain procedures are important to keep in mind when summarizing bivariate tables in this way. Hans Zeisel (1957) gives two rules in this connection that cover the general ground very well. These rules apply whenever we want to summarize the table in terms of conditional percentages.

The first rule is to percentage within a category of the independent variable, that is, in the direction of the attribute whose effect you are interested in examining. Since we place the categories of the independent variable across the top of the table this rule means that we should percentage up and down a column, as illustrated in Table 6.6. In other words,

Table 6.6 Illustration of directions in percentaging and comparing conditional distributions using figures from Table 6.5

		X_1	X_2	X_3	TOTAL
	Y_1	25%	41	67	44%
Y	Y_2	75	59	33	56
	Total	100%	100%	100%	100%

We percentage *down* and compare *across*. Note that the sum of the percents in each column totals 100 percent. In terms of a formula, each conditional percent is $(100) \dfrac{n_{ij}}{n._j}$

operationally, we will always form a percentage by dividing a cell frequency by the marginal total *in that same column.*

This first rule, however, also tells us essentially how to identify the independent variable. Generally speaking, we are interested in a bivariate table because we want to find out whether or not one of the variables has an effect upon or influences the distribution of the other variable. This effect may be causal or just conditional but in either case we are interested in the extent to which there is an effect. In these terms, the independent variable is the variable whose influence is being studied and the dependent variable is the variable whose distribution is influenced. For example, in the case of socioeconomic status and college plans we believe that status may influence the distribution of plans. In other words, we might say that the distribution of college plans is *dependent* upon socioeconomic status.

The second rule consists of a limitation on the first one. If one set of marginals is *not* representative of the population, then these marginals *must* be used as the base or denominator of the percentages. If the row marginals are not representative, then you must percentage within rows, and conversely. This rule takes precedence over the first rule.

As situations in which this rule applies arise rather frequently in social science research it is worthwhile to have a firm understanding of it. To gain this understanding it is necessary to consider what is called a *sampling fraction.* The sampling fraction is the ratio of the sample size to the size of the population from which the sample was drawn. Suppose, for instance, that you take a sample of 300 people from a city that has 50,000 residents whom you define as the population in which you are interested. The sampling fraction in this case is $300/50,000 = 0.006$. If we assembled the same number of cases in our sample, but from a city with a population of only 8000, the sampling fraction would be $300/8000 = 0.0375$, which is, of course, a much larger number than the first fraction.

We have mentioned several times that we usually visualize the bivariate table as a set of several conditional or univariate distributions. One common way to assemble the observations for such a table is to define a population and take *one* sample from it, recording the values of both variables for each individual in the sample. However, we do not need to proceed in this way. Sometimes it is more convenient to sample observations for each conditional distribution separately and then to combine the various samples into a single bivariate table. When the latter procedure is followed it is quite likely that *the sampling fraction will differ* from conditional distribution to conditional distribution. Whenever the sampling fractions differ we say that those sample sizes do not represent any population distribution and, hence, we apply Zeisel's second rule.

To illustrate this point consider taking samples of 300 people from each of five different cities. For each individual in each sample we record the observation of a variable such as *age*. We can construct a bivariate distribution from these samples by defining age as the dependent variable and city as the independent variable. The sample from each city is reported as a column in this table so that we have the general form:

		City A	City B	City C	City D	City E
	Y_1	f_{11}	f_{12}	f_{13}	f_{14}	f_{15}
	Y_2	f_{21}	f_{22}	f_{23}	f_{24}	f_{25}
Y = age	·					
	·	etc.				
	·					
	·					
	Y_k					
Total		300	300	300	300	300

What is important here are the marginal frequencies at the bottom of this distribution. Each of these marginal frequencies is 300 because we took a sample of 300 people in each city. These frequencies *in no way represent* how big the various cities are; that is, they do not represent the distribution of these cities by size. Therefore, Zeisel's second rule applies. Since these marginals are not representative of a population distribution they must appear in the denominators of the percentages. In other words, we *must* percentage within columns in a situation such as this one. In general, marginal frequencies will not represent any population distribution when they are based upon different sampling fractions. Expressed differently, the rule states that we must treat as the independent variable that variable whose *marginal* distribution is not representative.

6.6 THE SYMMETRIC INTERPRETATION OF A BIVARIATE TABLE

As we have stressed, the ordinary way in which we visualize a bivariate table is as a set of conditional distributions. Since this way of representing the table involves considering one variable as dependent upon the other, it is called an *asymmetric* treatment of the table. It is also possible, however, to consider the table from a *symmetric* point of view by considering each variable as on a par with the other. For example, if the two variables being considered are scores on two questions in a test there is no reason to consider one of these questions as dependent upon the other. In this case neither variable influences the other. Symmetry may arise also if each variable can be considered to be dependent upon the other.

There are two ways of handling a symmetric bivariate table. One is arbitrarily to select one of the variables to be X and the other to be Y and then to look at the conditional distributions of Y in the manner we have already discussed. Although this procedure is arbitrary it does permit us to analyze the table in an effective manner. This idea can be extended by analyzing the table twice, first using one variable as independent and then using the other variable as independent. The other way of handling the symmetric table is to ignore the conditional distributions altogether. Such a table may be percentaged by dividing each cell frequency (f_{ij}) by the grand total (N) and then multiplying the result by 100. We shall show in later chapters just when this treatment is sensible. For the present it is sufficient to recognize that this alternative method of handling a bivariate table is available.

6.7 BIVARIATE DISTRIBUTIONS PRESENTED IN SUMMARY FORM

Before concluding this chapter it is important to note that many bivariate distributions are presented, in articles and monographs, in a summary form rather than in the form of joint frequencies. Basically, the summary table consists of the measure used to summarize each conditional distribution; it does not present the conditional distributions themselves. When you see a table in this form it is important to be able to recognize it as the table of a bivariate distribution and to be able to visualize the frequency distribution that lies behind it. This ability is not entirely trivial since this type of table superficially resembles a univariate distribution in tabular form more than it does a bivariate one. Two examples will make these points clear. Table 6.7 presents the same information as Table 6.5 but in a slightly different way. In its general form, Table 6.7 appears to be the table of a univariate

Table 6.7 Percent of students planning to attend college, Milwaukee public school seniors, 1957, by socioeconomic status

Status	Percent
High	67
Medium	41
Low	25

distribution. It contains two columns, one listing categories of a single variable and the other listing percentages. However, closer examination reveals that this table actually is a summary of the conditional distributions in a bivariate distribution. The second variable is named in the title of the table. The original table has also been rotated so that the columns of the original table are now rows. Manipulations of this type may be confusing to the beginner. It is important to read the title, as well as the headings of the various columns, carefully to determine whether the table is univariate or summarized bivariate in form. One clue to the bivariate nature of this particular table is that the percentages do not sum to 100.

Table 6.8 is also bivariate although it has the same superficial resem-

Table 6.8   Mean age of college graduates at time of graduation by type of major (hypothetical data)

Major	Mean Age
Physics	20.3
Mathematics	20.2
German language	21.4
Humanities	22.1

blance to a univariate table. Here the clue lies in the use of the word "mean." A mean is clearly a summary measure so we should immediately suspect that the table will summarize a series of conditional distributions —in this case, conditional age distributions. The conditions will be the various possible majors. The two variables involved in this table, then, are age at graduation and major in college.

6.8 WHERE WE STAND

In this chapter we have presented the elements of bivariate table construction and table reading. We have seen that a bivariate distribution can arise when we make two observations on each individual in one population or when we make one observation on each individual in two (or more) populations. We have noted that ordinarily the best way to dissect and analyze a bivariate table involves three major steps: (1) we partition the table into its conditional, univariate components; (2) we summarize each of the conditional distributions using one or more of the concepts developed in Part I of this book; and (3) we compare the various conditional distributions as summarized. We have seen that this last step introduces the concept of *relationship* between the two variables. In particular, when the conditional distributions are different from each other, we say that the variables are related to each other. On the other hand, when the conditional distributions are all identical when expressed in percentage or proportion form we say that the two variables are not related or are *independent* of each other.

These various analytical steps were illustrated using percents as summary measures since percents can be used at all levels of measurement. We also learned how to label the two variables in the table. One of the variables is called the *dependent* variable; it is the one whose distribution is being studied. It can also be identified as the variable that is affected or influenced by the other variable. The other variable is called the *independent* variable; it is the one that we believe has some impact upon the dependent variable or its distribution. Generally, we study the distribution of the dependent variable under various conditions as defined by the categories of the independent variable. By widespread agreement the independent variable is symbolized by the letter X and the dependent variable is symbolized by the letter Y. We also mentioned that it is possible to view the two variables in a bivariate table as on a par with each other and to treat the table in a symmetrical manner. In Chapters 7 and 8 we shall consider much more deeply just how to analyze bivariate distributions at various levels of measurement.

7

THE BIVARIATE TABLE:
INTERVAL VARIABLES

We shall now consider in more detail just how to summarize and describe the information in a bivariate distribution. Basically, we shall be elaborating just what it means to *compare* the conditional distributions with each other and to *summarize* the results of that comparison. In this discussion we shall reverse our earlier order of presentation by beginning with interval variables (in this chapter) and proceeding down the measurement scale to ordinal variables and attributes (in the next chapter). The basic concepts are more easily learned in this order of presentation.

It will be recalled that the major concepts used to describe the distribution of a single variable are the concepts of central tendency and dispersion. When we compare the conditional distributions of an interval variable in a bivariate table we ordinarily compare either the central tendencies of those distributions or their dispersions. These two types of comparison, in turn, give rise to two major descriptive concepts. The comparison of central tendencies leads to the concept of *regression* and the comparison of dispersions gives rise to the concept of *correlation*. After showing how to draw a graph of a bivariate distribution we shall show how these two concepts are measured and used.

7.1 GRAPHING A BIVARIATE DISTRIBUTION

The basic graph of the joint distribution of two interval variables is called a *scatter diagram*. In this graph the horizontal axis is used to represent values of one of the variables and the vertical axis is used to represent values of the other variable. Thus, the basic format is as shown in Figure 7.1.

110

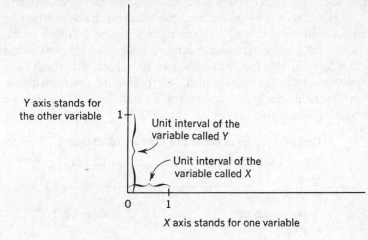

Y axis stands for the other variable

1

Unit interval of the variable called Y

Unit interval of the variable called X

0   1

X axis stands for one variable

Figure 7.1. Basic format of a scatter diagram.

As we noted in the last chapter, when one of the variables is considered the independent variable its values are placed on the horizontal axis and it is called X. The other variable, which is dependent, is then placed along the Y axis and is called Y. Using this convention the graph will be read in the same way that we read the bivariate table. In particular, any conditional distribution of Y will appear up and down on a (vertical) line on the graph, just as the corresponding frequencies in the table appear in a single column of the table.

Notice that both of the dimensions of the graph have been used in representing the variables and their values. It is a bit difficult to represent the frequencies on the same sheet of paper. If we tried to represent them in the same way as in a univariate distribution we would have to add a dimension—but then we would leave the sheet of paper and enter the three-dimensional world of solids. (In other words, although area represented frequency with one variable we would have to use volume to represent frequency with two variables.) The usual solution to this problem is to represent each bivariate observation (that is, each pair of X and Y observations) as a *dot* on the sheet of paper. The dot is placed at the intersection of the X and Y values observed for that object or event. This representation is ungrouped since the individual observations are listed separately. Frequencies never appear directly in the graph; but only as dots. A high frequency is represented by many dots in a small area whereas a low frequency is represented by dots that are widely scattered relative to each other (hence the term "scatter diagram").

As an example, consider the following observations. We have interviewed five people and from each person have received two pieces of information: his *age* and how many *siblings* he has. We want to know whether or not people who are older also tend to have more siblings. In other words, we consider age, or X, to be the independent variable. The original data come to us in the form of two columns of scores or values, one for X and one for Y. Another column is usually included to identify the individuals who have been observed. Each row stands for an individual. This information looks something like Table 7.1.

Table 7.1   Age as related to number of siblings

INDIVIDUAL (IDENTIFIED BY A CODE NUMBER)	X AGE	Y NUMBER OF SIBLINGS
1	45	3
2	20	2
3	35	4
4	10	1
5	30	2

The individuals are identified by number in order that we may keep track of them. Although the order in which they are listed is unimportant, it is vital to keep each pair of scores together, since the values in a given pair are for the same individual. For example, the first pair of numbers are (45, 3). These values could be listed in any row but they would both have to be placed in the same row. The identification numbers help us keep better track of the pairs of observations.

Let us see how we draw a graph of these joint observations, that is, of this bivariate distribution. First, we mark off intervals on the X axis to stand for ages and then intervals on the Y axis for numbers of siblings. Second, we enter each joint observation as a dot at the point where the X score and the Y score intersect. The first observation is 45 years of age and three siblings. Accordingly, we go out along the X axis to 45 and then up parallel to the Y axis until we reach the equivalent of 3. At this point we record a dot, as shown in Figure 7.2. We proceed in the same way to place dots on the paper for each other observation pair. The graph then needs only a number, title, and source to be complete. There are other ways of drawing graphs of bivariate distributions but this method is by far the most useful in statistical analysis.

The one problem that beginning students often have in using the scatter diagram is in visualizing the conditional distributions. This problem is

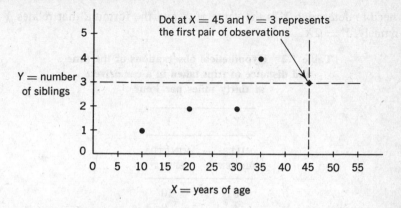

Figure 7.2. Graph of bivariate distribution.

solved by imagining intervals along the X axis and studying the region above each interval. The number of dots appearing at various heights in each interval represents the conditional distribution of Y for that class interval of X. That is, it is the distribution of Y given the condition that X has the value of the midpoint of the interval. In the following pages we shall illustrate various procedures using relatively few observation pairs. In such cases it is particularly difficult to visualize conditional distributions, although it is much easier to understand the procedures. A certain amount of imagination on the part of the reader will help.

7.2 THE BASIC IDEA OF REGRESSION

Let us suppose for the moment that there is a perfect relationship between two variables. A perfect relationship exists whenever one and only one value of the dependent variable corresponds to each value of the independent variable. Empirical observations never display literally perfect relationships but we can imagine such a relationship. For example, if a car moves at a constant speed, there will be a perfect relationship between the number of miles it is driven and the length of time it has been in use (provided we can measure these miles and times without error). If it travels at 30 miles per hour, it will have gone a distance of 30 miles whenever it has been driven for one hour, 60 miles whenever it has been driven for two hours, and so on. In this situation, if we measure (without error) both distance and time for each of several trips we will assemble observations such as those listed in Table 7.2. In this example, Y is obviously equal to $2X$ $(2 \cdot 5 = 10$ for the first trip, and so on). All of the information that we need to determine Y is the value of X and the formula that relates Y to X, namely, $Y = 2X$.

**Table 7.2   Hypothetical observations of the time
and distance of trips taken in a car driven
at thirty miles per hour**

X	Y
MILES DRIVEN	MINUTES SPENT
5	10
4	8
3	6
8	16
7	14
3	6
6	12
5	10
4	8
3	6

A graph of this distribution would look like Figure 7.3. Notice that in this graph a *line* rather than a series of dots has been used to represent the joint distribution. The dots can be imagined as points along the line, which is called the *regression* of Y on X. It is equivalent to the formula $Y = 2X$ and so this formula is also a description of the regression. The line on the graph is called a geometric description of the regression and the formula is called an algebraic description of it.

This particular line is straight. When a regression appears on a graph as a straight line it is called a *linear* regression. When it appears as a curve it is called a *curvilinear* regression. This particular straight line goes through the origin, which is the point where both X and Y are zero. (In other words, it takes no time to cover no distance.) The formula for this straight line has the number "2" in it:

$$\overset{\downarrow}{Y = 2X}$$

This number is called a *constant*. When Y is equal to some constant times X, we refer to the constant as the *slope* of the regression and symbolize it by the letter b. In this equation the slope is 2 or $b = 2$. This constant, b, appears on the graph of the regression as the amount of change in Y that accompanies a *unit* change in X. In this case, a one-mile change in X is

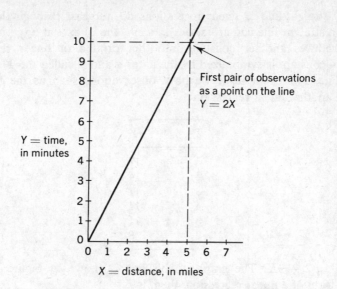

Figure 7.3. Graph of distribution of Table 7.2.

accompanied by a two-minute change in Y. In general, when Y changes a great deal for a given change in X the slope is steep (just like a steep hill). On the other hand, when Y does not change much for a given change in X the slope is shallow, as Figure 7.4 illustrates. Here the slope is much steeper in the graph on the left than in the other graph. (The reader may enjoy figuring out in which case the car is moving faster.)

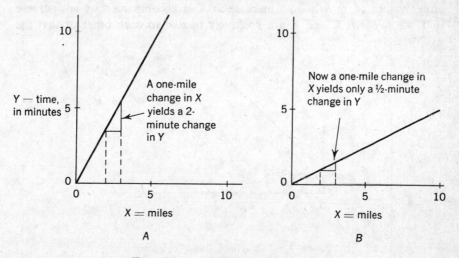

Figure 7.4. Steep and shallow slopes.

Many straight-line or linear regressions do not pass through the origin. In fact, a straight line can cross, or *intercept,* the Y axis at any point. This fact introduces another constant into the formula of linear regression. This new constant is symbolized by the letter a and is called the Y *intercept* of the line. For example, if we have observations such as the following we have another linear regression:

X	Y
5	17
4	14
3	11
4	14
3	11
2	8

Now, $Y = 2 + 3X$. The graph of this line is shown in Figure 7.5. The general form of a linear regression, then, is

$$Y = a + bX$$

where a indicates where the line crosses the Y axis and is called the Y intercept and where b indicates the rate of change of Y with respect to X and is called the slope of the regression. The formula tells us what to do if we know X and want to know Y. In particular, starting with X we first multiply it by b and then add a to this product. This sum is the value of Y.

So far we have illustrated regressions in which larger values of X imply larger values of Y. When an increase in X is accompanied by an increase in Y we say that X and Y are *positively* related to each other or that the

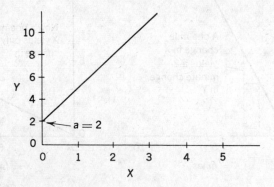

Figure 7.5. Graph of linear regression.

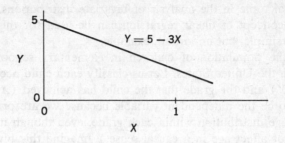

Figure 7.6. Graph of negative linear regression.

direction of the relationship is positive. Positive relationships occur quite frequently in social science. For example, there is a strong positive relationship between the number of years a person has gone to school (X) and the income he receives (Y). The longer his period of schooling the higher his income (on the average). This relationship is positive. The positive character of a linear relationship is reflected directly in the sign of the constant b. When b is a positive number the relationship between X and Y is also positive.

Of course, the relationship between X and Y can also be *negative*. That is, it is quite possible that as X increases there is a decrease in Y. When the relationship is negative and linear, the constant b has a negative sign. For example, the formula $Y = 2 - 0.5X$ tells us that for every increase of one unit in X there is a decrease of half a unit of Y. The graph of a negative linear regression is a line that slopes downward from left to right, such as shown in Figure 7.6. Negative relationships also occur fairly often in social science. For example, there is a negative relationship between distance and human interaction. The greater the distance between people the less frequently will they interact (on the average).

7.3 LINEAR REGRESSION AND THE CONDITIONAL DISTRIBUTIONS OF Y GIVEN X

The individual observations of two variables essentially never all occur along a straight line in practice. Despite this fact, the concept of linear regression is very important in statistical analysis. This concept is used to summarize the results of comparing the conditional distributions in bivariate tables or scatter diagrams. It will be recalled that these comparisons are the central topic in the analysis of bivariate distributions. In order to see how the concept of linear regression can be used for this purpose let us consider a simple, but important, example.

Consider the population of children in elementary schools (grades 1 through 6) in the United States. Let us classify each child according to his or her *age* (*Y*) and the grade that the child has achieved (*X*). (We consider grade to be the independent variable because we are primarily interested in the age distribution within each grade, even though it is clear that grade does not affect age in a causal sense.) Imagine this bivariate distribution divided into its conditional components; that is, visualize the distribution of age in each given grade. Table 7.3 shows these distributions using United States Census figures. In this table each column contains a set of conditional frequencies, as usual.

Table 7.3   Age of children at last birthday by grade in school, all elementary schools, United States, 1950*

	Grade					
AGE	1	2	3	4	5	6
14						1
13					1	3
12				1	3	7
11			1	3	7	9
10		1	3	8	9	1
9		2	8	10	1	
8	2	9	12	1		
7	10	15	1			
6	17	1				
5	1					

SOURCE: U.S. Bureau of the Census, Census of Population, 1950. Special Report PE 58, Table I.
* Each frequency represents 100,000 pupils.

Once we identify the proper conditional distributions we proceed to summarize each one. Since these distributions refer to an interval variable (age), it is appropriate to use the mean as a basic summarizing tool. Therefore, we compute the mean age for each grade. These conditional means

Table 7.4   Mean age of children by grade, United States, 1950

				Grade		
	1	2	3	4	5	6
Mean Age	6.9	8.0	9.1	10.2	11.2	12.2

are shown in Table 7.4. (The computations are not shown since we have already discussed how to calculate means. If you want to check these figures remember that each age is an interval extending up to the next age. Thus, for example, age 10 means "10–11" and has a midpoint at 10.5.)

The final step is to compare these means and summarize the results of the comparisons. From Table 7.4, for example, we see that, as expected, children average about one year older in each higher grade. (Note, incidentally, that the average age in each grade is such as to suggest that these children are about ready to enter the next grade. Thus, 6.9 years is almost 7 and seven year olds are expected to be in the second grade. The census is taken in April, which means that these children *were* about to enter the next higher grade.) The only problem involved in comparing these means directly with each other is that there are six of them, which implies that there are many comparisons that we could make. To aid us let us plot the means on a graph, as in Figure 7.7.

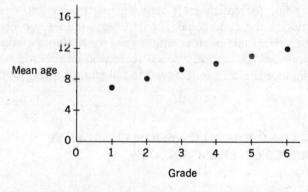

Figure 7.7. Mean age of children by grade, United States, 1950.

Notice that the *means* fall almost exactly along a straight line. This line is essentially $Y = 6.0 + 1X$ (we shall consider in the following paragraphs just how to estimate this line very accurately). The important point to recognize here is that this very simple equation describes quite accurately the mean or average age of children in each grade. Only two numbers are used in this description ($a = 6.0$ and $b = 1$). Note that Table 7.4 is also a description of the mean ages in each grade but it involves six numbers— the mean for each grade. By using the regression concept we have reduced the six numbers to just two. Obviously, the regression line is a very efficient way of summarizing the information.

In short, this example illustrates the fact that we use a linear regression line to summarize the results of comparing various conditional means with each other, whenever the graph of those means reveals that they fall more or less along a straight line. The constants a and b in this regression describe how the means are related to each other. If we want any particular mean, we can get it (or very closely approximate it) by using the regression equation. For example, suppose that we want to know the average age of children in the fourth grade. We use the linear equation

$$Y = 6.0 + 1(4) = 10.0$$

The actual mean was 10.2, which is very close to the figure derived from the regression. Usually the linear regression line will not reproduce the means exactly, but the slight inaccuracy is more than compensated by the fact that we have summarized the information so much more succinctly in the regression line.

The key point to remember is that the regression line describes the *average* values in the conditional distributions within some bivariate distribution. Sometimes this point is emphasized by calling the regression line the "line of means." Of course, a *linear* regression line should be used only when the conditional means in fact tend to fall along a straight line.

7.4 ESTIMATING THE REGRESSION CONSTANTS: THE PRINCIPLE OF LEAST SQUARES

Once we decide to use a linear regression line to summarize the information in a bivariate distribution the practical problem becomes one of estimating the constants in that equation. Clearly, there are a great many straight lines that *could* be drawn on a sheet of paper. From all of these possible lines we want to choose the one that is the *best*. But before we can choose the best one, of course, we must understand clearly just what we mean by "best"; we must establish the criteria by which we make our choice.

Basically, we want to choose a line that comes close to the conditional means. However, it proves to be unnecessary actually to compute these means. Instead, we choose the line that comes as close as possible to all of the individual observations. This line will also come as close as possible to the means of any arbitrarily chosen class intervals. To show how we develop the actual criterion it is important to introduce a new symbol. We have noted that the regression line gives us a way of estimating the average value of Y for any given value of X. In any study, of course, we also have certain observed values of Y that occurred with that value of X. We need a symbol to distinguish between the value of Y that we expect from the regression and the value of Y that we actually observe. We create this symbol by putting a prime (') after the expected value of Y. That is, we write

$$Y' = a + bX$$

Verbally, this formula reads, "the estimated (or expected) value of Y for a given value of X is equal to $a + bX$."

To say that we want to choose the regression line that is as close as possible to the actual observations is, then, to say that we want to choose that line whose expected values come as close as possible to the corresponding observed values. The difference between the observed value and the expected value, of course, is $Y - Y'$. We want to choose a and b such that we reduce as much as possible all of these differences between observed and estimated values. Beginning students often have difficulty in seeing that for each and every observation there corresponds an expected value. The key to understanding this point is to remember that each bivariate observation really is a pair of observations; namely, an observation of Y and an observation of X. We convert the observation of X into an expected or estimated value of Y through the use of the line of regression. Thus, we start with an observation of Y and one of X and we end with an observation of Y and an expected value of Y, or Y'.

The actual criterion that we use to estimate a and b is to choose those values of a and b that minimize the sum of the squared differences between the observed and expected values of Y. In terms of a formula we *minimize*

$$\Sigma(Y - Y')^2 = \Sigma(Y - a - bX)^2$$

(The differences are squared before we sum them for the same reason that we used when developing the concept of *variance*. In particular, the sum of the differences themselves will be near zero for many values of a and b since negative deviations will compensate for positive deviations.) This criterion is called the *least squares* criterion. When we choose a and b so that this sum is a minimum we say that we have used the least squares method of estimating the constants.

The student may be mystified at this point as to how to proceed to find the proper values of a and b given this criterion. Fortunately, a mathematical solution is available (through the use of calculus). However, we do not really need to know the derivation of the solution in order to be able to make use of it. All we really need to know is that someone has solved the problem in such a way that we can take advantage of his method. In this book we purposely avoid demonstrating how technical problems such as this are solved. The interested reader should consult any one of a number of texts written at a more advanced level if he wishes to pursue the matter further. We shall be content to show what the solution is and how it can be used in analyzing data.

7.5 COMPUTATION OF a AND b
FROM RAW OR UNGROUPED DATA

We usually calculate the values of a and b (as well as the other concepts introduced later in this chapter) from the original observations rather than from a table, because formulas that use tabled data are rather cumbersome. Furthermore, desk calculators and digital computers have been especially designed to facilitate making these calculations from the raw data. Accordingly, we shall present computational formulas for raw or ungrouped data only.

The basic formulas that should be used in calculating a and b are

$$b = \frac{\Sigma xy}{\Sigma x^2}$$

and

$$a = \bar{Y} - b\bar{X}$$

where Σxy is the sum of the cross products of the *mean deviates* of X and Y and Σx^2 is the sum of squares of the *mean deviates* of X. Notice that a is very easily calculated once we have found the value of b, but that b involves a rather long series of computations. Let us, then, consider the formula for b rather carefully.

In Chapter 5 we introduced the notion of a mean deviate and the sum of squares of mean deviates (Section 5.3). In that chapter we saw that the sum of squares of the mean deviates of X is the numerator of the variance. Now we see that this same sum of squares becomes the de-

Table 7.5   Example of worksheet

X	Y	X^2	Y^2	XY	
5	13	25	169	65	
4	9	16	81	36	$\Sigma xy = 576 - \dfrac{(47)(107)}{10} = 73.10$
3	6	9	36	18	
8	18	64	324	144	$\Sigma x^2 = 253 - \dfrac{(47)^2}{10} = 32.10$
7	16	49	256	112	
2	4	4	16	8	
6	12	36	144	72	$b = \dfrac{73.10}{32.10} = 2.28$
5	12	25	144	60	
4	10	16	100	40	$a = \dfrac{107}{10} - (2.28)\dfrac{47}{10} = -0.02$
3	7	9	49	21	
47	107	253	1319	576	
ΣX	ΣY	ΣX^2	ΣY^2	ΣXY	

nominator of the regression constant b. To calculate this sum of squares we use the formula introduced in Chapter 5, namely,

$$\Sigma x^2 - \Sigma(X - \bar{X})^2 = \Sigma X^2 - \frac{(\Sigma X)^2}{N}$$

Notice that the computational form is written in terms of the original X values rather than in terms of the mean deviates. (At this point you may wish to review the relevant section of Chapter 5 for further details.)

The numerator of b, which is the sum of the cross products of the mean deviates of X and Y, is usually calculated from the following formula:

$$\Sigma xy = \Sigma(X - \bar{X})(Y - \bar{Y}) = \Sigma XY - \frac{(\Sigma X)(\Sigma Y)}{N}$$

The best way to become familiar with these formulas is to see the way they are used in actual calculations. We shall go through a step-by-step analysis using hypothetical data. The important thing to recognize at the outset is that we calculate b in two stages. In the first stage we find the sum of squares and the sum of cross products. In the second stage we combine these two sums into the formula for b.

To make these calculations we set up a worksheet as shown in Table 7.5. Our raw data are the X and Y values listed in the first two columns. To the right of these two columns we write three more columns, which involve (1) finding the square of each of the observations of X, (2) finding the square of each observation of Y, and (3) finding the cross product of each of the X and Y pairs. (The column headed Y^2 is not actually used in these calculations. It will be needed later on in the chapter, however.) Once the proper numbers have been placed in the columns, each column is summed and the sums are entered at the bottom of the columns. We have labeled each of these sums for easy reference. Next, the sums are introduced into the formulas as at the bottom of Table 7.5. First we find Σxy, then we find Σx^2. From these two figures we then calculate b. Next we use b and the means of the two variables to find a. When we are finished, we have the formula that tells us what value of Y to expect for any given value of X, namely,

$$Y' = -0.02 + 2.28X$$

For example, suppose that we want to know what value of Y to expect when $X = 5$. We use the formula and find $Y' = -0.02 + 2.28(5) = 11.2$. Looking back at the original data we see that there were two actual observations of Y for this value of X; $Y = 12$ and $Y = 13$. Our expectation is, therefore, fairly close but not exact. We would not anticipate that it would be exact because it represents the *average* value of Y for each value of X rather than the individual observations of Y. In general, this line comes as close to the observations as any straight line would, and in this sense it is the best linear representation of these observations or, more accurately, of the average values of these observations in the various conditional distributions.

This computational procedure, as well as those given below, are summarized in a computation design at the end of the chapter.

7.6   THE STANDARD ERROR OF ESTIMATE

When we considered a single univariate distribution and summarized its central tendency by the mean, we also found it important to identify just how far, on the average, the observations deviated from this mean. This measure of deviation from the mean we called the standard deviation (s) or the variance (s^2). In the case of the bivariate distribution we are faced with essentially the same situation. The regression line, $Y' = a + bX$, summarizes the information about several conditional means, assuming that those means lie on a straight line. In this case, also, it is worth knowing by how much the actual observations deviate from these expected or estimated values, on the average. This measure of dispersion is called the standard error of estimate and is denoted by the symbol $s_{y.x}$ (read "s y dot x" or "the standard deviation of y given a particular value of x"). By definition, $s_{y.x}$ is the square root of $s_{y.x}^2$, which is defined as

$$s_{y.x}^2 = \frac{\Sigma(Y - Y')^2}{N - 2} = \text{residual variance in a sample of observations.}$$

Notice that the denominator in this expression is "$N - 2$." We subtract 2 from the sample size to correct for a bias in estimating the population standard error of estimate. A denominator such as this is called the number of *degrees of freedom*. When working with samples we almost always divide by degrees of freedom rather than by sample size itself.

As we have noted, the standard error of estimate ($s_{y.x}$) corresponds to the standard deviation (s) of a univariate distribution. It represents the dispersion of the observed values of Y around the estimated regression line, $Y' = a + bX$. If the distribution of the Y values about the regression line is normal, then about two thirds of the observed values will be within one standard error of estimate of the expected value. That is, an interval extending from $Y' - s_{y.x}$ to $Y' + s_{y.x}$ will contain about two thirds of the actual observations. The standard error of estimate can and should be interpreted as the *average* standard deviation in the set of conditional distributions of Y given X.

There is a technical way of considering this variance ($s_{y.x}^2$) that is useful in both statistics and sociology. If the relationship between X and Y is perfect there will be no dispersion around the regression line and $s_{y.x}^2 = 0$. In other words, we would make *no* errors in estimating the individual observations directly from the regression line. In this case we say that X *accounts for* or *explains* all of the variance in Y. Of course, when the relationship is less than perfect, X does not account for *all* of the variance in Y. Some other source of variation is present in the data—either measurement or sampling error, or the effects of other variables, or both. In this case we say that *some* of the variance in Y is explained by X and some of it is not explained or *unexplained* by X. The $s_{y.x}^2$ measures the amount of this unexplained variance in Y. We shall expand on this interpretation later.

The Computation of $s_{y.x}$ and $s_{y.x}^2$

As usual, there is one formula that defines the standard error of estimate and another that is most efficient in calculating it. We *could* make the calculation directly from the definition but it would take a long time because we would have to figure out the expected value (Y') that corresponds to each and every observed value (Y). In practice, it is much simpler to use the following formulas:

$$s_{y.x}^2 = \frac{(\Sigma y^2) - b(\Sigma xy)}{N - 2}$$

and
$$s_{y.x} = \sqrt{s_{y.x}^2}$$

The elements in the first equation are (1) the *sum of squares* of the mean deviates of Y, (2) the *regression coefficient b*, and (3) the *sum of cross products* of the mean deviates of X and Y. As we have seen before, a sum of squares is the numerator of the variance. In the same way, the sum of cross products is the numerator of what is called the covariance, or the common variance. The above formula gives a good idea of what the error variance is. In particular, it is essentially the *total variance* of the Y observations *minus* the *covariation* between X and Y. In other words, it is essentially the total variance of the Y observations minus that part of the total variance that is accounted for by variation in the X values. In this sense, $s_{y.x}^2$ is sometimes called the *residual* variance of Y because it is the variance that is left over after eliminating the influence of X.

Remember that we first compute sums of squares and sums of cross products by simple computational routines and then we put them together in the formulas that we want. Using the data presented earlier we can illustrate the process. We have already calculated b and the sum of cross products Σxy so all that we need is the sum of squares of the y values. The computational formula for a sum of squares is

$$\Sigma y^2 = \Sigma Y^2 - \frac{(\Sigma Y)^2}{N}$$

as we already know. Referring back to Table 7.5 we see that $\Sigma Y^2 = 1319$, so the sum of squares of y is

$$\Sigma y^2 = 1319 - \frac{(107)^2}{10} = 174.10$$

Using this information as well as the calculations already made the error variance is

$$s_{y.x}^2 = \frac{174.10 - (2.28)(73.10)}{8} = 0.93$$

and the standard error of estimate is

$$s_{y.x} = \sqrt{0.93} = 0.97$$

7.7   CORRELATION

Let us review briefly what we already know about summarizing the information in a bivariate distribution. We imagine the distribution to be divided into a series of univariate conditional distributions that we compare with each other. The linear regression line summarizes the connections among the means of these conditional distributions. The standard error of estimate describes the variation or dispersion of the observations around this regression line. Thus, in a sense, these two concepts effectively summarize the entire bivariate distribution.

In fact, however, it is very useful to carry the process of summarization one step further and thereby to arrive at a measure of the *amount of relationship* between X and Y. The basic idea here is to compare the error of estimate variance ($s_{y.x}{}^2$) with the original variance of the Y observations ($s_y{}^2$). Remember that we compare numbers either through the use of subtraction or division. In this case division is more appropriate. Therefore, we express the comparison as a ratio, which is technically called the coefficient of alienation. We have

$$K^2 = \text{coefficient of alienation} = \frac{s_{y.x}{}^2}{s_y{}^2}$$

Statisticians find it convenient to subtract this ratio from one, to define what is called the coefficient of determination or, more commonly today, the relative explained variance r^2. We have

$$\text{Coefficient of determination} = r_{yx}{}^2 = 1 - K_{yx}{}^2 = 1 - \frac{s_{y.x}{}^2}{s_y{}^2}$$

Finally, this comparison is often discussed in terms of the square root of the coefficient of determination, which is called the *correlation coefficient*. Thus,

$$r_{yx} = \text{correlation coefficient} = \pm \sqrt{r_{yx}{}^2}$$

In all of these formulas the subscripts yx are used to identify the variables being considered. The order in which these variables are written is quite important, because the first variable listed is always the *dependent* variable. Thus, r_{yx} is the correlation coefficient treating Y as dependent upon X, or when looking at the conditional distributions of Y given X.

Let us consider quite carefully just why this comparison of the residual variance of Y with the original variance of Y is so important and useful. By and large, in scientific work we attempt to account for or explain the variation in whatever variable we happen to be interested. An economist attempts to explain why some people have low incomes and others high incomes. In other words, he attempts to explain the variation in income in some population of people. A sociologist tries to explain why some people are hostile and alienated whereas others are enthusiastic and integrated. In other words, he attempts to explain the variation in morale or *esprit de corps* in some population of people.

One way to accomplish this objective is to identify other variables that tend to covary or vary along with the dependent variable's variation. When the variation in two different variables is associated it is quite possible that one of the variables can be used to account for the other. For example, one way to account for variations in income is to look for other variables that covary with income. In our society, for example, one of these variables is education. By observing the extent to which variation in education is associated with variation in income we learn something about how to explain the distribution of income. The coefficient of determination r_{yx}^2 is a measure of the extent of this covariation. It tells us what proportion of the variation in Y is associated with (or covaries with) variation in X. Similarly, the coefficient of alienation tells us what proportion of the variation in Y does *not* covary with variation in X. These two proportions, of course, add up to one because all of the variation in Y either does or does not covary with variation in X.

In terms of a formula we represent this relation as

$$r_{yx}^2 + K_{yx}^2 = 1$$

where the number "1" stands for the total variation in Y, which has been divided into two parts: (1) that part of the variation in Y that occurs *only when X* also varies (r_{yx}^2) and (2) that part of the variation in Y that occurs even when X is constant or does not vary (K_{yx}^2). We may also think of these two parts in a slightly different way, which, however, amounts to the same thing. In particular, the total variation in Y may be represented by the difference between an observation and the mean of all observations, or by $y = Y - \bar{Y}$. By introducing the expected value of Y given X (that is, Y') we may divide this total deviation into two parts:

$$y = Y - \bar{Y} = Y - Y' + Y' - \bar{Y}$$
$$= (Y - Y') + (Y' - \bar{Y})$$

When we square both sides of this equation and sum the results over all observations we have

$$\Sigma y^2 = \Sigma(Y - Y')^2 + \Sigma(Y' - \bar{Y})^2 + 2\Sigma(Y - Y')(Y' - \bar{Y})$$

The third term in this expression is identically equal to zero so the sum of the squares of the mean deviates reduces to

$$\Sigma y^2 = \Sigma(Y - Y')^2 + \Sigma(Y' - \bar{Y})^2$$

In other words, the total variation of the Y values (Σy^2) can be divided into two parts, one part being the variation of the Y values around the expected values $[\Sigma(Y - Y')^2]$ and the other parts being the variation of the expected values around the mean of all Y values $[\Sigma(Y' - \bar{Y})^2]$.

In short, we may refer to these two parts as variation *in* the *expected* values of Y and variation *around* these *expected* values. The coefficient of determination is a measure of the relative amount of variation that is in the expected values whereas the coefficient of alienation is a measure of the relative amount of variation that is around these expected values.

Because this concept of correlation is so important in sociological research it is useful to give a specific illustration of the interpretation that we have just made. For this purpose let us consider the distribution of children by age and year in school that was presented in Table 7.3. The dependent variable here is $Y =$ age. The mean age of *all* children in grade school was $Y = 9.4$ years. (The computations upon which these figures are based are not shown so that we may emphasize the main points more clearly.) The variance in age was $s_y^2 = 4.05$, which is a measure of the total variation in Y. Our problem is to discover what proportion of this total variation is associated with variation in the child's grade. To find this information we first calculate the line of regression, which (using least squares principles) is

$$Y' = 5.9 + 1.06X$$

where X stands for the grade that the child is in. Now we calculate the variation of the observed values of Y around these expected values found by applying the above formula. This residual variation is $s_{y.x}^2 = 0.76$. In other words, for any particular value of X (that is, within any particular grade) the variance in age is 0.76.

Next we compare the variation in age *within a grade* (or with X *not* varying) with the variation in age among all students. We have

$$K_{yx}^2 = \frac{0.76}{4.05} = 0.19$$

In other words, 19 percent of the original variation in age remains when we consider single grades. Of course, this fact also means that 81 percent of the variation in age is *not* found in the distributions within single grades but rather occurs as we change from one grade to another. In short, 81 percent of the variance in age is associated with or covaries with variation in X or the grade of the child in school. We summarize this by saying that

$$r_{yx}^2 = 1 - K_{yx}^2 = 0.81$$

Having identified both the regression and the amount of relationship we have completed our analysis of this particular bivariate distribution.

The Computation of r_{yx}^2 and r_{yx}

Fortunately, the computation of r_{yx}^2 involves precisely the same information that we have already used in finding the regression constants and the standard error of estimate. In particular, we have the following as the basic computational formula for r_{yx}^2:

$$r_{yx}^2 = \frac{(\Sigma xy)^2}{\Sigma x^2 \Sigma y^2}$$

The numerator in this formula is the square of the sum of the cross products of x and y and the denominator is the product of the sums of squares of the two variables. Each of these components, in turn, is calculated from the special computational formulas already discussed. For the illustrative data from Table 7.5 we have

$$\Sigma x^2 = 32.10$$
$$\Sigma y^2 = 174.10$$
$$\Sigma xy = 73.10$$

Given these figures it is a simple matter to calculate r_{yx}^2. In particular,

$$r_{yx}^2 = \frac{(73.10)^2}{(32.10)(174.10)}$$
$$= 0.9562$$

The correlation coefficient itself (r_{yx}) can be calculated directly from this result by taking its square root. However, to be sure that we assign the correct sign to r_{yx} it is preferable to calculate it from a formula that involves taking the square root of the numerator and denominator separately. We have

$$r_{yx} = \frac{\Sigma xy}{\sqrt{\Sigma x^2 \Sigma y^2}}$$
$$= 0.978$$

in our illustration. The computation design at the end of this chapter summarizes this procedure as well as all others introduced here.

7.8 POINTS TO REMEMBER IN INTERPRETING CORRELATION OR AMOUNT OF RELATIONSHIP

The correlation coefficient (or its square) is one of the most widely used of all statistical measures. Therefore, it is quite important that it be properly interpreted. For the most part this statement means that it is important to recognize certain limitations of the concept. Four major principles should limit and guide its use. The first point is that the concept of correlation or amount of relationship is *not* the same as the concept of a causal relationship. We shall discuss this point much more carefully in Chapter 9 because it is the key to understanding a great deal of quantitative research in sociology. At this point we shall only note that there are *several different reasons* why two variables may display relationship in a given population of observations. For example, when two variables are correlated it may be that X causes Y in some sense or it may be that both X and Y are the result of the action of some third variable. *In order to infer cause you must have additional information. It is not sufficient simply to note that the two variables are related to each other.*

The second principle to remember is that r_{yx} and r_{yx}^2 measure only the *linear* relationship between two variables. Many important relationships in sociology and other fields are not linear. For example, the relationship between *distance* and the *frequency of interaction* is *not* linear, the relationship between *age* and *income* is *not* linear, and the relationship between the *size* of an organization and the *complexity* of its structure is *not* linear. Obviously, the correlation coefficient should be used only when the relationship between X and Y is approximately linear. Fortunately, it is quite easy to tell whether or not this approximation exists in a set of observations. There are two ways to proceed. First, a scatter diagram may be constructed and inspected visually. If the relationship between X and Y is linear the basic arrangement of the dots should be elliptical (that is, approximately in the shape of a cigar). Second, the distribution may be put in a table and the mean of each conditional distribution in the table computed. These means may then be plotted on graph paper to see whether or not they fall approximately along a straight line. In general, one or the other of these acts should be performed by the researcher before reporting or interpreting a correlation coefficient.

The third principle is a bit more technical. It is that the value of r_{yx} is difficult to interpret directly. The usual direct interpretation that is made today is based upon r_{yx}^2 rather than upon r_{yx}. In particular, r_y^2 is the proportion of the variance in the Y observations that is accounted for by variations in X. No comparable interpretation of r_{yx} exists. It is possible to interpret r_{yx} directly through the use of the last formula presented above. We shall not develop this interpretation since it involves concepts that are beyond the scope of this text. For elementary or basic statistical analysis the interpretation that is most germaine is the interpretation of r_{yx}^2 that we presented above.

The fourth principle is of special interest to sociologists. It concerns the interpretation of correlations between characteristics of groups or aggregates of people. Such correlations are known in sociology as *ecological* correlations, because the aggregates are so often defined in terms of where they are located. Examples of this type of correlation include (1) correlating the average size of farms in a county and the average income of farmers in the county, (2) correlating the percentage of houses that are owner-occupied in a census tract (or urban neighborhood) and the percentage of people in the tract who are Negro, and (3) correlating the crime rate in a city and the percentage of people in the city who are foreign-born. In each of these cases, the unit that is being studied is some aggregate of individuals rather than the individuals themselves. Correlations of this type are perfectly legitimate (see Menzel, 1950) but *it is* also *very easy to misinterpret them.* In particular, it is *not* legitimate to use the ecological correlation *in place of* correlations based on individuals, as W. S. Robinson has shown (Robinson, 1950). Robinson shows, for example, that the correlation between the percentage of Negroes and the percentage of illiterates in regions of the United States is very high, namely, $r = 0.946$. On the other hand, the correlation between race and illiteracy when individuals are identified separately is only $r = 0.203$. The inflation of the ecological correlation between race and literacy is due largely to the fact that the more Negroes there are in a region the higher is the proportion of illiterate *whites* in the same region. In general, ecological correlations must not be interpreted as implying corresponding correlations between individuals. Such improper interpretations are examples of what is called the *ecological fallacy.*

7.9 WHERE WE STAND

In this chapter we have introduced two basic descriptive concepts relevant to bivariate data: the concept of *regression* and the concept of *correlation* or amount of relationship. The only regression that we have considered is linear regression, which is one way of describing how the means of conditional distributions are related to each other. There are, of course, many other regression lines, called curvilinear regressions, that can be studied. The only measure of correlation or amount of relationship that we have discussed is the coefficient called r_{yx} (or its square, r_{yx}^2). There are also many other ways of measuring the amount of relationship between two variables (some of which will be presented in Chapter 8). Other methods of handling regression and correlation are all roughly analogous to the two studied here. For this reason it is important that you understand the measures we have discussed. As an aid to the computational routines involved you should consult the accompanying computation design.

Computation design for linear bivariate analysis, ungrouped data

Individual	X	Y	X^2	Y^2	XY
1	X_1	Y_1	$X_1 X_1$	$Y_1 Y_1$	$X_1 Y_1$
2	X_2	Y_2	$X_2 X_2$	$Y_2 Y_2$	$X_2 Y_2$
.					
. .					
i	X_i	Y_i	$X_i X_i$	$Y_i Y_i$	$X_i Y_i$
.					
.					
N	X_N	Y_N	$X_N X_N$	$Y_N Y_N$	$X_N Y_N$
	ΣX	ΣY	ΣX^2	ΣY^2	ΣXY

1. The raw data come to us in the form of a table with three columns. The first column is a code identifying the particular individual object or event that has been observed. The second and third columns identify the two observations (X and Y) made on each individual. There are N individuals in all.
2. Three new columns are created; these are headed X^2, Y^2, and XY. Numbers are entered in these columns as indicated from the basic observations. For example, the entry in the ith row of the column headed X^2 is the product $X_i X_i$.
3. There are now five columns of data. Each of these columns is summed and the sums are recorded at the bottom of each column. Stage 1 in the calculation is now complete. These five column sums and N are carried over and used in stage 2.

$$\Sigma x^2 = \Sigma X^2 - \frac{(\Sigma X)^2}{N} \quad =$$

$$\Sigma y^2 = \Sigma Y^2 - \frac{(\Sigma Y)^2}{N} \quad =$$

$$\Sigma xy = \Sigma XY - \frac{(\Sigma X)(\Sigma Y)}{N} \quad =$$

$$\bar{X} = \frac{\Sigma X}{N} \quad =$$

$$\bar{Y} = \frac{\Sigma Y}{N} \quad =$$

1. The five sums found in stage 1 are now converted into the sums of squares and sum of cross products of the mean deviates. First, we find Σx^2 by squaring the sum of the column headed X, then dividing this square by N and subtracting the result from the sum of the column headed X^2. Second, we proceed in the same manner to find Σy^2 and Σxy.
2. Now we find the mean of each variable as indicated and enter the results as $\bar{X}$ and $\bar{Y}$. These calculations complete stage 2. We now have all of the basic information needed to calculate whatever summary measures we desire.

STAGE 3

$$b = \frac{\Sigma xy}{\Sigma x^2} \qquad =$$

$$a = \bar{Y} - b\bar{X} \qquad =$$

$$s_{y.x}^2 = \frac{(\Sigma y^2) - b(\Sigma xy)}{N - 2} \quad =$$

$$s_{y.x} = \sqrt{s_{y.x}^2} \qquad =$$

$$r_{yx}^2 = \frac{(\Sigma xy)^2}{\Sigma x^2 \Sigma y^2} \qquad =$$

$$K_{yx}^2 = 1 - r_{y.x}^2 \qquad =$$

$$r_{yx} = \frac{\Sigma xy}{\sqrt{\Sigma x^2 \Sigma y^2}} \qquad =$$

1. In this final stage of the computations we create whatever summary measures we desire. Each measure is calculated from one or more of the results found in stage 2. For example, to find b we locate Σxy in stage 2 and divide it by Σx^2, which is also found there. We proceed in the same manner for each other summary measure.
2. Note that we do not need to make all of these calculations each time we analyze data. Sometimes we will only be interested in the correlation coefficient, and at other times we will only be interested in the regression constants. Regardless of what eventual measure we want to compute, however, we should proceed through these stages rather than attempt to calculate the measure all at once.

Note: These computations can be quite tedious unless a desk calculator is available. The computational task can be reduced somewhat through the use of coding procedures similar to those discussed for the case of the mean. See your instructor for more details, if desired. However, in practice, the best solution is to find a desk calculator even if one is not readily available.

8

THE BIVARIATE TABLE:
ATTRIBUTES
AND ORDERS

In this chapter we shall consider all bivariate tables in which at least one of the variables has been measured at an ordinal level or is an attribute. Tables of such distributions are often called contingency tables. The basic problem in these tables is the same as in tables of interval variables, namely, to describe and summarize the differences among the various conditional distributions. In the preceding chapter we saw that two major concepts are used to solve this problem. These concepts are *regression* and *amount of relationship* or correlation. In the case of attributes and orders the concept of regression is of only secondary importance. For orders it is reduced to the basic question of whether the relationship between the variables is positive or negative, and for attributes even this distinction disappears. On the other hand, the concept of amount of relationship or association remains very important. Indeed, it is the key concept in terms of which we summarize the information in a contingency table. The amount of association summarizes the extent to which the conditional distributions of Y given X differ from each other in the various categories of X.

A great many measures of association have been proposed over the years for contingency tables. No one measure is universally accepted as the best one to use. In this text we shall describe only a few of these measures. Those that we do describe are widely used by sociologists today. Our main objective, however, is to provide an understanding of how the problem of measuring association is solved rather than to catalogue the various solutions that have been proposed.

To refresh your memory concerning the basic structure of a contingency table see Table 8.1. Here the various parts of such a table are described, using what is called the 2×2 table as an example. We usually identify the

135

Table 8.1   The General form of a contingency table

		X		
		X_1	X_2	*Total*
Y	Y_1	n_{11}	n_{12}	$n_{1.}$ ← The conditional distribution of X given Y_1
	Y_2	n_{21}	n_{22}	$n_{2.}$ ← The conditional distribution of X given Y_2
	Total	$n_{.1}$	$n_{.2}$	N ← The marginal distribution of X

↑ The conditional distribution of Y given X_1

↑ The conditional distribution of Y given X_2

↑ The marginal distribution of Y

size of a contingency table by noting the number of rows and the number of columns that it contains. Thus, a 2×2 table is a table with two rows (that is, two categories of Y) and two columns (that is, two categories of X). Notice that in Table 8.1 we refer to the marginal frequencies as giving the *marginal distribution* of X and the *marginal distribution* of Y. This phrase is just a new name for the original or univariate distribution of each variable. The contingency table, in general, then, contains joint frequencies that combine into *conditional distributions* and marginal frequencies that combine into *marginal distributions* or original univariate distributions. In every case, of course, the distribution includes the category designations as well as the frequencies.

8.1   THE PERCENT DIFFERENCE AND THE RATIO OF PERCENTS AS MEASURES OF ASSOCIATION

In Chapter 6 we studied how to analyze the general bivariate distribution by expressing each conditional distribution in percentage form and then comparing the percentages. This comparison, expressed as a difference or as a ratio, is a simple, yet useful, measure of the amount of association between the variables. That is, it is a measure of the extent to which the

Table 8.2   Professionalization in government agencies
by size of agency

	Size		
PROFESSIONALIZATION	SMALL	LARGE	TOTAL
High	31	28	59
Low	61	32	93
Total	92	60	152

SOURCE: Blau and others, 1966, adapted from Table 1.

conditional distributions differ. Since this measure is most useful in small contingency tables let us illustrate it in the case of a 2 $\times$ 2 table.

Blau, Heydebrand, and Stauffer compare the level of professionalization in small and large government agencies. Professionalization is defined as the extent to which members of the operating staff are required to have college degrees. They report the following (Table 8.2) among others. We may identify the extent to which professionalization is related to size by percentaging within each column and then comparing the percents within a row. In particular, the percent with high professionalization is 34 percent among small agencies and 47 percent among large agencies. The *difference* between these two percentages is 13 percent. This difference is a measure of the extent to which the two variables are associated.

Let us generalize this result by developing a formula for the percent difference. Under the condition X_1, that is, in the first column, the percent of Y_1s is

$$P_{11} = (100) \left(\frac{n_{11}}{n_{.1}} \right)$$

Under the condition X_2, that is, in the second column, the percent of Y_1s is

$$P_{12} = (100) \left(\frac{n_{12}}{n_{.2}} \right)$$

The difference between these percentages is the measure of association that we are considering. This difference is usually expressed as

$$\text{Percentage difference} = P_{12} - P_{11}$$

The percentage difference is an excellent *rough* measure of association. It is the measure we ordinarily use in scanning a table. In fact, it is very common today to report contingency tables in percent form. When this is the case the percent difference is extremely easy to calculate. However, the percentage difference is *not* the preferred measure for more systematic analysis for two reasons. First, except for 2×2 tables, all tables contain more than one such difference that could be used. In such tables it is better to have a measure that describes the entire table rather than just a part of it. Second, the percentage difference is strongly influenced by the relative frequency of Y_1 and Y_2 in the table as a whole (that is, in the marginal distribution of Y). Indeed, it is best to use the percentage *difference* only when Y_1 and Y_2 appear approximately equally often in the marginal distribution of Y. (In table 8.2, for example, there were 59 agencies with high professionalization and 93 with low professionalization. These two numbers are similar enough to make the percentage difference useful.)

When one of the marginal frequencies of Y is much larger than the other it is better to shift to the ratio method of comparison. The ratio of percentages is

$$\text{Ratio of percentages} = \frac{P_{12}}{P_{11}}$$

In our example this ratio is 1.4, meaning that a large agency is about 1.4 times as likely as a small agency to display high professionalization. This ratio is ordinarily computed only when one category of Y is quite rare. This situation does not often occur in sociology but it is very common in a field like medicine. Rare events (such as diseases) are of great interest in such a field. The ratio of percentages is subject to the same limitations that were mentioned for the difference between percentages. Because this ratio is not commonly used in sociology we shall not discuss it further.

In the remaining sections of this chapter we shall consider three more refined approaches to the measurement of association in contingency tables. The first approach, based on what is called statistical independence, is particularly appropriate when both measures are attributes, though it may also be used with ordinal variables. The second approach, based on comparisons of pairs of observations, is particularly appropriate when both measures are ordinal. The third approach, based upon ideas similar to those used in correlation analysis, is appropriate when the independent variable is an attribute or an order but the dependent variable is interval.

8.2   ASSOCIATION DERIVED FROM STATISTICAL INDEPENDENCE

To measure association, we proceed as follows. First, we create an imaginary table that describes what our observed bivariate table would look like *if there were no association* between the two variables (that is, if the two variables were statistically independent). We call this table the *expected* table. Second, we compare the table we have observed with this imaginary or expected table. The two attributes are associated to the extent to which the observed table differs from the expected table. Third, we find some way of summarizing the differences between these two tables and call the summary our measure of association.

The key to this procedure lies in understanding how the imaginary or expected table is created. Note first that association involves the conditional distributions and *not the marginal distributions*. (Remember, association is defined as existing when the conditional distributions of Y given X in percent form differ from each other.) To create a table similar to the one we have observed except that the two variables are independent of each other or *not associated*, we use the same marginal frequencies. However, we insert new cell frequencies (called E or expected frequencies). These expected cell frequencies are calculated in such a way that the conditional distributions would all be identical to each other when expressed in percentage form. This state of independence will be achieved if

$$E_{ij} = \frac{n_i. n_{.j}}{N} \qquad \text{for each cell}$$

For example, consider the frequencies in Table 8.2. What frequency would have to be in the upper-left-hand cell (cell$_{11}$) if the two variables were independent? The formula tells us that this number is found by taking the product of the two marginal frequencies that are in the row and column of this cell and dividing this product by the number of observations in the entire table. In particular, for this cell

$$E_{11} = \frac{n_1. n_{.1}}{N} = \frac{(92)(59)}{(152)} = \frac{5428}{152} = 35.7$$

$$= 36 \text{ (rounded to the nearest whole number)}$$

By proceeding in this manner we create the expected frequency in each cell. These results are presented in Table 8.3.

Table 8.3   Observed and expected cell frequencies
from Table 8.2

	Observed			Expected	
	X_1	X_2		X_1	X_2
Y_1	31	28	Y_1	36	23
Y_2	61	32	Y_2	56	37

Let us check the expected frequencies in this table to be sure that they really represent a table in which the variables are independent of each other. By definition, two variables are independent of each other if the conditional distributions (expressed in percentage form) of one variable given the other are identical. Since there are only two rows in our table all that we need to consider is the percent in the first row for each conditional distribution. We find these figures:

$$\text{The percent of } Y_1 \text{s given } X_1 = (100)\,\frac{36}{92} = 39 \text{ percent}$$

$$\text{The percent of } Y_1 \text{s given } X_2 = (100)\,\frac{23}{60} = 39 \text{ percent}$$

Therefore, the table of expected frequencies does display independence. (Of course, in actual calculations such as these rounding errors may produce slight discrepancies in the percentages.)

At the beginning of this section we said that we would measure the amount of association by identifying and summarizing the difference between the *observed* distribution and the *expected* distribution (assuming statistical independence). To accomplish this objective the next step is to compare the observed table with the expected table. We perform this comparison by subtracting each expected frequency from the corresponding observed frequency. Symbolically, we call this difference δ_{ij} (read "delta ij") and have

$$\delta_{ij} = n_{ij} - E_{ij}$$

Sometimes this difference is also referred to as "$O - E$" meaning the difference between the observed (O) and expected (E) frequencies. However, as we shall see later it is convenient to have a single symbol (namely, δ_{ij}) to represent this difference.

Of course, in any particular table there are as many δ_{ij} values as there are cells. Even in a 2×2 table there will be four such differences, and if the table is as large as 6×8 there will be 48 such differences. Somehow, we must summarize these individual cell differences into a measure that describes the deviation of the observations from the expectations in the table as a whole. This summarization can be accomplished in the following way. First, we square each difference to work with δ_{ij}^2. (As usual, we square to avoid the problem that the sum of the δ_{ij}s themselves will be zero, except for rounding errors.) Second, we divide each squared difference by the expected number, E_{ij}. We perform this division to adjust for the fact that a given deviation implies more association when the expectation is small than when it is large. At this point the adjusted number in each cell is δ_{ij}^2 / E_{ij}. The third step is to sum these ratios over all the cells in order to reduce the differences

Table 8.5   Calculation of ϕ^2 from its definitional formula

Column	Row			$\delta_{ij} =$			
i	j	n_{ij}	E_{ij}	$n_{ij} - E_{ij}$	$\delta_{ij}{}^2$	$\delta_{ij}{}^2/E_{ij}$	
1	1	31	36	-5	25	0.69	
1	2	28	23	5	25	1.09	$\phi^2 = \dfrac{2.91}{152}$
2	1	61	56	5	25	0.45	
2	2	32	37	-5	25	0.68	$= 0.0191$
		152				2.91	$\phi = 0.138$

to a single number. Finally, we divide the sum by N to express the deviation from expectation on a per person basis. (Clearly, the number of cases we choose to study has nothing to do with how much association there is between the variables we are considering. On the other hand, the above sum will get larger as we increase the sample size. We divide by N to eliminate this effect.) The measure that results from these operations is called ϕ^2 (read "phi squared"). It is defined by the following formula:

$$\phi^2 = \frac{1}{N} \Sigma \frac{\delta_{ij}{}^2}{E_{ij}},$$

where we sum over all cells. Table 8.5 illustrates its computation using the frequencies of Table 8.3.

The ϕ^2 is a summary of how much difference there is in the table as a whole, between the observed and expected frequencies. It forms the basis of a set of measures of association based upon the idea of statistical independence. In a 2×2 table (that is, a table in which each variable is a dichotomy) ϕ^2 itself is a sensible and widely used measure of association. For larger tables, however, ϕ^2 can be greater than one that is undesirable in a measure of association. Various modifications exist, which solve this problem. We shall not elaborate on these modifications except to present the oldest among them. It is called the coefficient of contingency and its square is defined as

$$C^2 = \frac{\phi^2}{1 + \phi^2}$$

The coefficient of contingency is the square root of C^2. It is a useful measure of association. It is important to recognize, however, that its maximum value depends to some extent upon the size of the table to which it is applied. For elementary analysis it is certainly adequate. In general, then, we can use ϕ^2 as a measure of association in a 2×2 table and C^2 as the measure in any larger table.

In a 2×2 table it is conventional to calculate ϕ^2 from a special formula. In particular,

$$\phi^2 = \frac{(n_{11}n_{22} - n_{12}n_{21})^2}{(n_{1.})(n_{2.})(n_{.1})(n_{.2})}$$

We can illustrate this computation with the following data:

	X_1	X_2	Total
Y_1	6	3	9
Y_2	4	5	9
Total	10	8	18

$$\phi^2 = \frac{(6 \times 5 - 3 \times 4)^2}{9 \times 9 \times 10 \times 8}$$

$$\phi^2 = \frac{324}{6480} = 0.050$$

or

$$\phi = 0.22$$

By way of contrast, we do usually calculate the coefficient of contingency C from the formula used earlier to define ϕ^2.

8.3   ASSOCIATION BETWEEN TWO ORDINAL VARIABLES

When the variables appearing in a contingency table are both ordinal we can approach the problem of measuring the amount of association between them in a very different way. In particular, we develop our measure out of the basic properties of ordinal measurement itself. It will be recalled that the essential property of ordinal measurement is the ability to determine which of two observations is the larger with respect to the variable being measured. This comparison can be generalized to the case of two variables. We can consider a *pair* of *individuals* and note whether or not the individual that is larger on X is also larger on Y. For example, suppose that two students each took two tests, with the following results:

	X	Y
	TEST 1	TEST 2
First student	A	B
Second student	C	C

The first student received the higher grade on test 1 (X) and also received the higher score on test 2 (Y). We say, then, that these two students are in the *same order* with respect to these particular observations.

Suppose, however, that two other students also took these two tests and received grades like these:

	$\bar{X}$	$\bar{Y}$
	TEST 1	TEST 2
John	A	B
Mary	C	A

The two variables rank this pair of students in a *different* order. As we shift from Mary to John the grade on X increases but the grade on Y decreases.

Now consider what we mean by association or relationship. If we say that two variables are *positively* related we mean that when we observe a relatively high value on one of the variables we will probably also observe a relatively high value on the other. In the same way, if we say that two variables are *negatively* related we mean that a high value on one variable will tend to occur with a *low* value of the other. Finally, when we say that two variables are *not* related we mean that we cannot tell anything about the value of the second variable from the first one. Notice that for the first pair of students that we considered X and Y generated the same order or appeared to be positively related. For the second pair of students X and Y generated different orders or appeared to be negatively related.

It turns out that we can use this very basic idea to build an effective measure of association. What we do is to consider *all of the possible pairs of individuals* in our sample or set of observations. For each pair we note whether the two variables rank the individuals in the same order or in a different order. Our measure of association is the relative preponderance of one or the other of these possibilities in the set of all possible pairs. We let N_s stand for the number of pairs in which the variables give the same order and N_d stand for the number of pairs in which the variables give a different order. The relative preponderance of one or the other order is given by the difference between these two numbers, that is, by $N_s - N_d$. For example, if this difference is positive there are more pairs in which both variables produced the same order. If the difference is negative then there are more pairs in which the variables produced different orders, that is, produced a different ranking of the individuals. To develop a measure of ordinal association all that we need do is divide this difference by the total number of possible pairs. This measure is called τ (read "tau") and is defined as:

$$\tau = \frac{N_s - N_d}{\text{all possible pairs}}$$

Because several new ideas are presented in the above paragraph it is worthwhile to consider an example using a small number of observations. Suppose that we have graded five students on two tests:

Student	X	Y
1	A	B
2	C	C
3	B	D
4	D	A
5	F	F

Our first problem is to identify all of the possible *pairs* of students that we could form from this group of five.

Consider the first individual. He may be paired with any one of the remaining four, giving the pairs $(1, 2)$; $(1, 3)$; $(1, 4)$; and $(1, 5)$. Now consider the second student. He may also be paired with any one of the remaining four individuals, yielding the pairs $(2, 1)$; $(2, 3)$; $(2, 4)$; $(2, 5)$. In general, for any one of the five individuals there are four others with whom he may be paired, giving 5×4 pairs in all or, in general, $N(N - 1)$ pairs. But wait!!! Notice that in the above lists pair $(2, 1)$ contains the same individuals as pair $(1, 2)$. When we define "all possible pairs" we agree to count such repeated pairs only once. The mathematician refers to this reduced number as the number of *combinations* of the individuals. In statistical work we almost always deal with combinations. In this case since each pair appears twice, that is, once as (a, b) and once as (b, a), the number of combinations is

$$\frac{N(N - 1)}{2} = \frac{5 \times 4}{2} = 10$$

In general, we speak of the number of combinations of N things taken two at a time as the number of "all possible pairs." We symbolize combinations by large parentheses, as follows:

$$\binom{N}{2} = \frac{N(N - 1)}{2} = \text{combinations of } N \text{ things taken two at a time.}$$

The next problem is to list the ten pairs and identify, for each one, whether the two variables rank the individuals in the same or in a different order. We might set up a worksheet something like Table 8.4.

Table 8.4 Sample worksheet

| | Student with higher grade on each variable | | |
PAIR	X	Y	ORDER
1, 2	1 (A vs. C)	1 (B vs. C)	same
1, 3	1 (A vs. B)	1 (B vs. D)	same
1, 4	1 (A vs. D)	4 (B vs. A)	different
1, 5	1 (A vs. F)	1 (B vs. F)	same
2, 3	3 (C vs. B)	2 (C vs. D)	different
2, 4	2 (C vs. D)	4 (C vs. A)	different
2, 5	2 (C vs. F)	2 (C vs. F)	same
3, 4	3 (B vs. D)	4 (D vs. A)	different
3, 5	3 (B vs. F)	3 (D vs. F)	same
4, 5	4 (D vs. F)	4 (A vs. F)	same

Now all we need do is count the number of pairs for which the order is the same (N_s) and the number of pairs for which it is different (N_d). We have

$$N_s = 6$$
$$N_d = 4$$

Therefore, the amount of association between X and Y is

$$r = \frac{6 - 4}{10} = 0.20$$

This measure, as defined above, is suitable for *ungrouped* data in which there are *no ties*. A tie occurs whenever both of the individuals in a pair have the same value on one or both of the variables. For example, this pair is tied on X but not on Y:

	X	Y
1	B	A
2	B	C

Ordinarily, when individuals are ranked on a variable there are many ties. For example, many students get the same grade on an examination in a large class. Ties are particularly common when the variable has been grouped. Then all of the individuals falling into the same category are tied with each other. Since we usually calculate our measure of ordinal association from a table it is very important to learn how to handle the ties that will be present.

The first step is to learn how to classify each possible pair according to order or ties. In general, there are five possible arrangements within any given pair.

1. X and Y may rank the individuals in the same order. The number of pairs for which this statement is true is called N_s.

2. X and Y may rank the individuals in different orders. The number of pairs for which this statement is true is called N_d.

3. The two observations of X may be the same (that is, tied) but the two observations of Y be different. The number of pairs for which this statement is true is called T_x.

4. The two observations of X may be different but the two observations of Y be the same (tied). The number of pairs for which this statement is true is called T_y.

5. The two observations of X may be tied and the two observations of Y may also be tied. The number of pairs for which this statement is true is called T_{xy}.

Notice that these five possibilities exhaust all of the arrangements that could exist within a pair. Therefore, the total number of these arrangements must be equal to the total number of pairs. In other words, we have

$$\binom{N}{2} = N_s + N_d + T_x + T_y + T_{xy}$$

As we shall see in the next section there are several different ways in which these various counts may be combined into measures of ordinal association. Before looking at these measurements, however, it is necessary to learn how to make these various counts when the data have been grouped into a table. Since this problem is far from trivial we have prepared a special computation design that should be consulted for detailed instructions. What we will do here is to look at a table and see how we identify pairs of observations in it and then how we decide what the order is within each pair.

Pairs of Observations in a Contingency Table

As we know, the main body of a bivariate table consists of a rectangle of cells each of which contains a frequency n_{ij}. This frequency refers to the number of people (or objects or events) who possessed both the ith value of Y and the jth value of X. In visualizing pairs it is convenient to visualize the tally sheet from which the table was constructed. On this tally sheet the frequency appears as a set of tally marks, with one tally mark for each individual in the cell. Thus, a pair of individuals is any one of these tally marks combined with any other one tally mark—either from the same cell or from a different cell. As an example consider the five students we listed before. Now, however, we shall group their test scores into "high" (C or more) and "low" (D or F) categories and table the results, as follows:

		TABLE			IMPLIED TALLY	
		X			X	
		LOW	HIGH		LOW	HIGH
Y	High	1	2	High	/	//
	Low	1	1	Low	/	/

In locating the pairs in a table we identify them according to the *cells* involved rather than in terms of code numbers applied to the individuals. Of course, there will be the same number of possible pairs as in the ungrouped data. For these five students let us now identify each of the ten possible pairs.

We start in the upper-left-hand corner, that is, with cell$_{11}$. It contains one person who may be paired with any of the remaining four persons. Two of these remaining four persons are located in cell$_{12}$ so we say that there are *two* pairs that we can form between cells "11" and "12." Notice that the number of pairs that can be formed from these two different cells is the product of the cell frequencies, $2 \times 1 = 2$ pairs. This statement is generally true. *The number of pairs that can be formed by taking one individual from one cell and the other individual from another cell is the product of the respective cell frequencies.* Let us proceed. We can also pair the individual in cell$_{11}$ with the individual in cell$_{21}$ and with the individual in cell$_{22}$. These, then, are the four pairs involving the individual in cell$_{11}$.

Now look at the cell in the upper-right-hand corner, that is, cell$_{12}$. This cell contains two individuals either of whom could be combined with any of the other four to make a pair. Consider the first person in that cell. He can combine with the person in cell$_{11}$, but notice that we already counted that pair when we started with cell$_{11}$. Remember that we are finding combinations and hence do not count any pair more than once. Therefore, we use the following rule. *In locating new pairs involving a given cell ignore all cells that have already been used as a starting point.* The next individual with whom our person may be paired is the other person in cell$_{12}$. In other words, we can form one pair from the two persons *in the same cell*. In general, *the number of pairs that can be formed within a single cell is* $\binom{n_{ij}}{2}$ *or the combinations of n_{ij} things taken two at a time.* In this case we have two things taken two at a time, or $(2 \times 1)/2 = 1$ pair. This person could also be paired with the individual in cell$_{21}$ or with the one in cell$_{22}$, giving two more pairs. Now consider the second person in that cell. He can also be paired with any of the other four individuals. However, we have already counted both the pair involving cell$_{11}$ and the pair involving the other student in cell$_{12}$. Therefore, his new pairs are with cell$_{21}$ and with cell$_{22}$.

If we proceed in this way through all of the cells we will locate all of the ten possible pairs. In general, a pair may be formed by two individuals in the *same cell* or by two individuals located in *different cells*. For our example we might list the set of ten possible pairs as shown in Table 8.6.

Table 8.6   Set of ten possible pairs

Cells involved in pair	Number of pairs involving these cells
11 and 11	0
11 and 12	2
11 and 21	1
11 and 22	1
12 and 12	1
12 and 21	2
12 and 22	2
21 and 21	0
21 and 22	1
22 and 22	0
	10 possible pairs

We have illustrated this method of identifying pairs in a 2×2 table, but, of course, the same procedure can be used in any contingency table. Although the larger the table, the more possible combination of cells, the same rules apply.

The next step in learning to read a table in this ordinal manner involves learning how to classify the pairs according to how the variables order the individuals. First, let us identify all cases in which at least one of the variables shows a *tie* in the pair. There are three types of tie that can occur and there are three corresponding sets of cells that would produce them. Suppose that both individuals in the pair come from the *same cell*. They are then necessarily tied on both X and Y. In other words, all such pairs form the number T_{xy}. Now suppose that the pair involves different cells, but the cells are both located in the same *row*, such as:

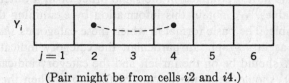

(Pair might be from cells *i*2 and *i*4.)

Any pair formed in this way is tied on Y but not on X. The set of all such pairs form T_y. Finally, suppose that the pair involves different cells, but the cells are both located in the same *column*, such as

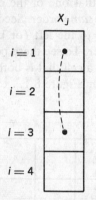

(This pair might be from cells 1*j* and 3*j*.)

Any pair formed in this way is tied on X but not on Y. The set of all such pairs form T_x.

Now that we see how to find the pairs involving ties let us consider finding those pairs that do not involve ties (in other words, all pairs such that the two variables order the individual in the *same* or in *different* orders). All such pairs will involve two different cells such that the two cells are located in different rows *and* different columns. Such a pair of cells might be

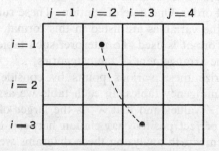

(This pair might be from cells 12 and 33.)

For any pair formed in this manner we also need to be able to tell whether the individuals in it are ranked in the same order or in a different order by the two variables. We obtain this information by examining the categories of each variable. The basic format in which these categories *should* be listed is the same as in a graph. In particular, the category indicating the least quantity of X should be on the far left and the category indicating the least quantity of Y should be at the bottom of the table. Then the values of X increase as we scan from left to right and the values of Y increase as we scan from the bottom to the top of the table.

When this format is used we have the following rules relative to order. First, any pair of cells such that one of the cells is both above and to the right of the other displays the *same* order. Second, any pair of cells such that one of the cells is above but to the left (or below but to the right) of the other displays a *different* order. To see these points consider two individuals, A and B. Let A be located in a cell that is both above and to the right of the cell in which B is located, as in Figure 8.1.

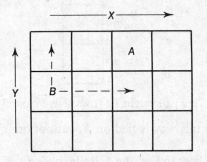

Figure 8.1.   Same order versus different order.

Here, it is clear that X and Y rank these two individuals in the same order because A has a higher value of X and also a higher value of Y, relative to B. Try to visualize on this diagram the other situation, that is, the one that leads to a different order. One note of caution: These rules apply only when the categories of the variables are listed in this format. In many published tables a different format is used. To interpret such tables you must modify the rules to suit the arrangement of the categories.

Let us summarize these various points by considering various hypothetical 2×2 contingency tables. In each table we assume that Y_1 is the larger of the two Y values and that X_2 is the larger of the two X values. First, consider a perfect positive association between two variables, as in diagram A. Remember, in analyzing these diagrams we are going to think in terms of the possible pairs of individuals that could be formed. Notice,

A. Perfect positive association

	X_1	X_2
Y_1	0	50
Y_2	50	0

first, that the only ties that can be formed are within a single cell. That is, in each and every case in which X is tied Y is also tied; or, in other words, $T_x = 0$ and $T_y = 0$. Second, note that any pair formed *between* cells will display the *same* order on both variables. For such a pair one must be chosen from $cell_{21}$ and the other from $cell_{12}$. In a pair from these cells the rule about being above and to the right applies; in other words, $N_d = 0$. No pairs can be formed in which the variables display a different order.

Diagram B displays a perfect negative association between the variables. Here, again, there are no ties involving just one variable. Now, however,

B. Perfect negative association

	X_1	X_2
Y_1	50	0
Y_2	0	50

all pairs from different cells show a *different* order between the individuals on the two variables. Whenever individual A has the larger value of X he also has the smaller value of Y. Diagram C is more difficult to interpret.

C. Perfect positive association

	X_1	X_2
Y_1	25	25
Y_2	50	0

Analyzing this diagram in terms of pairs of individuals we note that in all of the pairs in which both variables are different the *order* is the same, and therefore, $N_d = 0$. This fact suggests that the association is perfect. But now look at the ties. In some pairs (namely, those formed by choosing one individual from $cell_{11}$ and the other from $cell_{12}$) Y is tied but X is not. In other pairs (from $cell_{11}$ and $cell_{21}$) X is tied but Y is not. The question is, do these ties detract from the "perfectness" of the association? Experts disagree on this point. Some would argue that these ties do not detract and that the association is perfect because $N_d = 0$. Others would argue that the ties do detract because there are some cases in which a change in one variable was *not* accompanied by a change in the other variable. Whether or not this table displays perfect association the two variables are obviously positively associated.

Measures of Ordinal Association

We are now in a position to consider certain specific measures of ordinal association using the various concepts that we have just discussed. It turns out that τ itself is not a very sensible measure when there are ties, but that the principal alternatives are all based on the idea of τ. We shall discuss three measures here, all of which make use of the same numerator as does τ. In particular, the numerator of each ratio is $N_s - N_d$, which is, of course, the relative preponderance of pairs displaying the *same* order among those not containing ties. The measures develop somewhat different denominators, however.

The first measure is usually called γ (read "gamma"). It is defined as

$$\gamma = \frac{N_s - N_d}{N_s + N_d}$$

Notice that the denominator here consists of all nontied pairs. In diagram C this measure would equal 1.

The second measure is called d_{yx}, and is defined as

$$d_{yx} = \frac{N_s - N_d}{N_s + N_d + T_y}$$

Now we have included in the denominator all pairs in which Y is tied but X is not tied. The argument for including these ties is that Y is visualized as dependent upon X. Therefore, if X changes but Y does not, there is evidence of a lack of association, and hence these ties should be in the denominator where they decrease the value of the measure. In a similar way, incidentally, we can also define

$$d_{xy} = \frac{N_s - N_d}{N_s + N_d + T_x}$$

Here we have reversed the roles of X and Y. Now we visualize X as dependent upon Y.

The third measure is called τ' and is equivelent to the original τ corrected for ties. It is defined as

$$\tau' = \frac{N_s - N_d}{\sqrt{(N_s + N_d + T_y)(N_s + N_d + T_x)}}$$

Table 8.7 Class homogamy in the United States

| WIFE'S FATHER'S OCCUPATIONAL CLASS | *Husband's Occupational Class* | | | |
	LOWER	MIDDLE	UPPER	TOTAL
Upper	13	26	9	48
Middle	83	75	19	177
Lower	110	56	16	182
Total	206	157	44	407

SOURCE: Adapted from Centers, 1949.

It turns out that this measure is equal to $\sqrt{d_{yx}d_{xy}}$. In other words, it is a measure in which we assume that either X or Y might be dependent upon the other, and so we take both kinds of ties into account in the denominator. In practice, τ' is probably the best measure to use.

All of these measures of association, of course, are based upon the same set of counts, namely, N_s, N_d, T_x, T_y, and T_{xy}. The computational problem, therefore, involved in any of them is to make these counts in an efficient way. We shall illustrate how to find these various numbers using a 3×3 table. You should also study the computational design for further guidance.

Table 8.7 is a typical contingency table with ordinal variables. To analyze it we imagine all of the possible pairs of observations that we could form with the 407 individuals in the table, and then we divide these pairs into the various categories that we have discussed.

Counting N_s

Let us first identify the number of pairs for which the individuals would be ranked in the same order by both variables. As a preliminary we observe the format of the categories of X and Y. This format is the preferred one with Y increasing up the page and X increasing to the right. Therefore, we form pairs from cells such as that one cell is both above and to the right of the other. To find this number we take each cell in turn. We multiply the frequency in the cell by the sum of the frequencies in all cells both above and to the right of it. Then we sum these products over all the cells. Let us begin in the lower-left corner (that is, in cell$_{31}$). The frequency in this cell is $n_{31} = 110$. We multiply this frequency by the sum of all the frequencies in cells above and to the right of it, or by $(75 + 26 + 19 + 9)$. We then shift to the next cell and proceed in the same way, and in this way we go through all the cells. Of course, in several cells there will be no frequencies above and to the right (namely, for cells in the top row and in the right hand column), and the product will be 0. When we add these products we obtain N_s.

$$N_s = 110(75 + 26 + 9 + 19) + 56(9 + 19) + 83(26 + 9) + 75(9)$$
$$= 110(129) + 56(28) + 83(35) + 75(9)$$
$$= 19,338$$

Counting N_d

The procedure for counting N_d is very similar. In this case, however, we assemble cell frequencies in cells that are below and to the right of the cell we select. If we start in the upper-left cell for this purpose we have

$$N_d = 13(75 + 19 + 56 + 16) + 26(19 + 16) + 83(56 + 16) + 75(16)$$
$$= 13(166) + 26(35) + 83(72) + 75(16)$$
$$= 10,244$$

Counting T_x

Both members of pairs that are tied on X will be found in the same column. Since we want pairs that are *not* tied on Y we must choose them from *different rows*. That is, we choose pairs of cells from the same column but different rows.

$$T_x = 13(83 + 110) + 83(110) + 26(75 + 56) + 75(56)$$
$$\qquad\qquad\qquad\qquad\qquad\qquad + 9(19 + 16) + 19(16)$$
$$= 13(193) + 83(110) + 26(131) + 75(56) + 9(35) + 19(16)$$
$$= 19,864$$

Counting T_y

By analogy to T_x the ties on Y but not X will be all pairs in cells such that the two are in the same row, but in different columns of the table.

$$T_y = 13(26 + 9) + 26(9) + 83(75 + 19) + 75(19) + 110(56 + 16)$$
$$\qquad\qquad\qquad\qquad\qquad\qquad\qquad\qquad\qquad\qquad + 56(16)$$
$$= 13(35) + 26(9) + 83(94) + .5(19) + 110(72) + 56(16)$$
$$= 18,732$$

Counting T_{xy}

This term does not appear in any of the measures of association. It is easily obtained by subtraction, since

$$T_{xy} = \binom{N}{2} - N_s - N_d - T_x - T_y$$

$$= \frac{407(406)}{2} - 19{,}338 - 10{,}244 - 19{,}864 - 18{,}732$$

$$= 14{,}443$$

Once the various counts have been made the measures of association are readily found, as follows:

$$\gamma = \frac{19{,}338 - 10{,}244}{19{,}338 + 10{,}244} = \frac{9094}{29{,}582} = 0.307$$

$$d_{yx} = \frac{9094}{29{,}582 + 18{,}732} = \frac{9094}{48{,}314} = 0.188$$

$$d_{xy} = \frac{9094}{29{,}582 + 19{,}864} = \frac{9094}{49{,}446} = 0.184$$

$$\tau' = \sqrt{(0.188)(0.184)} \qquad = 0.186$$

Notice that γ gives a considerably higher figure than the other measures since its denominator does not contain any ties. All of the measures show that the variables involved are positively related to each other, meaning, in this case, that a woman's husband will tend to be from the same occupational class as her father. Expressed in terms of pairs, the positive association means that if we consider two married women and find that the father of A, say, was from the higher class we would also expect that woman A would have the higher-status husband.

8.4 RELATIONSHIP BETWEEN AN ATTRIBUTE AND AN INTERVAL VARIABLE

We have discussed two approaches to the measurement of association among attributes and orders. In practice, there are many bivariate distributions that are mixed in form in the sense that the two variables have been measured at different levels. One case that is particularly important is the situation in which the dependent variable (Y) is interval but the independent variable (X) is an attribute. (Remember, of course, that any variable can be reduced to the level of an attribute so that X can really be measured at any level. It is appropriate that X be an attribute in the sense that we use no other information about it.) Examples of this bivariate mixture are: (1) the age distribution of people in various religious groups,

Computation design for N_s and T_x for two orders with r and c classes

1. To find N_s = the number of pairs displaying the *same* order:

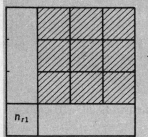

A. Start with n_{r1}, the lower-left cell. Add all the frequencies in the shaded area and multiply the result by n_{r1}.

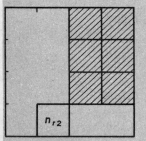

B. Now shift to n_{r2}, the adjacent cell in the same row. Again add all the frequencies in the shaded area and multiply the result by n_{r2}.

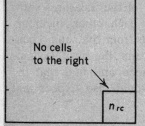

C. Then shift to n_{r3}, . . . always adding up the frequencies above and to the right of the selected cell. Cells in the last column have no cells to the right so may be ignored.

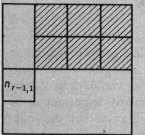

D. When done with row r shift up to the next row and proceed as before, working from left to right. Continue until you reach the top row, which may be omitted because there are no cells above this row.

E. Now sum the products that you have found. This sum is N_s.

Note: To find N_d proceed in a similar manner except that for each cell, cells *below* and to the right are chosen.

2. To find $T_x =$ the number of pairs tied on X but not on Y:

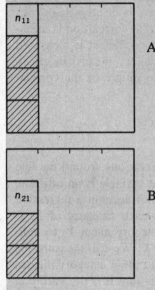

A. Start with n_{11}, the upper-left cell. Add all the frequencies in the shaded area and multiply the result by n_{11}.

B. Now shift to n_{21}, the adjacent cell in the same column. Again add the frequencies in the shaded area and multiply the result by n_{21}.

C. Then shift to n_{31}, ... always adding up frequencies below the indicated cell. The cell in the last row may be ignored since there are no cells below it.

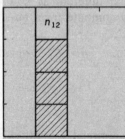

D. When done with the first column shift to the second and proceed as before, working down in the same column. Continue through all the columns.

E. Now sum the products that you have found. This sum is T_x.

Note: To find T_y proceed in a similar manner although now you will work within each *row*.

(2) weekly hours spent on the job in various occupations, and (3) income of individuals classified according to major leisure-time activities.

The measure of association that is appropriate here is directly analogous to the correlation coefficient. The only difference is that correlation is measured through the use of a line of regression and this coefficient is measured through the use of the category means. These category means, in effect, *become* the regression line. You will recall that the square of the correlation coefficient is

$$r^2 = 1 - \frac{s_{y.x}^2}{s_y^2}$$

where $s_{y.x}^2$ is a measure of the variation of the observations around the line of regression, $Y' = a + bX$. When the independent variable is an attribute the categories do not exist along a scale so we cannot develop a regression line. However, we can use the mean of Y within each category of X as equivalent to the regression line. We call such a category mean $\bar{Y}_j$ to indicate that it is the mean of Y in the jth category of X. We can measure the variation of the observations in each category around these category means. This variation is called the *within variance*, meaning that it is the variation in Y that occurs within a given category of X. We now define η^2 (read "eta squared") as

$$\eta^2 = 1 - \frac{\text{within variance of } Y}{\text{total variance of } Y}$$

The interpretation of η^2 is precisely analogous to the interpretation of r^2 that we have stressed in this text. It measures or tells us what proportion of the original variance of Y occurs only when X also varies.

The computational form of this measure is somewhat different as you should expect by now. The value of η^2 that we actually compute from observations is called E^2. We have

$$E^2 = 1 - \frac{\Sigma Y^2 - \sum\limits_{j} n_j \bar{Y}_j^2}{\Sigma Y^2 - N\bar{Y}^2}$$

where

ΣY^2 = sum of the squares of the Y observations summed *over all* of the observations

$\bar{Y}_j$ = mean value of Y in the jth category of X

n_j = number of observations of Y in the jth category of X

$\sum\limits_{j} n_j \bar{Y}_j^2 = n_1 \bar{Y}_1^2 + n_2 \bar{Y}_2^2 + \cdots$ through all the categories of X

$\bar{Y}$ = mean of *all* of the observations of Y

(Note: Those already familiar with E^2 will find this computational formula a little unusual. We introduce it here because it is the easiest formula to use, given only a knowledge of elementary statistics.) This formula should only be used when the Y observations are ungrouped, of course.

Let us illustrate the computations using hypothetical observations of students classified according to age and status. We arrange the data into two columns, one column for undergraduates and the other column for graduates. The first column represents $j = 1$ and the second column represents $j = 2$. The age of each student in the study is listed in the appropriate column, as follows:

	Undergraduates	Graduates	
	17	23	
	21	31	
	18	28	
	19	24	
	21	23	
	18	26	
		29	
ΣY_j	114	184	$\Sigma Y = 298$
n_j	6	7	$N = 13$
$\bar{Y}_j$	19.0	26.3	$\bar{Y} = 22.9$

We now sum the observations in each column and record the results as ΣY_j. These two sums are then added to give ΣY, which is written to the right of the other figures. Next we count the number of observations in each column (n_j) and then find $N = n_1 + n_2$. Finally, we get the mean of Y in each column and for all observations.

At this point, we square each observation and sum all of the squares, usually in a new place on the worksheet:

Y^2	
Undergraduates	Graduates
289	529
441	961
324	784
361	576
441	529
324	676
	841

$$\Sigma Y^2 = 7076$$

Now we enter these various elements in the formula and calculate E^2.

$$E^2 = 1 - \frac{7076 - 6(19.0)^2 - 7(26.3)^2}{7076 - 13(22.9)^2}$$

$$= 1 - \frac{7076 - 2166 - 4841.83}{7076 - 6817.33}$$

$$= 1 - \frac{68.17}{258.67}$$

$$= 1 - 0.264$$

$$= 0.736$$

In other words, approximately 74 percent of the variance in the ages of the students occurs only when we allow X to vary between undergraduates and graduates. Or we can say that 74 percent of the variance in the ages of the students disappears when we stay within the categories of X, namely, undergraduate and graduate.

This computational procedure can easily be extended to cases in which X possesses more than two categories, of course.

8.5 SIMILARITIES IN THE MEASURES OF ASSOCIATION: THE 2 x 2 TABLE

In this chapter and the last preceding one we have developed measures of association or relationship in three quite different ways. Each approach used information appropriate to a given level of measurement. At the *interval* level we introduced r^2, which is based upon the idea of variance and how much of the variance in Y is associated with variation in X. At the *ordinal* level we introduced τ' (and various related measures). τ' is based upon the idea of *order* and, in particular, is a measure of the extent to which two different variables will place a set of individuals in the same order. At the *nominal* level we introduced ϕ^2, which is a measure of the extent to which the frequencies in a table differ from those we would expect if the two variables were statistically independent of each other. Conceptually, these three approaches are really very different though each leads to a sensible measure of the amount of association or relationship.

Given this conceptual difference it is rather interesting to find that, in a 2 × 2 table,

$$r^2 = (\tau')^2 = \phi^2$$

We noted earlier that in the case of a dichotomy it is difficult to specify (uniquely) the level of measurement. Indeed, any dichotomy *can* be interpreted as involving measurement at any of the three levels. (Of course, this statement does not imply that any given dichotomy *should* be interpreted in this way.) When we are given only two values of X it is impossible to arrange them in such a way that they are "out of order." Therefore, we cannot definitely tell whether they are ordinal or not. Furthermore, we may assume that any interval between them represents "equal intervals" since there is just one interval. Thus, for example, we have the dichotomy "less than college education" and "college education or more." This dichotomy may be an all-or-none attribute since we can rephrase the categories to be "has not been to college" and "has been to college." Clearly, the categories can be interpreted in an ordinal manner also, since the categories are ranked relative to amount of education. It is even possible to think of these two categories as forming an interval scale. Each category presumably has a midpoint if we take the trouble to find it and there is a single interval between the midpoints. We could assign the code number "0" to the first category and "1" to the other category, thereby creating what we called a dummy variable. Using these code numbers for two variables we could compute the correlation between two dichotomies, for example. Thus, for any 2×2 table we can compute r, r', and ϕ without necessarily violating any assumptions regarding level of measurement. (Note that in this illustration the most sensible interpretation is an ordinal one.)

What is interesting, of course, is that we get precisely the same value for our measure of association whatever assumptions we make about the level of measurement, provided that we use one of the above three measures of association. The fact that these three measures are identical in the 2×2 table makes it more appropriate that they be used when measuring association, rather than some of the other measures that we have discussed. Incidentally, E^2 and r^2 will also be identical in a 2×2 table since, with only two categories of X, the linear regression will pass precisely through the category means of Y.

8.6 WHERE WE STAND

We have come a long way in this chapter because we have now introduced the elementary summary measures most frequently encountered in sociological research. This entire chapter has been devoted to the measurement of a single concept, namely, the amount of association between two variables. We focused attention primarily upon variables measured at either the nominal or ordinal levels. The concept of amount of association is the fundamental one we use in summarizing the result of comparing two or more conditional distributions. To the extent that the conditional distributions are similar there is no association between the variables represented in them. Indeed, when the conditional distributions are identical (in percentage form) we have what is called statistical *independence* between the variables. We have seen that sensible measures of association can be developed by determining how far an actual table departs from this state of independence. The important general point, however, is that measuring amount of association is equivalent to measuring the extent to which the conditional distributions differ in a bivariate table.

This point must be kept in mind in interpreting association or relationship. Unfortunately, it is often misunderstood. The statement that two variables are related to each other should not be taken as implying anything more. Naturally, when a relationship between two variables has been observed the researcher is very likely to also want to know how it came about—that is, he will want to find out why the conditional distributions of one of the variables are different for the various values of the other variable. This question is not easy to answer. In a sense, it is the key question in all scientific analysis. As such, it can never be answered in a completely definitive sense. Nevertheless, it is a crucial question. In the next chapter we shall consider certain elementary ways of attempting to answer it. For the moment you should simply note that the statement that two variables are related or associated signifies nothing more than that the conditional distributions of one variable given the other are different.

9

SELECTED MULTIVARIATE PROBLEMS

So far in this text we have discussed how to describe and summarize the information in univariate and bivariate distributions. In this chapter we turn to the analysis of what are called multivariate distributions, that is, joint distributions of three or more variables. These distributions arise when we make observations on three or more characteristics of each member of our population or sample. Our discussion will include only elementary problems in multivariate analysis because extensive treatment of this subject lies well beyond the scope of this book. Furthermore, we shall only consider those procedures that are appropriate at all levels of measurement.

Multivariate problems arise rather naturally in the research process. Ordinarily, research begins with the selection and study of a univariate distribution, that is, with the distribution of the dependent variable Y. We shift to the bivariate level in order to attempt to account for or explain this univariate distribution. In the same spirit, when we have cross-classified two variables and discovered that they are related, we want to know how to account for or explain that relationship. To solve this problem we introduce other variables into the analysis, in the hope that their introduction will clarify the original relationship between X and Y. Some sociologists call this process the *elaboration* of the original relationship (for example, Lazarsfeld and Kendall, 1950; see also Hyman, 1955, Chapters 6 and 7). We shall begin by showing what a multivariate table looks like and then consider just how it is used to account for or explain the relationship between two variables. Throughout the chapter we shall only consider dichotomies, although the procedures can also be applied to larger classifications.

9.1   THE GENERAL FORM OF THE MULTIVARIATE TABLE

Introducing a third variable adds a third dimension to our table. A 2×2 table, for example, becomes a $2 \times 2 \times 2$ table when dichotomized again. This step is sometimes called *stratifying* the 2×2. Table 9.1 is an example from a classic study of voting. The table on the left is subdivided into the

Table 9.1   Socioeconomic status, union membership, and the two-party vote, Elmira, 1948

						Union Membership						
						MEMBER				NONMEMBER		
	Status					*Status*				*Status*		
	LOW	HIGH	TOTAL			LOW	HIGH	TOTAL		LOW	HIGH	TOTAL
Rep.	150	242	392	STRATIFIED BY UNION	Rep.	37	14	51	Rep.	113	228	341
Dem.	111	78	189	MEMBERSHIP BECOMES	Dem.	56	14	70	Dem.	55	64	119
Total	261	320	581		Total	93	28	121		168	292	460

SOURCE: Berelson, Lazarsfeld, and McPhee, 1954, p. 47.

two tables on the right. The frequencies in corresponding cells of these two "partial" tables (on the right) sum to the frequency in that cell in the table on the left. For example, in cell$_{11}$ (the upper-left-hand cell) $150 = 37 + 113$. The table on the left is referred to as the marginal table or the original table and the tables on the right are called partial tables. Dividing the table into two partial tables is a way of representing the three dimensions on a two-dimensional surface. Actually, the eight cells of the overall table form a three-dimensional cube but the two layers of this cube have been separated and placed side by side.

Let us now consider how to read or understand the set of partial tables. Actually, we read *each one* in just the same way as we read any bivariate table. In particular, we divide the table into its conditional distributions, which are univariate, and then compare these conditional distributions with each other. In this example the univariate distribution in which we are interested is the party receiving each person's vote. In each of the three bivariate tables we see this distribution under two conditions, namely, among low-status individuals and among high-status individuals. If we wish, we can summarize each bivariate comparison by computing one of the measures of association discussed in Chapter 8. Now, however, we can carry this process of comparison one step further. Once the relationship between X and Y has been established in each partial table, *we can compare the relationship in one table with that in another*. Actually, two types

Table 9.2   Symbols identifying the parts of partial contingency tables

Categories of the control variable →		Z_1				Z_2	

Categories of the control variable → Z_1 Z_2

Categories of the independent variable → X_1 X_2 X_1 X_2

Categories of the dependent variable

	X_1	X_2			X_1	X_2	
Y_1	n_{111}	n_{121}	$N_{1.1}$	Y_1	n_{112}	n_{122}	$N_{1.2}$
Y_2	n_{211}	n_{221}	$N_{2.1}$	Y_2	n_{212}	n_{222}	$N_{2.2}$
	$N_{.11}$	$N_{.21}$	$N_{..1}$		$N_{.12}$	$N_{.22}$	$N_{..2}$

of comparison can be made. First, we can compare the relationship in all of the partial tables with that found in the marginal table. Second, we can compare the relationship in one of the partial tables with that in the other partial table(s). The extra comparisons that are now possible form the heart of multivariate analysis.

Before proceeding further with the analysis, however, it is important to understand the general symbols used for the parts of the multivariate distribution. First, consider the variables themselves. We continue to call the dependent variable Y and the independent variable X. The third variable is called Z and is referred to as a *control* variable. Each partial table shows the distribution of X and Y with Z held constant at some particular value. That is, a particular value of Z is included in the definition of the population from which the partial table arises. The marginal table also shows the distribution of X and Y but Z no longer appears in the definition of the population.

The designations of the frequencies in the partial tables are shown in Table 9.2. Notice that we have to add a third subscript to identify each frequency properly. This third subscript identifies which partial table contains the frequency; it is called k. Thus, the general cell frequency is n_{ijk}, where i identifies the row, j the column, and k the particular partial table. Notice that the periods or dots in the various marginal totals indicate the direction of the summation. Thus, for example, $N_{.11}$ is the marginal total in the first column of the first partial table. Sometimes it is convenient to refer to the total frequency in one of the partial tables as N_k rather than $N_{..k}$. Whenever N_k appears in the text it will mean the total frequency in the kth partial table. Also note that the symbols have been presented for the $2 \times 2 \times 2$ table. It is easy to generalize the symbols by extending the range of the subscripts. For example, if there are four categories of Z there will be four separate partial tables and the third subscript will range from 1 to 4. If there are three categories of Y there will be three rows in each partial table, and so on. We will not consider larger tables further.

9.2 WAYS TO ACCOUNT FOR THE OBSERVED RELATIONSHIP BETWEEN X AND Y

An observed association between variables can be explained in several different ways. We use multivariate analysis primarily as a means of identifying which among these possible explanations is correct in any specific case. To show how this objective is accomplished we shall first identify the various possible explanations of association or relationship, and then show how multivariate analysis helps us discriminate among these possibilities. The first phase will be discussed in this section and the second phase in the next section. Throughout the discussion, however, you should keep in mind that the problem of determining just why two variables are related to each other is one of the most difficult problems in all of science. At best we can assemble all of the evidence that is available and make a considered estimate of the reason. It is practically impossible to identify the reason in a positive and definite manner such that all would agree with the identification. Various techniques, including multivariate analysis, help us reach a decision but it is always possible that new evidence will undermine whatever reasons seem most plausible on the basis of any given analysis.

There are five major ways of accounting for or explaining the fact that two variables are related to each other in some set of observations. We shall consider each of these explanations in turn.

The Causal Explanation

A relationship may be manifest in our bivariate table because a change in one of the variables results in a change in the other, either always or "on the average." When the change in the other variable always occurs the relationship is called *determinate*. When it occurs on the average or only over a series of repetitions, it is called *stochastic*. In social science most relationships in which one variable directly affects the value of the other are stochastic. The stochastic relationship is one in which the change in one variable (X) does not really force the change in the other variable (Y) but does make this change *more likely*.

There are many ways of interpreting such direct or "causal" relationships, but a discussion of them is beyond the scope of the present text.

What is important to recognize here is that when two variables are causally related, joint observations of these variables will almost always display relationship when the observations are assembled into a bivariate table. Therefore, when we see a table in which X and Y are related one possible explanation is that the variables are causally related. By the same token, if the joint distribution displays independence (that is, lack of association) then it is quite possible that the variables are *not* causally related to each other. Of course, as we shall see, there are other possible explanations also.

Examples of direct or causal relationships, especially in stochastic form, are quite common in social science. For example, one way to get a higher income (Y) in the United States is to acquire more knowledge through further education (X). The relationship between education and income is stochastic in that your income does not *have* to go up just because you go back to school, but that it is *likely* to go up as a result of your possession of extra knowledge. Virtually all tables showing the joint distribution of income and education of people in this country display a close relationship between these two variables. That is, in these tables the income distributions for specific levels of education (the conditional income distributions) differ substantially from each other, *no matter how the observations have been assembled.*

Symbolically, we can represent this direct or causal explanation by an arrow pointing directly from X to Y, as follows:

$$X \rightarrow Y$$

The Joint-Result Explanation

A relationship may be manifest in our bivariate table because both of the variables are affected by the same phenomenon, such as change in a third variable. Sometimes we refer to this explanation by saying that the two variables, X and Y, are both measures of the *same thing*. Indirect relationships of this type can be visualized in many ways but from a formal point of view they all represent one kind of explanation.

The classic example of this explanation is the correlation of physical characteristics between brothers, such as the relationship between the weight of the older brother (X) and the weight of the younger brother (Y) (from the same family). Observations of X and Y drawn from a population of families will show substantial relationship. In this case there is no direct or causal connection between the two weights. If we modify the weight of the *older* brother (by inducing him to go on a diet, for example), we will not create any change in the weight of the *younger* brother, *per se*. The relationship between the weights that we observe exists because brothers in the same family have the same parents (same heredity) or because they have the same food preferences (same environment), or both. Were we systematically to modify the diet of the older brother in each family, it is likely that the only effect would be to reduce the amount of relationship that would appear in any future observations that we might assemble from the population.

Scores on tests provide another example. These scores are often correlated or associated despite the fact that performance on one test rarely if ever actually influences performance on the other test. Instead, they are related because they both measure some common thing, perhaps knowledge or attitudes and beliefs, depending upon the nature of the tests.

Symbolically, we can represent this indirect explanation through the use of symbols for three variables, X, Y, and Z. Both X and Y are influenced by Z so there is an arrow pointing from Z to each other variable. On the other hand, there is no direct connection between X and Y so there is no arrow connecting them.

The Interacting Effects Explanation

A relationship may be manifest in our bivariate table because a change in one variable produces a change in the other variable *under some conditions but not under other conditions*. If the right conditions are present in some of the observations that have been assembled then the table of the observations will show some relationship between the variables. If the right conditions are always absent, of course, then no relationship will appear in the table. Statisticians refer to this situation as involving *interaction* between two or more independent variables. We say that two variables, such as X and Z, interact in their impact upon Y. We shall discuss this explanation in greater detail later in the chapter. In one sense it introduces no new source of relationships but in another sense it does. Relationships do not just exist. Rather, they exist in some context. To explain the relationship it is often necessary to consider the context as well as the effect itself.

The relationship between education and income provides a simple example. Increased education may lead to higher income under some conditions, such as among young people. On the other hand, increased education may have no such effect under other conditions, such as among the elderly or retired. In situations such as this one we may say that there are two independent variables that interact or we may say that there is a variable that *intervenes* between the independent and the dependent variables. That is, we may refer to the control variable (Z) as an *intervening* variable.

Symbolically, we can represent this explanation of the observed relationship between X and Y by placing the categories of Z between the symbols for the other variables. An arrow goes from X to Z_1 to Y meaning that when Z_1 is present X affects Y. Another arrow goes from X to Z_2 and stops, meaning that when Z_2 is present there is no direct relationship between X and Y. We have illustrated interaction in connection with a causal or

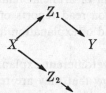

direct relationship. It can also arise in connection with a joint effects pattern. That is, two variables can measure the same thing under some conditions but not under others.

The Chance or Sampling Fluctuation Explanation

A relationship may be manifest in our bivariate table because a chance sampling fluctuation has occurred in drawing a sample from a population in which there is no association. This possible explanation should always be considered when dealing with empirical observations. Such observations are subject to errors of various kinds, including sampling errors. The relationship that appears in our table may well be more apparent than real, that is, it may itself be an error. We shall not discuss this possible explanation further in this chapter because it is considered in detail in Part III of this book. Fortunately, there are firmly established statistical procedures for deciding whether or not an observed relationship is just a sample fluctuation.

The Related Observations Explanation

A relationship may be manifest in our bivariate table because we are looking at related *observations* rather than because the *variables* are related to each other. In particular, the observations may represent the same object (or a very small number of objects) observed at different times or in different places. In this case very high relationships between variables may appear in our tables. These relationships, in turn, may result from the fact that the various observations are not really independent of each other.

For example, there is only one Federal tax system in the United States. If two aspects of this system were to be studied as they appear in each state it would seem that 50 pairs of observations have been assembled, although in actual fact only one object has been observed. This same problem exists for events that take a long time to occur (such as the development of automated factories). We shall not consider this problem further here; it is usually discussed at length in texts dealing with economic statistics under the title of time series analysis. Here we shall assume that the observations are independent of each other in the sense that only one observation has been made per variable on each object being studied. With this assumption met, the problem of artificial relations in time and space does not exist. However, when you read reports of research you should always check as to whether this kind of explanation applies in the particular study you are examining.

In summary, there are five different explanations of the fact that observations of two variables show that they are related to each other, as listed below. Our problem is to decide, in any given table, which explanation is the most sensible. In making this decision we use various techniques. In particular, to discriminate among the first three explanations we use multivariate analysis; to decide about the fourth explanation we use sampling theory (see Part III); and to handle the fifth explanation we make sure that our observations are all independent of each other (which eliminates this possibility). Schematically, we have

Explanation	*How we study it*
1. Causal	Multivariate analysis
2. Joint results	Multivariate analysis
3. Interacting effects	Multivariate analysis
4. Chance fluctuation	Sampling theory
5. Related observations	Instead of studying it we try to eliminate it as a possibility

In the remaining sections of this chapter we shall show how to use multivariate analysis to discriminate among the first three possible explanations of relationship. The procedures to be discussed are generally appropriate for data that have been assembled through a survey, a census, or any other field technique. Most of the data with which sociologists work arise in this way. Another set of procedures are applicable when the data have been assembled through an experiment. We shall discuss experimental designs briefly in Chapter 13.

9.3 THE BASIC PROCEDURE: HOLDING A THIRD VARIABLE CONSTANT

In the last section we identified the basic problem that leads the sociologist to turn to multivariate analysis. In this section we shall show how the multivariate table may be analyzed so as to yield at least a preliminary solution to the problem. The problem is to account for or explain why two variables are related in a set of observations. The basic solution is to make the two comparisons that are possible when we have partial contingency tables, namely, (1) to compare the relationship found in the set of partial tables with that found in the original or marginal table, and (2) to compare the relationship found in one partial table with that found in the other partial tables. These comparisons solve the problem because each explanation, if correct, will produce a different pattern in the partial tables than would each other explanation were it correct.

However, it is very important to recognize that we *cannot,* through this procedure, directly establish whether or not there is a *causal* connection between X and Y. The only way to establish one variable as the cause of another in any direct sense is actually to manipulate the values of the variable (X) that is presumed to cause the other and see if the values of the other variable (Y) really do change. What we can do is establish whether or not the relationship between X and Y is *independent* of a particular third variable (Z). If the relationship between X and Y is independent of Z then we *infer* that it is causal and if it is affected by Z then we infer that it is not causal. This inference, taken by itself, is weak in the sense that it may well be wrong. However, if we repeat the process on each of several different control variables and in each case find that the relationship between X and Y is independent of the control, then the inference concerning cause becomes strong in the sense that it is quite likely to be correct. We shall only show how to analyze a single control variable in this text. The logical structure is the same whether we work with only one or with a hundred such variables. In actual applications, of course, more than one control variable should be introduced in order to strengthen the plausibility of the inference.

Let us now see how to read a $2 \times 2 \times 2$ table to decide which explanation is the most sensible. We first consider certain simple cases. Throughout this discussion remember that we begin this analysis with the observation that X and Y are related in the original (or marginal) table. We introduce the third variable to account for this relationship. When we introduce the third variable we also introduce the partial tables.

Case 1. The relationship between X and Y is independent of Z, which means that it is not affected by Z. (Remember, if this situation occurs with many different control variables we will conclude that X is causally related to Y.) In this case, it does not matter whether we observe the variables (X and Y) with Z also varying (that is, in the marginal table) or with Z constant (that is, in one of the partial tables). Regardless of what is happening to Z in our observations we shall see the *same* relationship or association between X and Y. Symbolically, we may represent this situation as follows:

$$\phi_{YX} = \phi_{YX.Z_1} = \phi_{YX.Z_2}$$

In other words, the amount of association found in the marginal table will be equal to the amount of association in either partial table. (Notice the subscript notation here. For example, "$YX.Z_1$" refers to the relationship between Y and X with Z constant at the value Z_1, which is to say that it refers to the relationship in the first partial table.)

Case 2. There is no direct relationship between X and Y but a relationship appears in our observations because both variables are affected by variation in Z. In this case, it matters a great deal whether we observe X and Y with Z varying or with Z constant. In particular, the relationship between X and Y will appear only as long as Z also varies. In other words, the marginal table will show X and Y to be related, but the partial tables both will show X and Y to be independent of each other. Symbolically, we represent this situation as

$$\phi_{YX} \neq 0$$
$$\phi_{YX.Z_1} = \phi_{YX.Z_2} = 0$$

Case 3. There is a direct relationship between X and Y provided Z has a certain value. Remember, this case is what we have called interaction between X and Z in their impact upon Y. Here it not only matters whether Z is constant or not but it also matters at what value Z is constant. When Z is held constant at one value we will observe a relationship between X and Y but when Z is held constant at another value we will see no relationship between X and Y. Symbolically, we represent this situation as

$$\phi_{YX} \neq 0$$
$$\phi_{YX.Z_1}{}^2 > \phi_{YX}{}^2$$
$$\phi_{YX.Z_2} = 0$$

In other words, one of the partial tables will show more relationship than is present in the marginal table whereas the other partial table will show no relationship.

These three cases, then, give us the three basic patterns that we look for in order to decide which explanation of the original relationship is correct. Of course, in practice these patterns do not appear in quite such clear-cut form but they do give us a way to organize what we find. To illustrate the examination of actual tables let us consider Table 9.1. This table shows the relationship between political affiliation (Y) and socioeconomic status (X) with union membership as the control variable (Z). The original or marginal table and the two partial tables are all shown in Table 9.1. The first step in analyzing these tables is to measure the amount of association in each one. Since Y is an attribute it is appropriate to summarize the relationship by calculating ϕ. When we make the calculations (not shown) we get these results:

Marginal Table	First Partial	Second Partial
(in entire sample)	(among union members)	(among nonmembers)
$\phi_{YX} = 0.193$	$\phi_{YX.z_1} = 0.087$	$\phi_{YX.z_2} = 0.119$

The second step is to examine these coefficients and interpret them in terms of the cases already discussed. There are two major comparisons which we make. First, we compare the associations found in the two partial tables. These figures are approximately the same, since each of them is very close to 0.1. This fact enables us to eliminate Case 3 or to conclude that there is essentially no interaction between socioeconomic status and union membership as far as political affiliation is concerned. Now consider the average of the two partial coefficients. (We shall see later in this chapter how to find this average in a more accurate manner.) The sum of the two partial coefficients divided by two gives us

$$\phi_{YX.z} = 0.103$$

This number, which is the association between Y and X with Z held constant, is about half the size of the original measure of association. From this fact we conclude that both Case 1 and Case 2 are operating. That is, Z (union membership) accounts for some of the relationship but not all of it. In other words, to some extent we observe a relationship between socioeconomic status and party because union members are both more likely to be of lower status and also to be Democrats. On the other hand, some of the relationship between status and affiliation is direct, possibly causal, but also possibly due to some other variable not included in this analysis.

When an association between X and Y can be entirely explained by variation in a third variable (that is, when Case 2 applies) it is common to refer to that relationship as *spurious*. The implication is that the relationship does not really exist but only is apparent in the observations and hence is spurious. This phraseology is acceptable as long as it is recognized that the word "spurious" means only that the relationship is *not* causal. There is a negative connotation to the term, however, which is somewhat unfortunate. In some situations the existence of associations of this type is just annoying, but there are many situations in which researchers actually seek out these "spurious" relationships. A case in point occurs when we want to measure something through an index consisting of more than one individual measurement. One of the tests that we have found two measures that belong in the same index involves precisely this kind of partial analysis.

If we hold constant whatever both measures are measuring then their association should drop to zero. Instead of being annoyed with this situation, however, the researcher is likely to be happy to have found two different ways of measuring the same phenomenon. The term "spurious" therefore must be used with caution. Any implication that a spurious (that is, noncausal) relationship is unimportant should be avoided.

Demography is one of the earliest sciences systematically to explore the analysis of partial tables. In this field rates are often used to summarize conditional distributions. When these rates are obtained from partial tables they are called *specific* rates. Thus, rates developed from tables in which age is the control variable (Z) are called age-specific rates, and rates controlled for sex are called sex-specific. We often use age- and/or sex-specific rates in connection with mortality, morbidity, crime, fertility, hospital admission, and so on. Age and sex appear so often as the variables to control because most social variables are related in one way or another to age and sex. We shall not use the demographic terminology very much in this book but shall speak of relationships as existing in partial and marginal tables. The logical structure of the analysis is the same, of course, whatever terminology is used.

9.4 A FORMULA FOR MULTIVARIATE ASSOCIATION

An important formula summarizes our results so far and a proper grasp of its meaning will enable you to understand many multivariate problems. We present the formula in terms of δ quantities; this quantity was introduced in Chapter 8. It represents, for any cell in the bivariate table, the difference between the observed frequency and the expected frequency if the variables are independent of each other. In short, $\delta_{ij} = n_{ij} - E_{ij}$ where i and j identify cells of the table. In the 2×2 table all four δ values are the same except for sign. We shall define δ to be one of these values, namely, that value appearing in the upper-right-hand cell; that is, $\delta = \delta_{12}$. This value summarizes the association or departure from independence in the entire table.

In the multivariate distribution, of course, we work with more than one bivariate table. We shall therefore introduce a new set of subscripts to indicate which particular table we are considering. These subscripts are the same as those we used earlier in this chapter. Thus, δ_{YX} refers to the difference between observation and expectation in the original or marginal table of Y and X. The general formula is

$$\delta_{YX} = \delta_{YX.Z_1} + \delta_{YX.Z_2} + \frac{N}{(N_{..1})(N_{..2})}\delta_{XZ}\delta_{YZ}$$

In this formula δ_{YX} represents the relationship between X and Y in the marginal table, $\delta_{YX.Z_1}$ and $\delta_{YX.Z_2}$ represent this relationship in each partial table, and δ_{XZ} and δ_{YZ} represent the marginal relationships between X and Z and Y and Z respectively. The last term in the formula also contains a ratio of frequencies, namely, the total frequency divided by the product of the frequencies in the two partial tables. The logical structure of this formula may be generalized to contingency tables of any size, although the details of the expression would have to be modified somewhat.

This formula is not primarily for computation. It is given here to help you think about and understand multivariate problems. It says that the total or marginal departure from independence of X and Y is the sum of the departure from independence in each partial table *plus* a function of this departure in the table relating X and Z and in the table relating Y and Z. We can see quite clearly now what we have been discussing in the last few pages. Assume that X and Y are *not* related to each other except through the fact that each is related to Z. In this situation $\delta_{YX.Z_1} = 0$ and $\delta_{Y.XZ_2} = 0$ so that both of these terms vanish from the equation. However, by definition each variable *is* related to Z. Because of these relations to Z the marginal table displays a relationship between X and Y. This situation is the one in which it is reasonable to conclude that X and Y are not causally related or that their relationship in the marginal table is spurious. We might also say that X and Y are related to each other only to the extent that they both measure the same thing, namely, Z.

9.5 THE AVERAGE PARTIAL TABLE: STANDARDIZATION AND PARTIAL ASSOCIATION

In analyzing partial tables one thing that we do is to compare them with the corresponding marginal table. In making this comparison it is much more sensible to use an *average* partial table than the individual partial tables. The average partial table is usually called the *standardized* table of the relationship between X and Y. There are various ways to standardize a table. We shall consider the simplest method, which is called *direct standardization*. In discussing this method it is convenient to begin with partial tables that have already been converted to percentage form in each conditional component. In other words, we begin with the structure presented in Table 9.3. In this table the frequencies have been converted into percentages such that each column sums to 100 percent. Our problem is to construct, from this arrangement, a single table that is an average of these individual partial tables.

Table 9.3   Partial tables in column percentage form

	Partial table 1			Partial table 2		
	X_1	X_2		X_1	X_2	
Y_1	P_{111}	P_{121}	Y_1	P_{112}	P_{122}	
Y_2	P_{211}	P_{221}	Y_2	P_{212}	P_{222}	
T	100	100	T	100	100	

The general percent is P_{ijk} where i is a row, j is a column, and k is a particular table. The percentages in each column sum to 100. Symbolically,

$$P_{ijk} = \frac{n_{ijk}}{N_{.jk}}(100)$$

The simplest (though not the best) way to accomplish this objective is to take the percents in the same cell of each partial table and average them. For example, for the upper-left-hand cell (that is, cell$_{11}$) we might have

$$\text{Average cell percent} = \frac{P_{111} + P_{112}}{2}$$

This expression may also be written as

$$\text{Average cell percent} = \tfrac{1}{2}P_{111} + \tfrac{1}{2}P_{112} = \bar{P}_{11}$$

The number "½" in this formula is called a *weight* because it shows the relative importance of each partial percent in the average. When the weights of the various percentages are all equal we sometimes say that we have the "unweighted" average. The term "unweighted" is somewhat misleading, however, since there are weights but they are all equal. We can generalize this formula by calling the weights W_1 and W_2. We now have

$$\bar{P}_{11} = W_1 P_{111} + W_2 P_{112}$$

where $W_1 + W_2 = 1$.

Notice that the sum of the weights must equal 1. Finally, this formula can be generalized to any cell of the table, say the ijth cell, as follows:

$$\bar{P}_{ij} = W_1 P_{ij1} + W_2 P_{ij2}$$

where $W_1 + W_2 = 1$.

(In this form the formula can easily be extended to larger tables by adding terms if there are more partial tables or by letting i and j range above two if there are several rows or columns.)

The average percent obtained in this way is called a standardized average because *the same weights have been used for each and every cell in the table*. In other words, W_1 and W_2 have been used to find the average in each cell or for each value of i and j. Using the same weights for every cell eliminates the confounding effect of the third variable, Z. The original or marginal table of the relationship between X and Y is also an "average" of the partial tables but it is a poor average because the weights used vary from cell to cell—that is, these weights depend upon Z.

The one problem that exists in standardization concerns the selection of the weights to be used. In one sense, it does not matter what weights are selected. Whatever the weights chosen, the basic objective of eliminating the confounding influence of Z will have been achieved. However, it is also the case that the average table that is created will depend somewhat on the weights selected. Theoretically, this dependence exists only when the tables contain interaction or only when the individual partial tables differ from each other in the way that X and Y are related. In practice, however, frequencies are always subject to sampling fluctuation (see Part III) so some differences between the partial tables will be apparent whether there is interaction or not.

We do not ordinarily make all of the weights equal because this practice gives extra weight to the smaller tables. Unfortunately, the percentages in these tables are more subject to sampling fluctuation and hence are less reliable than tables with larger N's. This comment suggests a solution to the problem of selecting the weights—to make each weight proportional to the total number of observations in the corresponding partial table. Remember, we use the symbol N_k for the number of observations in the kth partial table. Symbolically, the solution is to make the kth weight

$$W_k = \frac{N_k}{N}$$

By using this solution to the weighting problem we have as the final formula to be used for creating the average percentages in our standardized 2×2 table

$$\bar{P}_{ij} = \frac{N_1}{N} P_{ij1} + \frac{N_2}{N} P_{ij2}$$

These standardized percentages may be compared directly or they may be converted back into frequencies so that a measure of association for the standardized table can be computed. Whatever procedure is followed, the basic idea is to compare the amount of association in the standardized table with that in the original table. In general, if the measure of association in the standardized table is much smaller than in the original table then the relationship between X and Y is primarily due to variation in Z. On the other hand, if the measure of association in the standardized table is about the same as in the original table then the relationship between X and Y is pre-

Table 9.4 Partial from Table 9.1 converted to column percentage form

		Partial table 1					Partial table 2	
Frequencies		STATUS Low	High				STATUS Low	High
Rep.		37	14		Rep.		113	228
Dem.		56	14		Dem.		55	64
Total		93	28	121	Total		168	292	460
Column percentages		STATUS Low	High				STATUS Low	High
Rep.		39.8	50.0		Rep.		67.3	78.1
Dem.		60.2	50.0		Dem.		32.7	21.9
Total		100.0	100.0		Total		100.0	100.0

sumably independent of the influence of Z. In this case, the relationship might be causal.

We may illustrate direct standardization by using the distribution presented in Table 9.1. Remember, our problem is to calculate the average partial table. The first step in this process is to convert each of the partial tables into column percent form. Table 9.4 shows this step. The second step is to find the weights to be used. The relative number of cases in each partial table is a sensible weight to use for that table as we discussed above. For the first table, then, we have $W_1 = 121/581 = 0.208$. Similarly, for the second table we have $W_2 = 460/581 = 0.792$. The third step is to apply these weights to the cell percents in the partial tables to find the average percentage in each cell. For example, for cell$_{11}$ (the upper-left-hand cell) we have

$$\bar{P}_{11} = (0.208)(39.8) + (0.792)(67.3)$$
$$= 61.6.$$

This number (61.6) is the weighted average of the two percents in cell$_{11}$ of the partial tables (namely, 39.8 and 67.3). Proceeding in this manner through all of the cells we construct the standardized table, as in Table 9.5. We have included the original table here for purposes of comparison. This comparison can be accomplished directly from these tables (using the idea of percent difference) or we can recover the frequencies and then calculate

Table 9.5 Original (marginal) table of relationship between status and party and standardized table showing same relationship with union membership controlled

Original table			Standardized table		
	STATUS			STATUS	
	Low	*High*		*Low*	*High*
Rep.	57.5	75.6	Rep.	61.6	72.3
Dem.	42.5	24.4	Dem.	38.4	27.7
Total	100.0	100.0	Total	100.0	100.0

a measure of association for each table and compare them. Let us use the percent difference approach. In the original table as we shift from low to high status there is a shift from 57.5 percent Republican to 75.6 percent Republican. In other words, there is an increase of 18.1 percent in the percent Republican. In the standardized table (eliminating the influence of union membership) the corresponding increase is 10.7 percent. In other words, just about half of the increase in percent Republican due to status remains when we control for union membership. (Remember that this conclusion is the same as was reached earlier using the actual partial tables and ϕ as the measure of association.)

The Partial Correlation Coefficient

When all of the variables, X, Y, and Z, are at least ordinal it is possible to shortcut this process somewhat. If what is desired is the average partial association to compare with the original association we may compute the average partial association directly. The formula is

$$r_{YX.Z} = \frac{r_{YX} - r_{XZ}r_{YZ}}{\sqrt{(1 - r_{XZ}^2)(1 - r_{YZ}^2)}}$$

This formula has been written in terms of the product moment correlation, r. Precisely the same formula is used for the partial ordinal coefficient $\tau_{YX.Z}$ except, obviously, that all of the associations are τ values rather than r values. Similarly, in the case of 2×2 tables, $\phi = r$ so the formula may be used with dichotomies. (Of course, to do so it should make sense to interpret the dichotomy as an ordinal or interval variable that has been dichotomized.)

In our example it is not very meaningful to interpret the dichotomies as ordinal in character. Therefore, in this case we would not ordinarily compute the partial correlation coefficient. However, to illustrate the computations we shall go through the steps. The three elementary or zero-order coefficients are

$$r_{YX} = 0.193$$
$$r_{XZ} = 0.591$$
$$r_{YZ} = 0.277$$

$$
\begin{aligned}
r_{YX.Z} &= \frac{0.193 - (0.591)(0.277)}{\sqrt{(1 - 0.591^2)(1 - 0.277^2)}} \\
&= \frac{0.029}{\sqrt{(0.651)(0.923)}} \\
&= 0.037
\end{aligned}
$$

9.6 INTERACTION

We have now considered one major use of the multivariate distribution—namely, to determine whether or not the relationship between X and Y can be accounted for by the variation in a third variable, Z. To make this determination we introduced the concept of average partial association and the standardized table. We compared the average partial association with the original or marginal association and concentrated upon two major outcomes. First, if the partial association is approximately the same as the original association we conclude that the relationship between X and Y is independent of variation in Z. Second, if the partial association is approximately zero whereas the original association is quite far from zero we conclude that the relationship between X and Y is accounted for by their relations to Z and the fact that Z varies in our original observations. In this case we conclude that the relationship between X and Y is not causal or is spurious.

As we have already considered to some extent, however, there is another important comparison that can also be made in multivariate analysis. This comparison involves comparing the individual partial tables with each other. As we already know, if the association in each partial table is the same as in each other partial table then there is no interaction between X and Z with respect to how they are related to Y. On the other hand, if each partial table is different from each other partial table in association then X and Z do interact in their impact upon Y. Among sociologists it is also quite common to refer to this phenomenon as *specification* and sometimes as *interpretation*

Table 9.6   Annual suicide rates (per million), by religion and
community in France

	Rural		Urban	
	CATHOLIC	PROTESTANT	CATHOLIC	PROTESTANT
Rate	88	414	309	378

SOURCE: Originally adapted from Halbwachs, *Les Causes de Suicide,*
Paris, 1930. Quoted from Zeisel, 1957, pp. 184–186.

where Z is interpreted as an intervening variable. In this section we shall illustrate interaction and also consider why it is important to take it into account.

An interesting illustration of the interaction is found in Halbwachs (see Zeisel, 1957). Halbwachs found that suicide rates for Catholics in France were significantly lower than suicide rates for Protestants, just as Durkheim had. The Catholic rate was approximately 198 per million annually whereas the Protestant rate was approximately 396. When, however, rural versus urban residence is introduced as a third variable, the results shown in Table 9.6 are obtained. Notice, incidentally, that this table is presented in summary form rather than in the form of frequencies. The student may wish to identify the three variables and their categories, which are implicit in this table.

Compare these two partial tables. Under rural conditions there is obviously a much greater difference in rate between Protestants and Catholics than under urban conditions. The original, or marginal, table (summarized in terms of the original rates given in Table 9.6) conceals this sharp difference between rural and urban. This shift in the amount of association from one condition to another is interaction or specification.

There are two primary reasons why it is important to consider interaction. First, when interaction is present the average partial table (the standardized table, for example) must be interpreted with caution. When a substantial amount of interaction is present it is better to avoid calculating this average table. When interaction is present the relationship between X and Y is different in each partial table. These differences should be taken into account rather than concealed in the form of an average. It is also important, however, to recognize that chance fluctuation may make it appear that interaction is present in data when in fact it is not. In such a case the tables should be averaged. The formal procedure for deciding when an average partial table is useful and when it is not useful involves principles that are beyond the scope of this textbook. A simple and useful rule to apply is to avoid using the average table when the partial tables individually show relationships *in different directions*. For example, if X and Y appear to be positively related in one partial table and negatively related in the other, then do not find their average.

The second reason for considering interaction is theoretical in nature. When interaction is present the combined effect of X and Z cannot be determined by studying either X or Z separately in relation to Y. Indeed, when interaction is present we may get very misleading results if we try to study the effect of either variable by itself. Consider, as an example, all-or-none attributes. It is quite possible that when one attribute (X) is present nothing much happens to Y and when another attribute (Z) is present nothing much happens to Y, *unless they are both present at the same time,* in which case a lot may happen. A very decisive example is a cake—when the ingredients are combined in the right proportions we have a pleasant dessert but when they are not combined (or not combined in the right way) we only have a mess. The point is that when interaction is present the variables X and Z cannot meaningfully be studied apart from each other.

9.7 WHERE WE STAND

In this chapter we have introduced some elementary ideas involved in multivariate analysis. We have stressed the use of multivariate analysis as a means of accounting for the relationship between two variables. We began by noting that there are five different kinds of explanation of the fact that observations display a relationship. We can discriminate among three of these explanations through multivariate analysis. The major tool in multivariate analysis is what is called the *partial* table, which is a table showing the relationship between X and Y for some particular value of Z. There are two basic comparisons that we make in multivariate analysis. First, we compare one partial table with another. If they differ in the amount of relationship displayed we say that X and Z interact in relation to Y. If there is little or no interaction we may find the average partial table through standardization. Second, we compare this standardized table with the original or marginal table. If the relationship between X and Y is the same in the standardized and the original tables then we conclude that Z has no effect upon the relationship. On the other hand, if the relationship between X and Y is much smaller (ideally, absent entirely) in the average partial table than in the original table then we conclude that X and Y are related to each other only because each is related to Z. In this case we are likely to lose our interest in X and shift our attention to Z if our objective is to explain the distribution of Y.

It must be stressed at this point, however, that another kind of explanation may account for our findings, whatever they are. This explanation is that the findings are just sampling or chance fluctuations. When our observations are a sample we must be especially careful to consider this possibility. For example, before we conclude that there is interaction present we should be reasonably sure that the differences between the partial tables cannot be accounted for as just sampling fluctuations. The study of the role of chance fluctuation in statistical observations is very important. We shall introduce this subject in Part III.

Steps in multivariate analysis illustrated for dichotomies

We begin with a set of observations on three (or more) variables, say, X, Y, and Z.

STEP 1

Cross-classify the two variables, X and Y, creating their bivariate distribution. (Marginal frequencies not shown.)

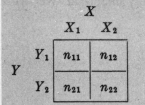

Detailed analysis:
(1) Summarize each conditional distribution of Y using percentages, ratios, or rates. (2) Compare these distributions using an appropriate measure of association, such as ϕ or γ or τ'.

STEP 2

Introduce a control variable, Z, and show the bivariate distribution of X and Y for each value of this control variable. These tables are called *partial* tables. (Marginal frequencies not shown.)

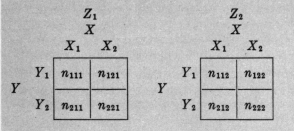

Detailed analysis:
Summarize the information in each of these partial tables in the same way that you summarized the information in the original table (in Step 1).

STEP 3

Compare the amount of association in each partial table with that in each other partial table.
  (a) If the amount of association is substantially different in the partial tables conclude that X and Z *interact*. Study the pattern of interaction and attempt to interpret it. This interpretation completes your analysis.
  (b) If each partial table displays approximately the same amount of association as each other partial table, proceed to step 4.

STEP 4

Find the average partial table (the standardized table) and measure the amount of association in it.

In column percent form the entries in this standardized table are

$$\bar{P}_{ij} = W_1 P_{ij1} + W_2 P_{ij2}$$

where $W_1 + W_2 = 1$.
These column percents may be converted back into frequencies by the formula:

$$\bar{n}_{ij} = n_{.j}\bar{P}_{ij} = \text{the standardized frequency}$$

STEP 5

Compare the amount of association in the standardized table with that found in the original or marginal table.
   (a) If the amounts in these two tables are approximately the same conclude that the relationship between X and Y is independent of Z (and may, therefore, be causal).
   (b) If there is substantially less association in the standardized table than in the original table conclude that the relationship between X and Y is spurious; that is, is due to the fact that both are related to Z.

Note: Throughout this analysis be careful to recognize that the result you are looking at may be just a chance sampling fluctuation.

part III

Introduction to Statistical Inference

Introductory Comments

In the first two parts of this book we discussed how to describe and summarize distributions of variables, first by considering one variable at a time, then two, and finally three. We noted in passing that these distributions might exist either in a sample or in a population of objects, events, or observations. The population consists of all of the objects, events, or observations in which the researcher is interested. The sample is a subset of the members of the population. In actual fact, researchers rarely if ever work with populations of data. Instead, each researcher assembles a *sample*. This fact creates a very serious problem. The researcher wants to make a statement about the distribution in the population that he has defined but he only has information about this distribution in his sample. He must, therefore, use the information in his sample to *infer* what the population is like. This problem is very easy to state but quite difficult to appreciate. At best this kind of inference is risky—quite subject to error. Indeed, for many kinds of samples the risks of error are so great as to make it prudent *not to make* any inferences at all. In general, though, it is vital to solve the problem, that is, to learn how to make sensible inferences, because the researcher really has no choice. He *is* interested in populations and he *does* gather information about samples. In the past century the labors of many men have essentially solved this problem of inference. We know now what kinds of samples should be taken and also how to measure the error that is involved in using the sample information in place of population information. This part of the book presents an introduction to the nature of these solutions.

10

THE ELEMENTS
OF STATISTICAL
INFERENCE

In this chapter we shall consider how to draw samples in such a way that
sensible statements about the population can be made. We shall also discuss
what kinds of assertions may be made about population distributions.

10.1 A FORMAL STATEMENT OF THE PROBLEM OF INFERENCE

Let us begin with a clear understanding of the nature of the problem to
be solved. We want to complete the research with a statement that describes
the distribution of one or more variables in some specified population. In
Parts I and II we learned how to describe distributions in terms of concepts
such as percents, means, correlations, and measures of association. The
statement we shall make will involve these concepts. For example, we might
want to conclude our research by saying "The mean income of families in
the United States is $7,500" or "The relationship between alienation and
conservatism in the South is $r' = -0.30$." (These statements are illustrative only and may well not be correct, which is precisely the problem.)
Values of descriptive measures used in statements about populations are
called *parameters*. The mean age of the members of a population is a
parameter, as is the proportion of laborers in the labor force, and the association between exposure to politics and membership in voluntary
associations.

We shall make the statement about the parameter from evidence existing
in our sample. There are two fundamental situations in which we want to
proceed in this way. In the first place, we may not have a very good idea of

191

the value of the parameter and so we use the sample to give us some information about it. When we proceed in this way we say that we are *estimating* the parameter. In the second place, we may *think that we know the value of the parameter* and so we use the sample to *test* or confirm what we think we know. When we proceed in this way we say that we are *testing an hypothesis* about the parameter. Notice that we only think that we know the value of the parameter before we take the sample. If we really knew the value beforehand, of course, there would be no point in taking the sample.

To make our statement about the parameter we assemble a sample and use the observations in the sample to develop an estimate of the parameter. For example, if we want to make a statement about the mean in a population we calculate the corresponding mean in our sample and if we want to make a statement about a percent in a population we calculate the percent in our sample. These sample values are called *statistics* or *estimators*.

The statement that we make about the parameter should have two properties: it should be *relatively precise* and it should be *correct*. Consider a specific example. Our objective is to make a statement about the percent of people in Chicago who are Republican. This percent is the parameter in which we are interested. We draw a sample and find that the percent of Republicans in the sample is 46 percent. On the basis of this sample we now want to say something about the percent in the population and, ideally, we want this statement to be both precise and correct (or a balance of these criteria). We could say, for example, that the percent in the population is just the same as the percent in the sample, namely, 46 percent. This statement is very precise. It is called a *point estimate*. The only problem is that this statement is very likely to be incorrect. It is very unusual for the value we find in our sample to be exactly the value that we are looking for in the population. For this reason statisticians do not ordinarily use point estimates alone. Consider the other extreme. We could say that the percent of Republicans in Chicago is between 0 and 100 percent. We *know* positively that this statement is correct because all percents are between 0 and 100. A statement of this general type is called an *interval estimate* because it puts the parameter inside some interval. This particular interval is so broad, of course, that it really tells us nothing—it is too imprecise. These are the extremes: a very precise statement that is almost certainly wrong and a very imprecise statement that is certainly correct, but useless. Somewhere in between lies a sensible estimate of the parameter. We might make the statement, for example, that the percent Republican is between 40 percent and 52 percent, using an interval that extends 6 percent on either side of 46 percent. This statement is somewhat imprecise but still conveys a good deal of information. Of course, there is some risk that the statement is wrong—that the actual percent Republican is outside of the interval. The key problem in statistical inference is learning how to identify this risk and how to build sensible intervals that take the risk into account.

In the above paragraph we have illustrated the basic problem in relation to *estimation*. When we wish to test an hypothesis about a parameter we proceed in approximately the same way, as you will see in the pages to follow. In either case the basic problem is to discover how to measure the risk that a given statement is wrong (or, conversely, that it is correct). Only when we know how to identify this risk can we control it. For a given amount of risk we want to make as precise a statement as possible. But first we must have some method of determining just what the risks are. The first step in this process of identifying the risks of an incorrect statement is to identify carefully just what kinds of error occur in sampling.

10.2 THE TWO BASIC KINDS OF SAMPLING ERRORS

Let θ stand for any particular parameter (that is, any measure that describes or summarizes a distribution in a population). Let S stand for the corresponding statistic (that is, the same measure computed from a sample of observations from that population). The difference between these two quantities is called *sampling error*. We have

$$\text{Sampling error} = S - \theta$$

This difference will not ordinarily be zero; that is, there will usually be some deviation between the sample statistic and the parameter being estimated. It turns out that there are two very important, but very different, kinds of error in sampling procedures. These are called *random sampling errors* and *biases*. To understand these kinds of error we first specify just how we are going to take the sample. These specifications are called the *design* of the sampling procedure. One design might be to stand on a street corner and talk to whomever passes by; another might be to call every 20th person in a telephone book; and another might be to scan a list of persons and decide whether or not to include each one in the sample by tossing a coin—heads he is in the sample, tails he is not in it. (These designs are not necessarily the best ones to use but nevertheless they are designs.)

All statistical inference is concerned with the problem of identifying the extent to which a given sampling procedure or design produces error, on the average, or if used over and over again. This problem has, therefore, been studied very carefully. It has been found that there is one kind of error that has a very interesting property it tends to become smaller as the sample *size* becomes larger. The size of a sample is just the number of observations that it contains. It is noteworthy and very fortunate too, that one kind of error in sampling tends to disappear when larger and larger samples are taken. This kind of error is called *random sampling error*. We can measure quite accurately the amount of random sampling error that there is in any given sampling procedure or design once we know the size of the sample.

There is, unfortunately, another kind of error in many sampling designs. This kind of error does not respond to increasing the size of the sample. It is called *bias*. A bias is a deviation between the sample estimator, S, and the parameter, θ, which would continue to exist even if we took an extremely large sample—one so large that random errors would all but vanish.

These ideas can be summarized by introducing a new concept, which we shall call S. This concept, S, is the estimate of the parameter that we would make using an indefinitely large sample from a given sampling design. We may visualize the total error contained in a sample as consisting of two components, as follows:

$$S - \theta = \text{the total error in a particular sample}$$

It can be divided into

$$S - \theta = (S - \bar{S}) + (\bar{S} - \theta)$$

$$\underset{\substack{\text{random} \\ \text{sampling} \\ \text{error}}}{\uparrow} \qquad \underset{\text{bias}}{\uparrow}$$

Statisticians and others who have studied these two types of error have discovered some important things about them. Random sampling error cannot be eliminated from a finite set of observations, for example, but this kind of error can be *measured* and *controlled*. On the other hand, there are sampling designs in which bias can be essentially eliminated, although it is very difficult to measure or control bias when it is present. For these reasons, the statistician and the researcher make every effort to *eliminate* bias and to *control* random sampling error.

Let us consider an example to make sure that you understand these very basic points. Suppose that you want to know the mean age of people in the United States. This mean age is the parameter, θ, that you wish to estimate. Since there are well over 190,000,000 people in this country you quite understandably decide not to ask each one his age. Instead, you decide to take a sample of people according to some specific plan. This plan is the *sample procedure* or *design*. Suppose that your plan is to ask each person you see walking into a college dormitory how old he or she is. You follow this plan and, after asking 100 people, you get tired and stop sampling. You now take these 100 observations and find the mean age for them. This mean in your sample is the statistic or estimate, S.

The sample mean, S, will deviate from the true population mean for two reasons. The first is that you stopped sampling after assembling 100 observations. By considering only a limited number of cases a certain unreliability is introduced into your statistic. This unreliability can be measured. It is called *random sampling error*. At the same time, there is a problem with the procedure that you used. If you continued collecting observations indefinitely using the same plan or design, you would still not get a very good estimate of the average age of people in the United States. The mean that you would have computed had you continued sampling indefinitely is called $\bar{S}$. Clearly, this mean would deviate from the parameter because of a *bias* in your method of selecting the sample. The people walking into a college dormitory are not representative of all people in the United States. In particular, a very high proportion of those entering the dormitory will be young adults. Their average age would be perhaps 21 years, if the college is mainly undergraduate. The average age of people in the entire country is about 31 years. This difference of ten years is the bias resulting from your sampling procedure. It will remain no matter how many cases you collect, so long as you collect them all in the same way.

Since biases are very difficult to measure when they are present, it has been found through long and often painful experience that the only safe way to handle them is to eliminate them; the only safe way to sample is to use a design that is *not* biased. There is only one general way to assemble observations so as to eliminate bias. It is called probability sampling, and the basic form of this is random sampling. In this book we shall assume that all sampling is random. When samples are taken in a random manner there is no bias so the only problem is to measure and control the random sampling error that will be present. Let us now see how to draw a random sample.

10.3 DRAWING RANDOM SAMPLES

A random sample is very easy to define. It is a sample drawn in such a way that each and every object in the population has an equal chance of appearing in the sample. This definition is usually extended by considering the *simple random sample* in which each and every *set* of objects of the same size has the same chance of appearing in the sample. This notion of equal chance takes us into the realm of probability—the mathematical domain out of which virtually all statistical inference has emerged. The various outcomes of a process are equally likely if and only if they occur equally often in an indefinitely large series of repetitions of the process in question. Simple empirical examples of processes whose outcomes are equally likely are (1) tossing a coin (the two outcomes, heads and tails, are equally likely) and (2) tossing a die (the six outcomes, one, two, three, four, five, and six, are each equally likely). How do we know that these processes have equally likely outcomes? Only because if we actually do the tossing often enough each outcome will appear approximately as often as each other outcome. In actual fact, using manufactured coins or dice, it turns out that the outcomes are not quite equally likely, though it takes a great many tosses (several hundred thousand) to display the slight imbalances. Statisticians, therefore, talk about an ideal coin or an ideal die, meaning that the concept of equal likelihood has been abstracted out of the world of observation and made an elementary concept in its own right. However, we need not be concerned too much with this abstraction. We know that certain processes give very nearly equally likely results simply because we have tried them many, many times and found that the various outcomes do, in fact, occur (approximately) equally often.

The basic sampling procedure that is followed in taking a random sample involves two steps, once the population has been defined. The first step is to assemble a *list* of the objects that are in the population. The second step is to decide, for each object listed, whether or not to include it in the sample; this decision is made on the basis of a *random device* (such as tossing a coin). Although there are many more or less random devices that could be used, the one in most common use today is the *random number table*. A random number table is a listing of digits such that the choice of which digit is to be placed in each position is random (that is, such that each digit has a one-tenth chance of being in any given position). The random number table is created by the use of some known random device and, once created, can be used over and over again.

The random device most frequently discussed in statistics books is what is called the *urn* or *bowl model*. Imagine a bowl that contains ten balls that are identical, except that each ball has a different digit written upon it. The bowl is opaque so that we cannot see into it. We shake the bowl vigorously, which causes the balls to shift about. Then we reach into the bowl and draw one ball (that is, we remove it from the bowl). We note the number appearing on this ball (we write it into the random number table we are preparing, for instance) and then return the ball to the urn. We then repeat the process, first vigorously shaking the bowl, then drawing a ball, recording its number, and so on, and on, until we have generated as many random numbers as we want. This random device is quite appropriate both for thinking about the meaning of randomization and also for making simple choices on a random basis. (It was used to decide which men to draft first just before World War II, for instance.) Since a random device, such as this bowl, can be quite easily constructed, there is no particular problem involved in this aspect of random sampling.

One distinction is worth making at this point. In the urn example we drew a ball and *then replaced it* in the urn before drawing the next ball. Sampling in this way is called *sampling with replacement*. In samples that sociologists actually draw it is much more common to *sample without replacement;* that is, to select an object into the sample and then keep it out of the list so that it cannot be selected again. Basic sampling theory is built upon the idea that sampling occurs with replacement. When the population is large it does not matter much which way we sample. When the population is small, however, it can make a difference.

To take a a random sample we need both a *random device* and a *list* of the objects in the population to be sampled. This list is sometimes called the *sampling frame*. Unfortunately, it is rather rare to find a list for an entire population. When the list that is available is incomplete a substantial bias may be introduced if it is used. For example, if we wished to sample adults living in some specific community or city, it is very unlikely that we could find any actual complete listing of those adults. There are, of course, lists of *some* of the adults in a community—in telephone books, utility company records, voting records, and the like. Each of these lists is incomplete, how-ever, and usually in quite a systematic way. When such incomplete lists are used a considerable amount of bias can be introduced into the sampling process. The most famous example is the *Literary Digest* poll predicting the 1936 election. The *Literary Digest* took its sampling from lists of its sub-scribers and from telephone directories. A very large sample was taken involving approximately 2,000,000 people. Using the sample results the *Literary Digest* predicted that Landon would win the election by a consider-able margin. Of course, Roosevelt actually won—in a landslide. The prob-lem was simple but decisive. The sample was not random with respect to the population of voters because those voters who did not subscribe to the magazine and did not possess a telephone had no chance of being included in the sample. Such people were more likely to be poor, which means that the poor were more or less systematically excluded from the sampling. The poor, in this election, voted Democratic. The result of excluding them from the sample was the introduction of a very substantial bias. (Note, inciden-tally, that random sampling error was virtually eliminated by the extreme size of the sample but its elimination was essentially irrelevant because of the bias.)

When a complete listing of the population is not available the researcher is faced with a difficult problem. There is no exact solution to this problem but there are approximate solutions that are quite sound. The best solution developed so far is what is called *area sampling* or *multistage sampling*. Populations ordinarily occupy territory. This territory may be subdivided into small areas, each presumably containing a small number of the total population. The *areas* can then be listed and selected randomly in a proper manner. Within such randomly selected areas it is possible either to interview all persons or to prepare a list and then randomly sample people. For example, in a city we may select blocks randomly and then people within blocks. It is possible to develop principles of statistical inference that are exactly correct for such multistage samples (see Kish, 1965). However, since these samples are such close approximations to simple random samples it is more conventional to treat them in this way and to apply the inferential procedures of simple random samples to them. As far as we know today, this sampling procedure effectively solves the problem of random sampling when no list or frame of the ultimate units to be sampled exists.

One other kind of sampling procedure that is valid and occasionally encountered is what is called a *stratified random sample*. In such sampling the total population is first divided into several subpopulations according to some classification related to the dependent variable of the study. Independent simple random samples are then taken within each subpopulation. These component samples are combined using weights based on *population* figures so that the weights are not subject to sampling error. Such population figures are available for certain variables in such sources as Bureau of the Census reports. (The weighting procedure is very similar to that used in standardization; see Chapter 9.) We may take a stratified sample either to make sure that the overall sample is precisely representative with respect to the categories used in subdividing it or because it is desired to draw relatively more cases in some categories than in others. Stratification has one major advantage with respect to random sampling and one major disadvantage. The advantage is that the sampling errors are somewhat smaller. The disadvantage is that the dependent variable cannot be changed after the sampling is completed, for the reason we discussed in Chapter 6. When category sampling fractions are different, percentaging and comparing may be done in only one direction, which means that we must continue to use the same dependent variable.

10.4 THE SAMPLING DISTRIBUTION

Random sampling not only eliminates sampling bias, but it also permits us to measure the remaining error, which is called random sampling error or just sampling error. This error is usually measured by the standard deviation of a special distribution called the *sampling distribution*. The standard deviation of this particular distribution is called the *standard error* of the statistic we are using. The sampling distribution is a theoretical or conceptual distribution rather than a distribution that arises through counting existing objects or events (though it may be approximated through empirical observation). To visualize it we go through the following steps.

1. We treat the statistic in a particular sample as a *single observation*. The sample itself becomes the event that has been observed. The statistic that we compute (the mean of X in the sample or the proportion of females there or whatever) is the observation that we make on this event.

2. We define the population of these events to be all of the possible samples that we might have drawn from our original population (a) using the same sampling procedure and (b) having the same size as our sample. Remember that the particular sample we happen to observe or draw is very coincidental or "chancey" in the sense that we looked at those particular objects only because of random decisions. If the random numbers had come out differently we would have looked at another sample. The population now being considered consists of all of the possible samples that might have been drawn, including the one that actually was drawn.

3. We imagine computing our statistic for each sample in the population of all possible samples. Notice that the statistic itself now becomes the *variable* being studied and its values in the possible samples become the set of observations of the variable.

4. We now have a set of observations of a variable in a population. With this information we construct the distribution of that variable in that population. This particular distribution is called the sampling distribution.

5. Finally, in many cases we compute the mean and standard deviation of the sampling distribution. Its standard deviation is the standard error that we have been seeking.

Since there are several new ideas in these steps let us go over them again rather carefully with a simple example. When we say that we "imagine" this or that we do not mean that it is fanciful but only that we need not actually observe existing objects or events. Instead, we can create objects in our heads and study them. Let us, then, imagine a population consisting of six balls in an urn (or hat, if you prefer). Each ball has a number written on it. Except for the number, all of the balls are identical. The number on the ball is the variable, X, in which we are interested. In particular, we want to know the average or mean number on the balls (that is, in the population). This mean is the parameter in which we are interested. We refer to it as μ_X (read "mu X"). The Greek letter μ stands for a population mean. The subscript X identifies the variable whose mean it is. We shall suppose, for this illustration, that the six balls in the urn are numbered consecutively from 1 to 6. The parameter that we are trying to estimate is, then,

$$\mu_X = \frac{1 + 2 + 3 + 4 + 5 + 6}{6}$$

$$= 3.5$$

(In this case, of course, we already know the parameter that we will estimate but later we shall see that we can proceed in the same manner even when we do not know the parameter value.)

We have now defined the original population (the six balls in the urn), the original variable (the number on a given ball), and the parameter of the distribution of this variable in which we are interested, namely, μ_X. To estimate this parameter we shall take a sample of two balls from the urn, removing the balls one at a time and then replacing the ones selected. The number of observations in our *sample,* then, is $n = 2$. We are now ready to go through the steps that create the sampling distribution.

Step 1. Treat the statistic in a particular sample as a single observation. In this example, the average number on the two balls drawn from the urn is the statistic that we will treat as a single observation. For example, if we drew balls numbered 1 and 5 the mean in our sample would be $\bar{X} = (1 + 5)/2 = 3$. (Notice that we use the symbol $\bar{X}$ to refer to the mean in a sample.) This sample mean is an observation.

Step 2. Imagine all of the possible samples that we might draw from this population of balls keeping the sample size two and the sampling design random. In particular, we could get any one of the six numbers on the first draw and any one of the six numbers on the second draw. Let us make a table of these possible samples. We begin by identifying the possibilities as cells in a bivariate table where the number on the first draw is written across the top of the table and the number on the second is written up the left-hand side. Table 10.1 shows this format. Notice that there are $6 \times 6 = 36$

Table 10.1   Possible outcomes in samples
of size two

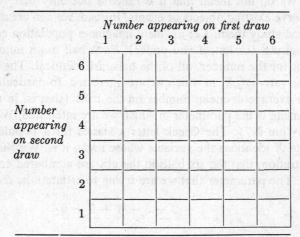

cells in this table, which indicates that there are 36 different outcomes of this sampling procedure. Each cell indicates the *joint* occurrence of a particular number on the first draw and a particular number on the second draw. Thus, for example, the cell in the upper-left-hand corner is the joint outcome of a "1" on the first draw and a "6" on the second draw.

Step 3. Now calculate the statistic for each of these possible outcomes. In this case we find the mean for each possible pair of observations and record these means in the cells of the table, as shown in Table 10.2. These

Table 10.2 Mean of each different sample from urn population

	Number appearing on first draw					
	1	2	3	4	5	6
6	3.5	4.0	4.5	5.0	5.5	6.0
5	3.0	3.5	4.0	4.5	5.0	5.5
Number appearing 4	2.5	3.0	3.5	4.0	4.5	5.0
on second draw 3	2.0	2.5	3.0	3.5	4.0	4.5
2	1.5	2.0	2.5	3.0	3.5	4.0
1	1.0	1.5	2.0	2.5	3.0	3.5

means are computed from the usual formula for a mean: $\bar{X} = \Sigma X/n$. Here $n = 2$. In the upper-left-hand corner, for example, we have the observations 1 and 6. We add these numbers together and divide by two to get the cell entry, $3.5 = (1 + 6)/2 =$ the mean of one of the possible samples that we might have drawn.

Step 4. These 36 observations (the various sample means) can be formed into a distribution by grouping them. To develop this distribution we need to know just how likely each of these possible sample means is. Because we are using a simple random sample design *each possible sample is just as likely to occur as each other possible sample*. Therefore, the distribution of sample means will be as in Table 10.3. This distribution is called the *sampling distribution* of the mean. In this distribution the proportions are the key indicators of the relative frequencies. The frequencies themselves (in column f) must be interpreted rather carefully. They identify the 36

Table 10.3   Distribution of sample means for samples
of size two from the urn population

Sample mean	f	Proportion
6.0	1	0.028
5.5	2	0.056
5.0	3	0.083
4.5	4	0.111
4.0	5	0.139
3.5	6	0.167
3.0	5	0.139
2.5	4	0.111
2.0	3	0.083
1.5	2	0.056
1.0	1	0.028

different samples that could be drawn and also represent the fact that each of these different samples is just as likely to be drawn as each other one. However, in another sense there is no limit to the actual number of samples one could draw. A person could start drawing balls from the urn and form samples of two balls, and continue the process for years and years. In fact, infinitely many samples could be drawn given enough time. No matter how many actual samples were drawn, however, each one would be one or another of the 36 possible samples we have listed.

Step 5. We now compute the mean and standard deviation of this sampling distribution using the formulas and procedures developed in Chapter 5. The results are

$$\text{Average value of sample mean} = 3.5$$

$$\text{Standard deviation of sample means} = 1.21$$

This standard deviation is also called the standard error of the mean. This step completes the presentation and description of the sampling distribution. At this point it is important to pause and make sure that we know how to symbolize and visualize the different distributions.

There are three basic distributions that we consider. Each of these distributions has a mean and standard deviation, which can be confusing until we see clearly how to distinguish among them. The first distribution is the distribution of X in the population we want to study. The mean of this distribution is written μ_X and the standard deviation, σ_X. The second distribution is the distribution of X in any particular sample from our population. (This distribution is represented in our example by any one cell in Table 10.2.) The mean in our sample is written $\bar{X}$ and the standard deviation, s_X. The third distribution is the distribution of *sample means* among all of the possible samples that we might have drawn. The mean of these means is written $\mu_{\bar{x}}$ and the standard error of the mean is written $\sigma_{\bar{x}}$. When we estimate the standard error we write it as $s_{\bar{x}}$.

With these symbols we now can say that the mean and standard errors of our example are

$$\mu_{\bar{x}} = 3.5$$

$$\sigma_{\bar{x}} = 1.21$$

Let us now consider how to interpret these figures. We will begin with the mean of the sample means, $\mu_{\bar{x}}$. This number is the value that we *expect* the sample mean to have (even though we know that the actual sample means will vary somewhat from this expectation). Notice that the mean of the sample means is precisely the same number as the mean of X in the original population (see page 200). In other words,

$$\mu_{\bar{x}} = \mu_X$$

or the expected value of the sample mean is precisely equal to the parameter in which we are interested. This fact says that our sampling procedure is *unbiased*. We *expect* to get the same result from our sample as actually exists in the population, subject to our knowledge that some random sampling error is present in the sample.

Now consider the standard error, $\sigma_{\bar{x}}$. This figure identifies the amount of error that we expect in any one sample. To interpret it consider an interval extending one standard error on both sides of the expected sample mean, which equals the parameter in which we are interested. Symbolically, we consider the interval

	from $\mu_{\bar{x}} - \sigma_{\bar{x}}$	to	$\mu_{\bar{x}} + \sigma_{\bar{x}}$
or	from $3.5 - 1.2$	to	$3.5 + 1.2$
or	from 2.3	to	4.7

Look back at the table of the sampling distribution in Table 10.3. Note how many of the sample means fall into this interval. (All of the means from 2.5 to 4.5 fall into the interval.) Of the 36 different samples we could take, 24 have means in this interval. That is, two thirds of all the sample means fall within one standard error of the parameter we are trying to estimate.

Now, think about this next statement very carefully, for it is the key to understanding statistical inference. *If two thirds of the sample means are within one standard error of the parameter in which we are interested, then it is also true that in two thirds of the samples actually drawn the parameter will be within one standard error of the mean of that sample.* Notice that the role of the sample estimate and the parameter have been reversed in this statement. We begin by asserting that the sample values are likely to fall relatively near the parameter but we conclude that the parameter is likely to be relatively near the sample value. This reversal means that *we can make a statement about the parameter on the basis of the sample and know how likely it is that the statement will be correct.* This statement is that the parameter is in a certain interval around the sample estimate when our objective is estimation. When our objective is hypothesis testing a comparable kind of statement is made by developing an interval around the hypothesis.

Consider a specific illustration of estimation. Suppose that we already know the sampling distribution of samples of size two from the population of balls in the urn. (A little later we shall see how to accomplish the same result by estimating the nature of the sampling distribution.) We take an actual sample and find that the numbers on the two balls in the sample are 1 and 4. We find the mean of these observations, which is 2.5. Now we construct an interval extending one standard error above and below this sample figure, that is, from 1.3 to 3.7. We assert that the mean in the population is somewhere inside this interval. We not only are able to make this statement but we are also able to identify just how likely it is that the statement is correct. In this case, we can say that statements made in this way will be correct two thirds of the time. Statisticians usually call this likelihood "confidence" and say that we have a confidence of two thirds that this statement is correct. Symbolically, we write

$$C(1.3 \leq \mu_X \leq 3.7) = \tfrac{2}{3}$$

which should be read "our confidence that the mean of the population is inside the interval 1.3 to 3.7 is two thirds."

From this general illustration of a sampling distribution and how it is used we can see how important a concept it is. In fact, one of the major tasks of the mathematical statistician is to discover just what the sampling distribution is for any particular summary measure. The search for and study of sampling distributions has revealed a set of basic findings, which include the following:

1. It is possible, in the case of most descriptive measures, *to deduce* the nature of the sampling distribution without ever taking any samples. These deductions flow from the fact that the sampling is random. By using probability theory as applied to random sampling, the sampling distribution can

be identified. (We shall show a simple but important example of such a deduction in Chapter 11.)

2. For many basic statistics, such as the mean and the proportion, the sampling distribution is approximately normal in shape whenever the sample is reasonably large. (See Chapter 12 for a further discussion of the meaning of "large" in this connection.) This fact means that we can use the table of the normal distribution as the sampling distribution in many situations. Through the use of this table we can translate the standard error into a likelihood statement or a confidence statement.

3. Perhaps the most interesting finding of all, however, is that the standard error can be very accurately estimated *from the sample itself*. This fact means that we can, just on the basis of the single sample that we have gathered, (a) estimate the parameter in which we are interested and (b) also estimate the likely error contained in that estimate.

10.5 THREE BASIC STANDARD ERRORS

As noted above, the sampling distributions of many elementary descriptive measures are approximately normal when the sample is large. We have discovered how to measure the standard errors of these measures. The formulas are quite simple, and the information needed to make the computations is available in the sample of observations. In this section we shall present the formulas for the standard error of a *mean*, of a *proportion*, and of a *difference* between two means or two proportions. You will recall that means and proportions are our basic tools in describing univariate distributions and also that the difference between two (conditional) means or two (conditional) proportions is a way of summarizing a bivariate distribution. (At this point you may wish to review Parts I and II of this text. Chapter 6 may be especially helpful.)

The Standard Error of a Proportion

Let p stand for the proportion of objects in a population who possess some characteristic. Let p_s stand for the corresponding proportion in a random sample drawn from that population. The standard error of p_s is

$$\sigma_{p_s} = \sqrt{\frac{p(1-p)}{n}}$$

Note that this formula contains the parameter p. Ordinarily, of course, this parameter is not known. A very good estimator of this standard error is given by the formula

$$s_{ps} = \sqrt{\frac{p_s(1 - p_s)}{n}}$$

This formula is identical to the first one except that p_s (the sample proportion) has been substituted for p (the parameter). In both formulas n is the size of the sample.

To illustrate the computation of this standard error suppose that we have taken a sample of 400 voters and found that 46 percent of them were Republican. We wish to estimate the standard error of the proportion, $p_s = 0.46$. Since we do not have the parameter available we use the formula for s_{ps}. We have

$$s_{ps} = \sqrt{\frac{(0.46)(0.54)}{400}} = \frac{0.498}{20} = 0.025$$

The Standard Error of a Mean

Let μ_X stand for the mean of X in the population and σ_X stand for the standard deviation of X in the population. Let $\bar{X}$ be the mean of a random sample from this population and s_X be the standard deviation of X in that sample. The exact and approximate formulas for the standard error of $\bar{X}$ are

$$\sigma_{\bar{x}} = \frac{\sigma_X}{\sqrt{n}}$$

$$\text{and } s_{\bar{x}} = \frac{s_X}{\sqrt{n}}$$

Notice once again that the exact formula is given in terms of the parameter, σ_X. A good approximation exists, however, in the form of $s_{\bar{x}}$, which requires only information that is available from the sample. In ordinary practice, of course, we use the approximation formula.

The structure of this formula should be studied carefully. In particular, study the role of the sample size, n. The variation in the mean of several observations is equal to the variation in an observation divided by the square root of the number of observations. The larger n is the smaller will be the error in the mean, but the error decreases only as the square root of the sample size. In other words, to reduce the error by half the sample size must be increased fourfold.

Computationally, this formula presents little difficulty provided that you remember to calculate s_X first and *then divide this quantity by the square root of n.* (Review Chapter 5 if you are in doubt as to how to calculate s_X.)

The Standard Error of a Difference Between Two Means
or Between Two Proportions

When working with bivariate distributions we ordinarily compare the conditional distributions with each other. If the independent variable is a dichotomy there will be two conditional distributions to compare. As we have noted before we may also visualize this situation as one in which we are studying the distribution of a single variable in two populations, where the populations are defined in terms of the categories of the second variable. The direct comparison of these two conditional distributions involves the difference, *d*, between two proportions or two means. We use the subscript "1" to identify the first population (or the first category of the independent variable) and the subscript "2" to identify the second population. Thus, the difference in which we are interested is either

$$d_p = p_{s_1} - p_{s_2}$$

or

$$d_{\bar{Y}} = \bar{Y}_1 - \bar{Y}_2$$

In these expressions d_p means the difference between two sample proportions and $d_{\bar{Y}}$ means the difference between two sample averages. Notice that we have identified the variable as Y in this case to call attention to the fact that it is the dependent variable whose distribution is being studied.

In general, the *square* of the standard error of a difference between two independent samples is equal to the *sum* of the squares of the standard errors of the components of the difference. Specifically, we have

$$\sigma_{d_p}{}^2 = \sigma_{p_{s_1}}{}^2 + \sigma_{p_{s_2}}{}^2$$

and

$$\sigma_{d_{\bar{Y}}}{}^2 = \sigma_{\bar{Y}_1}{}^2 + \sigma_{\bar{Y}_2}{}^2$$

It will be noted that these formulas have been written in their exact form using parameters and *not* in the form of sample approximations. The reason is that the best way to approximate these formulas when only sample information is available varies somewhat from situation to situation. To keep this discussion relatively simple we shall consider only the most commonly encountered situation, namely, the situation in which it is appropriate to *pool* the estimates derived from each sample. This situation arises whenever it is reasonable to assume that there is the same amount of variation in our variable in each population. This assumption is referred to as the assumption of *homoscedasticity*. Given this assumption, the best estimate of σ_{d_p} is

$$s_{d_p} = \sqrt{\bar{p}_s(1 - \bar{p}_s)\left(\frac{1}{n_1} + \frac{1}{n_2}\right)}$$

where $\bar{p}_s$ refers to the pooled (or weighted) estimate of the proportion in both samples. It is computed as follows:

$$\bar{p}_s = \frac{n_1 p_{s1} + n_2 p_{s2}}{n_1 + n_2}$$

In a similar manner the best estimator of the standard error of a difference between means when the assumption of homoscedasticity is appropriate is

$$s_{d_{\bar{Y}}} = \sqrt{\bar{s}_Y^2\left(\frac{1}{n_1} + \frac{1}{n_2}\right)}$$

where $\bar{s}_Y^2$ is the pooled estimate of the variance of Y using both samples and is computed from the formula:

$$\bar{s}_Y^2 = \frac{\Sigma(Y_1 - \bar{Y}_1)^2 + \Sigma(Y_2 - \bar{Y}_2)^2}{n_1 + n_2 - 2}$$

The two sums of squares in this formula should be computed in the manner shown in Section 5.3. For a summary of the calculations involved in the standard error of a difference, see the accompanying computation design.

10.6 CONFIDENCE INTERVALS: LARGE SAMPLE PROCEDURES

We are now in a position to present one basic set of solutions to the problem of statistical inference. This set of solutions is referred to as "large sample theory," because the sampling distributions of means, proportions, and differences are approximately *normal* whenever the sample(s) is (are) large enough. In this section we shall show how to *estimate* a parameter using large sample procedures and in the next how to *test an hypothesis* about a parameter using these procedures. We shall illustrate estimation using a single mean or a single proportion. We shall illustrate hypothesis testing using a difference between means or proportions. (At this point you may wish to review our earlier discussion of the normal curve and how to read the table of this curve. This discussion will be found in Section 5.4.)

Computation design for the standard error of a difference using pooling

A. The standard error of the difference between two proportions.
1. Arrange the data to be analyzed into the form of a 2×2 table in which the first row (Y_1) identifies the proportions. In other words, $p =$ the proportion of Y_1s in the population(s). Calculate p_s for each column in this table. Use $p_{s_j} = n_{1j}/n_j$.

	Column					Column	
	1	*2*	*T*			*1*	*2*
Y_1	n_{11}	n_{12}	$n_{1.}$		Y_1	$p_{s_1} =$	$p_{s_2} =$
				becomes			
Y_2	n_{21}	n_{22}	$n_{2.}$		Y_2	$1 - p_{s_1}$	$1 - p_{s_2}$
T	$n_{.1}$	$n_{.2}$	$n_{..}$		T	1.00	1.00

2. Calculate the pooled estimate of p. That is, calculate $\bar{p}_s$.

$$\bar{p}_s = \frac{n_{.1}p_{s_1} + n_{.2}p_{s_2}}{n_{.1} + n_{.2}} =$$

An alternative formula that can be used when the frequencies are available (as in the table on the left above) is

$$\bar{p}_s = \frac{n_{1.}}{n_{..}} =$$

(In other words the average p is the *marginal* proportion of Y_1s.)
3. Now calculate the standard error of the difference using the formula:

$$s_{d_p} = \sqrt{\bar{p}_s(1 - \bar{p}_s)\left(\frac{1}{n_{.1}} + \frac{1}{n_{.2}}\right)} =$$

B. The standard error of the difference between two means.
1. Divide the observations into the two samples (or according to the two values of the independent variable). Calculate the sum of squares of $y = Y - \bar{Y}$ for each sample. The general formula you will use is

$$\Sigma Y_j^2 = \Sigma(Y_j - \bar{Y}_j)^2 = \Sigma Y_j^2 - \frac{(\Sigma Y_j)^2}{n_j}$$

Sample 1	*Sample 2*
$\Sigma Y_1 =$	$\Sigma Y_2 =$
$\Sigma Y_1{}^2 =$	$\Sigma Y_2{}^2 =$
$n_1 =$	$n_2 =$
$\dfrac{(\Sigma Y_1)^2}{n_1} =$	$\dfrac{(\Sigma Y_2)^2}{n_2} =$
$\Sigma(Y_1 - \bar{Y}_1)^2 =$	$\Sigma(Y_2 - \bar{Y}_2)^2 =$

2. Combine these two sums of squares into the pooled estimate of $\bar{s}_Y{}^2$ using the formula

$$\bar{s}_Y{}^2 = \frac{\Sigma Y_1{}^2 + \Sigma y_2{}^2}{n_1 + n_2 - 2} = \frac{\Sigma(Y_1 - \bar{Y}_1)^2 + \Sigma(Y_2 - \bar{Y}_2)^2}{n_1 + n_2 - 2}$$

$$=$$

3. Finally, calculate the standard error of the difference, $d = \bar{Y}_1 - \bar{Y}_2$.

$$s_{d_{\bar{Y}}} = \sqrt{\bar{s}_Y{}^2 \left(\frac{1}{n_1} + \frac{1}{n_2} \right)} =$$

The general procedure that we use to construct an interval estimate of a proportion or a mean is as follows:

1. Select the desired level of confidence (you are free to choose this level but most people prefer either a 95 percent level or a 99 percent level).

2. Use the normal curve table to convert the level of confidence into a z score; that is, into the number of standard errors to be included in the interval.

3. Now construct the interval using either

$$p_s \pm zs_{p_s}$$

$$\text{or} \quad \bar{Y} \pm zs_{\bar{Y}}$$

depending upon whether you are estimating a proportion or a mean. In either case you assert that the parameter is inside the interval that you have constructed.

Since you already know how to find the standard error, the key problem here is to find z, which is the value in the normal curve table corresponding to your level of confidence. It is convenient to show how to find z (and the confidence interval itself) in terms of a specific example.

Let us suppose that we have taken a sample of 400 adults in a large city and have identified whether or not each individual in the sample was *born* in the indicated city. We wish to estimate the proportion of adults in the entire city who were born there. Suppose that in our sample we found that 46 percent of the respondents were born in the city. We now proceed through the steps listed above.

1. We select a confidence level. We decide that we want any statement we make about the parameter to have a 95 percent chance of being correct. Our desired confidence is, then, 0.95.

2. We now use the normal curve table (because a sample of 400 is a large sample) and convert our level of confidence into a z score. The normal curve describes the distribution of sample estimates (p_s values in this case). The mean of this sampling distribution is the parameter we wish to estimate. We want to find out how many standard errors away from this mean we must go to include 95 percent of the sample proportions. Since the normal curve is symmetrical the table only lists the upper half of it. To include 95 percent of the area in the entire distribution is to include half of this area, or 47.5 percent, in the upper half of the distribution. The probability (or area) listed in the table is $0.500 - 0.475 = 0.025$ (or, in general, $0.500 - \frac{1}{2}$ of our confidence). We therefore look in the body of the table until we find the probability 0.025 and then look at the edge of the table to identify the z score that corresponds to this probability. We see that a probability of 0.025 corresponds to a z score of 1.96. Therefore, we use $z = 1.96$.

3. Now we construct our confidence interval by finding s_{p_s} and then the interval itself. We have

$$s_{p_s} = \sqrt{\frac{(0.46)(0.54)}{400}} = 0.0249$$

The confidence interval itself then is

$$\begin{aligned} p_s \pm z s_{p_s} &= 0.46 \pm (1.96)(0.0249) \\ &= 0.46 \pm 0.049 \quad \text{or} \quad 0.46 \pm 0.05 \end{aligned}$$

It is conventional to write this interval in the form:

$$C(0.41 \leq p \leq 0.51) = 0.95$$

meaning that our confidence that the parameter is in the indicated interval is 0.95. Remember that this confidence refers to the proportion of times that statements made in this way will be correct.

Except that the computational details are different, we follow this same procedure in making an interval estimate of a mean.

10.7 TESTS OF HYPOTHESES: LARGE SAMPLE PROCEDURES

Researchers very frequently use statistical inference as a means of testing hypotheses about parameters rather than making estimates of those parameters. We use inference to test an hypothesis when we think that we already know the value of the parameter and want to test whether or not we are right. The hypothesis that we test is referred as as H_0. It is the hypothesis that the parameter in which we are interested has a certain value. To test the hypothesis we assemble a random sample and calculate the corresponding statistic in the sample. We then compare the statistic, say S, with the hypothesized parameter, say θ_0, forming $S - \theta_0$. In general, if there is no deviation between our evidence (S) and our hypothesis (θ_0) we will conclude that our test confirms the hypothesis. On the other hand, if there is a deviation between our evidence (S) and our hypothesis (θ_0) we would like to conclude that our evidence does *not* support the hypothesis and, hence, that the hypothesis is wrong. A moment's reflection shows, however, that we cannot proceed in quite such a direct way because *our evidence is also subject to error,* namely, to random sampling error. In other words, if

$$S - \theta_0 = 0$$

we cannot necessarily conclude that our hypothesis is correct because the zero difference may be due to a sampling fluctuation in S; similarly, if

$$S - \theta_0 \neq 0$$

we cannot necessarily conclude that our hypothesis is wrong because the deviation between our evidence and our hypothesis may be due to sampling errors in the evidence.

At first glance, it would appear that the existence of random sampling errors makes it impossible to reach any decision at all. In fact, however, we can reach a decision *under certain conditions*. Random sampling errors can be measured in the sense that their probable extent can be determined. If we get a deviation between statistic and hypothesized parameter that is larger than would be reasonable were sampling fluctuation the explanation we can conclude that the hypothesis is wrong. On the other hand, if the deviation is small or even absent we can never be sure that the hypothesis is correct because of possible sampling fluctuation.

Let us illustrate this point intuitively. Suppose that we have some reason to believe that an event occurs about 25 percent of the time. We take a reasonably large sample to test this belief. As a first outcome, suppose that the sample percent is 75 percent. We would feel quite confident in rejecting our hypothesis because the discrepancy between the hypothesis and our evidence (75 percent — 25 percent) is just too big to be accounted for as a chance fluctuation. As a second outcome, suppose that the sample percent is 30 percent. What should we conclude? A small discrepancy such as this one (30 percent — 25 percent) *might* just be a sampling fluctuation in our sample so the hypothesis might be correct. On the other hand, we could also get a sample of 30 percent if, say, the correct parameter were 32 percent or 27 percent or any other percent in the vicinity of 30 percent. Therefore, the hypothesis might still be wrong even though our sample outcome was close to it. In short, in this second situation we remain in doubt as to whether or not our hypothesis is correct whereas in the first situation we were able definitely to conclude that our hypothesis is incorrect. Basically, all that the statistician does is to systematize this line of reasoning so that he can tell where to draw the line between a "large" and a "small" discrepancy between the statistic and the hypothesized parameter.

The actual procedure that we follow is quite straightforward. First, we decide what deviation between statistic and hypothesis ($S - \theta_0$) is the largest one that could reasonably occur as a chance fluctuation, *if our hypothesis were true*. The largest deviation that is consistent with the hypothesis may be called the *critical deviation*. Second, we take our sample, compute the statistic in it, and calculate the deviation between this empirical statistic and our hypothesis. This discrepancy may be called the *actual deviation*. Third, we compare the actual deviation with the critical deviation: (1) If the actual one is larger than the critical one we reject the hypothesis. (2) If the actual one is smaller than the critical one we remain in doubt about the hypothesis but agree that it *might* be correct. There are several ways to state this conclusion. We may say that we "fail to reject" our hypothesis; we may say that we "tentatively accept" our hypothesis; or we may say that our sample evidence is "consistent with" our hypothesis. Note that we *never* say that we definitely accept our hypothesis, because a small deviation can arise quite easily even though our hypothesis is wrong.

Since we already know how to calculate the sample estimate of the parameter, the only really new problem here is to find out how to identify the critical deviation. (This term, incidentally, is introduced in this book, though similar terms are used elsewhere and the concept itself is in use wherever hypotheses are tested in a statistical manner.) To find the critical deviation you must first identify the sampling distribution of the statistic you are using. The critical deviation can then be found in a table of this sampling distribution or it can easily be calculated from the table. For this reason, the critical deviation is sometimes referred to as a "table value" to be compared with the observed value.

When dealing with samples that are sufficiently large, the sampling distribution of means, proportions, and differences between means or proportions will be normal. The critical deviation in these cases is defined in terms of the standard error of the statistic. In particular, we have

$$\text{Critical deviation} = z \times s_S$$

where s_S refers to the standard error of whatever statistic we are considering. In calculating this standard error use the hypothesized parameter value wherever possible. For example, if our hypothesis concerns a proportion, then we use p_0 and $1 - p_0$ in calculating the standard error. Otherwise, the procedure here is the same as in statistical estimation.

The letter z in the above formula refers to z score in the normal curve table. The researcher himself selects this value of z. Remember, the critical deviation, the largest difference between statistic and hypothesized parameter, *could reasonably be* regarded as a chance fluctuation in the sample around a true hypothesis. The key phrase here is "could reasonably be," which must be determined by the researcher himself. This determination is made by deciding what risk you are willing to run of rejecting a true hypothesis. This risk is called α (read "alpha"). Generally speaking, we want this risk to be quite small. Most researchers set α either at 0.05 (called the 5 percent level of significance) or at 0.01 (called the 1 percent level of significance). When $\alpha = 0.05$ we shall reject a correct hypothesis only about one time in every 20 tests. Once we select α we divide it in half and look it up in the body of the normal curve table (remember the normal curve table really only gives half of the table.) We then note the z that corresponds to this probability. For example, if $\alpha = 0.05$ we find the probability "0.025" in the normal curve table and see that a $z = 1.96$ corresponds to this figure. This value of z is placed in the formula for the critical deviation.

We shall be studying this general procedure using several different sampling distributions in Chapter 12. There you will have a chance to become more familiar with some of the aspects of this argument. Instead of continuing here with an abstract discussion we shall conclude this section with an extended example, which should make the basic procedure quite clear.

An Example Using Means

Suppose that we design the following experiment to see whether or not there is any relationship between pressure toward conformity in a group and the level of cohesiveness in the group.[1] We establish the hypothesis that there is *no* relationship between $Y =$ number of pressures to conform and $X =$ the amount of cohesion in the group. (See Chapter 13 for a discussion of when it is appropriate to test this particular hypothesis.) We randomly assign 80 subjects to 40 two-person groups. Half of these groups are randomly selected and receive instructions that create high cohesiveness. The other half receive instructions that create low cohesiveness. (In this discussion we will assume that the instructions are valid and reliable.) Now we watch each group perform some activity and count the number of times that each member exerts pressure on the other to conform to some standard. The total number of these attempts to create conformity is our dependent variable, Y. We can now translate our hypothesis into statistical form; designating low cohesiveness as category 1 and high cohesiveness as category 2. Our hypothesis states that the distribution of Y under condition 1 will be the same as the distribution of Y under condition 2. Specifically, we interpret the hypothesis to say that there will be no difference in the *average* value of Y under these two conditions. Symbolically, then, our hypothesis is:

$$H_0: d_{\mu_Y} = \mu_{Y_1} - \mu_{Y_2} = 0$$

To test this hypothesis we shall compare the difference in our sample with that hypothesized, using as a standard for comparison the critical deviation, $(z)\bar{s}_{dy}$.

[1] This example is adapted from a Swedish replication, by Zetterberg (1952), of a famous group dynamics experiment.

Table 10.4   Number of pressures toward conformity per group

Pressures under Low cohesion	Pressures under High cohesion	
3	4	Let Y_1 be an observation in the low-cohesion group. We have, for this group:
5	7	$\Sigma Y_1 = 162$
6	8	
6	8	$\Sigma Y_1^2 = 1416$
6	9	
7	9	$s_1^2 = 103.8/19 = 5.46$
7	9	
8	10	$\bar{Y}_1 = 8.10$
8	10	
8	10	Let Y_2 be an observation in the high-cohesion group. We have, for this group:
8	10	
8	10	
9	10	$Y_2 = 200$
9	11	
9	11	$Y_2^2 = 2104$
10	12	
10	12	$s_2^2 = 104/19 = 5.47$
10	12	
12	13	$\bar{Y}_2 = 10.00$
13	15	

SOURCE: Adapted from Zetterberg, 1952. The actual observations shown here are *not* from the original source but are fictitious. The means, results, and so forth, approximate those in the original, however.

Before we take the sample (or before we examine its results) we select our α level and from it, determine the value of z in the critical deviation. Suppose that we select $\alpha = 0.02$ (remember we can make it any value we wish). To convert this figure into a z score divide it in two and look up the result in the normal curve table. We have $(\frac{1}{2})\alpha = 0.01$ and the z score corresponding to this probability is $z = 2.33$. To complete the specification of the critical deviation we must take the sample, divide it into the two groups, and estimate the pooled standard error of the difference between the means of the two groups. The necessary calculations are shown in Table 10.4. In this table we have also included the calculations for the variance within each group to show that the assumption of homoscedasticity is reasonable. In particular, $s_1^2 = 5.46$ and $s_2^2 = 5.47$, so pooling is appropriate.

To pool the variance estimates we proceed as in the computational design given earlier. First, we find

$$\Sigma(Y_1 - \bar{Y}_1)^2 = 1416 - \frac{162^2}{20} = 103.8$$

and

$$\Sigma(Y_2 - \bar{Y}_2)^2 = 2104 - \frac{200^2}{20} = 104.0$$

Next, we add these two results together and divide by $(n_1 + n_2 - 2)$ to get

$$\bar{s}_Y^2 = \frac{103.8 + 104.0}{20 + 20 - 2}$$

$$= \frac{207.8}{38}$$

$$= 5.47$$

Finally, we calculate s_d, which is used in the formula for the critical difference. We have

$$s_d^2 = 5.47 \left(\frac{1}{20} + \frac{1}{20} \right) = 5.47(0.1) = 0.547$$

$$s_d = \sqrt{0.547} = 0.74$$

The critical deviation itself, then, is

$$\text{Critical deviation} = zs_d = 2.33(0.74) = 1.72$$

Remember, this critical deviation tells us the largest deviation between sample outcome and hypothesis that could reasonably occur just from sampling fluctuation.

Now we are ready to make the test (although virtually all the work has been done). Our hypothesis was that $d_{\mu Y} = 0$. The difference between the two means in our samples was $10.00 - 8.10 = 1.90$. In other words, we expected 0 and calculated 1.90. The deviation between outcome and hypothesis, therefore, is $1.90 - 0 = 1.90$. This actual deviation is compared with the critical deviation. We note that the actual deviation is the larger. *Therefore, we reject the hypothesis that $d_{\mu Y} = 0$* and conclude that the two variables are related to each other. In other words, we conclude that there is greater pressure to conform in highly cohesive groups than in low-cohesive groups. Notice that we were able to reach this conclusion because the observed deviation of 1.90 could not reasonably be considered to be just a chance deviation. If it is not just a chance deviation then there must be a real difference between the two types of group.

A graphical illustration of this finding may help to make the point, and the argument, clear. Under our hypothesis we *expect* there will be no difference in the means. Graphically, this expectation is a point on a line representing the possible differences between the means, as shown in Figure 10.1.

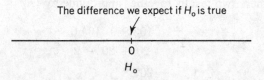

Figure 10.1. Possible differences between means.

We also recognize, however, that the actual sample differences we observe will vary somewhat around this expectation *even if the hypothesis is true.* That is where the critical deviation comes in. It identifies the largest difference that could reasonably be considered just a chance fluctuation. Graphically, this critical deviation defines an interval around the hypothesis, as shown in Figure 10.2.

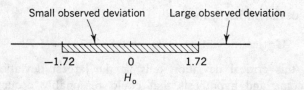

Figure 10.2. Possible differences between means.

Any smaller deviation *could* be due to chance. Any larger deviation could not reasonably be considered just a chance deviation so we conclude that our hypothesis is incorrect or we reject the hypothesis. On the graph the interval below -1.72 and above $+1.72$ is often referred to as the *rejection region* because whenever a sample outcome occurs there we reject our hypothesis.

One final comment is in order. We have only illustrated the process of hypothesis testing in this chapter. In Chapters 11 and 12 we shall delve further into this aspect of statistical inference. Some of you may have been puzzled about the fact that when we tested the hypothesis there was *no difference* between the two means. Our reason was that by *rejecting* the hypothesis of *no difference* we were able to conclude that there is, in fact, a difference. In a situation such as this one there are alternative procedures that can be followed but the procedure of testing the hypothesis of no difference is by far the most widespread and conventional one in statistical anaylsis. See Chapter 13 for more details.

10.8 THE POWER OF A TEST

In the preceding section we noted that there are two reasonable explanations of a small deviation between sample outcome and hypothesis. On the one hand, our hypothesis may be correct—in which case the deviation is a random sampling fluctuation. On the other hand, our hypothesis may be wrong—in which case the true parameter is relatively near the hypothesis. We also noted that, when the deviation is small, we cannot determine which of these alternatives is the right one. In this section we shall see that by careful study of the situation we can often reach certain reasonable conclusions with respect to these explanations, however. That is, we shall show you how to develop at least a partial solution to the problem of selecting the correct explanation. This solution involves measuring what is called the *power* of the test.

What we do, basically, is to compare our hypothesis with some *specific* alternative hypothesis. As usual, we call our hypothesis H_0. In the same spirit, the alternative hypothesis is referred to as H_1. Once we have specified H_1 we can determine, very accurately, just how likely we are to reject H_0 when H_1 is true in the population we are sampling. This probability is referred to as the power of the test. Clearly, if H_1 is true, we want to reject H_0; hence, the term *power*. The more powerful a test is, the more likely we are to be able to discriminate between H_0 and H_1 (by rejecting H_0 when H_1 is true).

To calculate the power of a test we proceed in two major steps. The first step involves identifying the rejection region for H_0. To perform this step we proceed in the manner of Section 10.7. The second step involves determining how likely we are to get a sample in this rejection region if H_1 is true. Let us illustrate these steps by considering a very elementary hypothesis.

Suppose that we have reason to believe that the proportion of marriages that end in divorce within ten years is 0.2 in some population of marriages. We wish to test whether or not this belief is correct by drawing a random sample from the population and testing the hypothesis, $H_0 : p_0 = 0.2$. We decide to test the hypothesis with a random sample of 400 marriages. The first step is to find the rejection region for this hypothesis using this test. We may apply large sample theory to construct the rejection region because the sampling distribution of the sample proportion, p_s, will be approximately normal if H_0 is true. Accordingly, we select a level of significance, say,

$$\alpha = 0.03$$

Next, we find the z corresponding to this α using the normal curve table. We have

$$z_{0.03} = 2.17$$

Then we determine the standard error of p_s assuming that H_0 is true.

$$\sigma_{p_s} = \sqrt{\frac{0.2 \times 0.8}{400}}$$

$$= 0.02$$

Finally, we use this information to construct the rejection region. In particular, we will reject H_0 whenever

(a) $\quad p_s \le 0.20 - 2.17(0.02) = 0.157$

or

(b) $\quad p_s \ge 0.20 + 2.17(0.02) = 0.243$

We have now completed the first step in determining the power of our test.

The second step involves calculating the power itself. First, we must select some alternative hypothesis. Suppose, for example, that the proportion of divorces in the population actually is $H_1 : p_1 = 0.3$. How likely are we to reject H_0 in this case? If the parameter actually is 0.3 and we take a sample of $N = 400$ marriages, we are once again in a situation in which large sample theory applies. The standard error of p_s now is

$$\sigma_{p_s} = \sqrt{\frac{0.3 \times 0.7}{.400}}$$

$$= \sqrt{\frac{0.21}{400}}$$

$$= 0.023$$

We use 0.3 in this formula because we are now assuming that H_1 is true. We want to determine how likely we are to be in the rejection region of H_0. This rejection region consists of the two parts listed above.

Consider the interval, $p_s \ge 0.243$, first. The probability of getting a sample proportion of 0.243 or more if $p = 0.3$ can be found from the normal curve table by converting 0.243 into a z score, as follows:

$$z_1 = \frac{0.243 - 0.300}{0.023} = \frac{-0.057}{0.023} = -2.48$$

Upon looking this value up in our table we see that the probability of being equal to or above -2.48 is

$$\text{Prob}\{z \geq -2.48\} = 0.9934$$

To find the corresponding probability that p_s is less than 0.157 we convert 0.157 into a z score. This z is

$$z_2 = \frac{0.157 - 0.300}{0.023} = \frac{-0.143}{0.023} = -6.22$$

The probability of getting a z less than or equal to -6.22 is so small that it is not even entered in the table. It is, essentially, 0.0000. Accordingly, the power of our test is

$$\text{Power} = 0.9934 + 0.0000 = 0.9934$$

Clearly, against this particular alternative, we have a very powerful test because we would reject H_0 more than 99 percent of the time if we sampled from a population in which this H_1 was true.

This procedure is perfectly general in the sense that we can use it to determine the power of our test relative to *any particular* alternative. Table 10.5 shows the power of this test against several of these alternatives. Note that the power is small when the alternative hypothesis is close to H_0 and that it becomes larger as we consider more and more remote alternatives. For example, the probability that we would reject H_0 is only 0.077 if the actual parameter is $p = 0.21$ whereas this probability is 0.879 if the actual parameter is $p = 0.27$.

Table 10.5   The power of $H_0: p_0 = 0.2$ against
various alternatives given a random sample
of $N = 400$ and $\alpha = 0.03$

Alternative	Power of H_0
$p = 0.21$	0.0771
0.22	0.1618
0.24	0.4484
0.27	0.8790
0.30	0.9934

There is another important point about power that should be recognized. The power of a test against any particular alternative depends upon (a) the choice of α and (b) the choice of N or the sample size. For example, if we choose only $N = 100$ cases for our sample the power relative to $H_1 : p_1 = 0.30$ drops to 0.6103. In general, the smaller is α and the smaller is N, the less is the power. Basically, it is for this reason that we should take reasonably large samples when testing hypotheses and that we should *not* select an α that is extremely small.

To make these points more clear, it is customary to talk about $1 -$ power, which is referred to as β. By definition, then,

$$\beta = 1 - \text{power}$$

Clearly, β is the probability that we will fail to reject H_0 when (a specific) H_1 is the true parameter value. A sensible test of an hypothesis is one in which β is kept reasonably small. Thus, there are two probabilities that we wish to keep small: α and β. Usually, we keep α small by choosing it to be small and we keep β small by taking a sample that is large enough to permit effective discrimination between H_0 and important alternative hypotheses. However, we must be careful not to choose too small an α lest we lose control over β, even with a reasonably large sample. There is no fixed rule as to how to balance these two probabilities. The researcher's personal judgment is necessarily involved in the decision as to where to set α and N so as to achieve a reasonable degree of control over β as well.[2]

10.9   WHERE WE STAND

We have introduced several new concepts in this chapter, all centering around how to use information in a sample to describe distributions in populations. We considered the kinds of error that can arise in sampling (sampling bias and random sampling errors) and indicated that bias can be eliminated through the practice of taking *random samples* but that random errors can only be controlled through manipulating the number of observations that are included in the sample. Next we introduced the key idea

---

[2] In the statistical literature, failing to reject a false hypothesis is sometimes referred to as an error in the same sense that rejecting a true hypothesis is an error. It is preferable to avoid this terminology, however, since the two situations are not quite analogous. In particular, we do not assert that our hypothesis is true just because we have failed to reject it. Therefore, we have not really made an error in failing to reject. On the other hand, we do assert that H_0 is false when we reject it. Hence, in this case we do commit an error when H_0 actually is true.

in statistical inference, the *sampling distribution,* which is the distribution of the statistic we are using to estimate the parameter in all possible random samples of the same size. We noted that for certain elementary statistics this sampling distribution is approximately normal provided only that our sample is large enough. Because of this fact, random sampling error is well measured by what is called the *standard error,* which is the standard deviation of the sampling distribution. We then showed how to use the standard error to *estimate* the parameter by constructing a confidence interval and also to *test an hypothesis* about a parameter by establishing a critical deviation.

In the next chapter we shall continue this discussion by considering rather carefully just how we develop an exact sampling distribution. This discussion will permit us to gain further insights into the construction of tests of hypotheses.

11

THE BINOMIAL
SAMPLING
DISTRIBUTION

In the preceding chapter we saw how to develop interval estimates of population parameters such as means and proportions. We also saw how to test hypotheses about parameters. To accomplish these objectives we used a sample estimate of the parameter and then worked with the sampling distribution of that estimator. In many cases this sampling distribution is approximately normal when the samples are sufficiently large. Therefore, we were able to use the standard error and the normal curve table to generate the interval estimates and to test our hypotheses. All statistical inferences are built up in essentially this same way. Each inference begins with some measure that describes the distribution in a sample and that is considered to be an estimator of the corresponding measure in the population. Next we identify and make a careful study of the *sampling distribution of the estimator*; that is, of the distribution of the estimator in all possible random samples of the same size from the population. The sampling distribution tells us how much the estimator varies from sample to sample, which is to say that it tells us how unreliable our estimator is. Finally, we use the relevant information in the sampling distribution to solve our estimation or hypothesis-testing problem.

Actual sampling distributions have many different shapes, depending primarily upon the estimator we use and the size of the sample. The general study of these sampling distributions lies far beyond the scope of this book. Indeed, this study is usually included only in texts on mathematical statistics. It is very useful, however, for the researcher who uses statistical procedures to have some grasp of how the mathematical statistician proceeds in his task of identifying sampling distributions. Fortunately, there is one exact sampling distribution that can be constructed without the use of any mathematics beyond simple algebra. Furthermore, the ideas used in constructing this distribution are just the same as those used when more complicated distributions are identified. We refer to what is called the *binomial distribution,* which is the sampling distribution of the simplest possible type of variable, the all-or-none attribute. In this chapter we shall show how the binomial sampling distribution is created. Then we shall use it to deepen our understanding of estimation, and especially of hypothesis testing. Actually, we have already discussed *all* of the concepts required to study this sampling distribution. However, we shall recast these concepts somewhat, with rather profound results. Our major objective is to study the binomial distribution for the light that it casts upon the general problem of testing and estimation.

11.1 THE CONCEPT OF A RANDOM VARIABLE OR VARIATE

In sampling theory a single observation is called a *random variable* or *random variate.* It is a variable because we do not know its value until the observation has actually been taken. It is a *random* variable because its value depends upon a random decision; in particular, its value depends upon which object or event is selected into the sample, and this selection is random, as discussed in the preceding chapter. Each observation in a sample is a separate random variable. Thus, if there are n observations in our sample we speak of having n random variables or random variates. These variates are identified as $X_1, X_2, \ldots, X_n$, according to the order in which they are drawn. That is, X_1 is the first observation in the sample, X_2 is the second, and so on.

As with any other variable, the important thing to know about a random variate is its distribution. If we start with the distribution of X in a population we also call an observation of that variable X, or X_i if we want to identify which particular observation it is. We can properly use the same symbol to refer to the distribution of the variable in the population of objects or events and to refer to the random variable obtained by choosing an observation from that population. The reason is that *these two distributions are identical* whenever we choose the observation in a (simple) random manner. However, we must be a bit careful in making this statement. A random variate describes the distribution of a *single* event (namely, making a single observation). Therefore, the concept of *frequency* of occurrence is not relevant. It is replaced by the concept, *probability of occurrence.* Thus, the two basic columns that describe the distribution of a random variate are (1) a column identifying the various values that might be observed and (2) a column identifying the probability that each value will, in fact, be observed. When we take simple random samples these probabilities are identical to the proportions in the table of the distribution of a variable. These proportions describe the relative frequency (f/N) with which each category or value of X occurs in the population. They also describe the relative likelihood that each category or value will occur in our single observation. The concepts of proportion and probability may be substituted for each other in this way whenever the sampling is *random*. Otherwise, the identity breaks down. We may summarize these ideas in these two sentences. (1) The distribution of the random variate, X, is identical to the distribution of the variable, X, in the population provided that the random variable is the outcome of an observation from that population and the object observed has been selected in a random manner. (2) In this situation the proportion of times that some value occurs in the population is equivalent to the probability that it will occur in the single random observation.

Let us illustrate these points by imagining the distribution of some dichotomy, X, in a large population such as the population of the United States. An example is the population of politically active Americans, each of whom either is a Republican ($X = 1$) or is not a Republican ($X = 0$). We have already considered variables of this type quite extensively. To construct the *distribution* of the variable we count the number of times that each value of X appears in the population. Since we are usually not interested in the size of the population itself, these counts or frequencies are often converted into proportions before reporting the distribution. A table of the distribution of X then looks like Table 11.1.

Table 11.1   Distribution of X in a population

Value of X	Proportion of times this value occurs in the population
1	p
0	$q = 1 - p$
Total	1

Here $p =$ the proportion of times that $X = 1$ in the population. The proportion of times that $X = 0$ is usually referred to as "q" and we have $q = 1 - p$.

Now imagine drawing a single object from the population and observing its value of X. In other words, take a sample of size $n = 1$ from the population. Take the sample in a random manner. Each and every object in the population has the same chance of appearing in the sample (or of being observed). Let X be the value of this observation. It may be either "1" or "0." (In other words, the categories of the random variate, X, are identical to the categories of the variable, X, in the population.) The distribution of the random variate is constructed by specifying the probability that each of these categories will actually be observed. We establish these probabilities from the definition of random sampling. If each object in the population has the same chance of being observed as each other object, then the probability that a given category will be observed in a single observation is equal to the proportion of objects in the population that possess that category. A table of the random variate, X, will look like Table 11.2. Notice

Table 11.2   Distribution of X in a randomly selected observation from the population

Value of X	Probability that this value will occur in a random observation
1	p
0	$q = 1 - p$
Total	1

that Tables 11.1 and 11.2 are identical except for the different heading over the second column.

At this point you may feel that we are somewhat belaboring the obvious and being quite repetitive. If so, excellent—for then you have mastered the idea. This idea is so crucial, however, that it bears examination from several angles. An observation of X randomly selected from a population may be visualized as a random variate that possesses the same distribution as X in the population.

If you understand what has been said so far, you will see that we have already *created a sampling distribution*; namely, the sampling distribution for samples of size $n = 1$ from the population. Since there is only one observation in this sample we must use it in estimating any parameter. Thus, the observation itself becomes a kind of universal estimator, since it is the only available information.

11.2   THE JOINT DISTRIBUTION OF TWO RANDOM VARIATES: SAMPLES OF SIZE TWO

Ordinarily, we do not consider observations one at a time. Instead, we combine randomly selected observations into samples of larger size. It is vital that we understand the rules that govern this combination. We shall begin by considering the distribution of two random variates. We shall see that once this very elementary joint distribution is understood, it is easy to extend the principles to larger samples. Just as the key to establishing the connection between the variable in the population and an observation of that variable lies in the concept of random sampling, so does the key to understanding the joint distribution of two random variates lie in another property of random sampling. This property is the *independence* of the observations, which is to say, the independence of the individual random variates. We have already defined what it means to say that two variables are independent of each other (see Chapter 8). Random sample observations are independent of each other because the selection of one object (or event) for observation does not affect the selection of the next object (or event). (Technically, this result exists only when each object that is selected is returned to the population before the next selection occurs. As we know, this process is called sampling with replacement and will always be assumed in this discussion.)

Remember, in sampling theory the basic unit of quantity is a probability rather than a frequency. In random sampling the probability of an object being in a certain location (such as a cell) is equivalent to the proportion of *all* objects that are there. If N stands for the number of objects in the population and n_{ij} for the number of objects in the ijth cell, then $p_{ij} = n_{ij}/N$ gives the proportion of objects in that cell or the probability of observing an object in that cell. Note that these proportions *are not conditional proportions* or probabilities. Each cell frequency is divided by the grand total of the entire table rather than by the column totals. Table 11.3 illustrates this method of calculating proportions.

Now consider the bivariate distribution of two randomly selected observations from a population in which X takes on the values 1 and 0, with

Table 11.3   A bivariate table where frequencies are expressed as proportions of the grand total

	Frequencies				Proportions		
	X_1	X_2	T		X_1	X_2	T
$Y_{.1}$	n_{11}	n_{12}	$n_1.$	Y_1	p_{11}	p_{12}	$p_1.$
Y_2	n_{21}	n_{22}	$n_2.$	Y_2	p_{21}	p_{22}	$p_2.$
T	$n_{.1}$	$n_{.2}$	N	T	$p_{.1}$	$p_{.2}$	1

$$p_{ij} = \frac{n_{ij}}{N} \text{ for any location in the table}$$

proportions p and q respectively. The bivariate distribution of these two random variates will have the form of Table 11.4 (cell probabilities omitted temporarily). The marginal probabilities in this table are the univariate probabilities that were discussed in the last section. Since the sampling is done with replacement a proportion, p, of the objects have the property $X = 1$ at each draw, so the probability that $X = 1$ is p at each draw.

Table 11.4   Form of bivariate sampling distribution

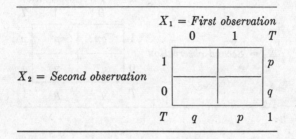

The cell probabilities have not been entered in this table. These are the probabilities of the joint occurrences of pairs of observations. In the upper-left-hand cell, for example, we want the value of p_{11}, which is the probability that X will have the value "0" on the first observation *and* "1" on the second observation. Our basic problem now is to determine how to calculate this joint probability.

We do it from the property of independence. Two variables are independent of each other when their joint occurrence is entirely a function of their separate occurrences. In other words, independence means that cell numbers depend entirely upon marginal numbers. In Chapter 8 we defined independence in terms of frequencies as existing whenever

$$\frac{n_{ij}}{n_{.j}} = \frac{n_{i.}}{N} \text{ for all } i \text{ and all } j.$$

Rearranging the elements in this formula we say that independence exists whenever the cell frequency n_{ij} is defined by the marginal frequencies so that

$$n_{ij} = \frac{n_{i.}n_{.j}}{N}$$

This same idea may now be expressed in terms of proportions or probabilities. The formula is even simpler in this case. Independence exists whenever

$$p_{ij} = p_{i.}p_{.j}$$

for all combinations of i and j. Now we may complete our table of the joint distribution of two random variates, since these variates are independent of each other through the fact that the sampling is random. Table 11.5 shows

Table 11.5   The bivariate sampling distribution of a dichotomy

		$X_1 = First\ observation$		
		0	1	T
	1	qp	p^2	p
$X_2 = Second\ observation$	0	q^2	pq	q
	T	q	p	1

this distribution. This formula for independence is sometimes referred to as the "multiplication law" of probabilities. In that form you may remember it from algebra.

Because this bivariate distribution is so important we shall present two examples. First, suppose that we are sampling from a population in which 60 percent of the individuals are male and 40 percent are female. We agree to make two random observations, thus generating two random variates. What is the joint distribution of these variates? Table 11.6 contains the

Table 11.6   Example of a sampling distribution where $n = 2$ and $p = 0.4$

Second observation	First observation		
	Male	Female	Total
Female	0.24	0.16	0.40
Male	0.36	0.24	0.60
Total	0.60	0.40	1.00

solution. This table tells us, for example, that the probability of getting a male on the first observation *and* a female on the second is $(0.6) \times (0.4) = 0.24 = p_{11}$. We are entitled to use the marginal probabilities to calculate the cell probabilities because of the condition of independence.

Consider another example. Let us make two tosses of a coin and observe which side is up each time. What is the bivariate distribution of outcomes? Pause a moment and consider carefully what population we are considering in this example, because it is often misunderstood. We have a coin with two sides, a head and a tail. These two sides are the population. The proportion of heads to sides is one half and the proportion of tails to sides is one half. Therefore, the proportion of heads in the population is 0.5, as is the proportion of tails. (We often speak loosely of this population as consisting of "all possible tosses" or something similar, as in Chapter 8, but the characterization given here is more precise.) Now we wish to identify the probability that a head will be facing up if we toss this coin. Here we make the random assumption. We *assume* that a head is just as likely as a tail. This assumption permits us to convert the proportions into probabilities. Note that the word "assumption" is used in its technical sense here. There is no guarantee whatever that the indicated probabilities will exist for any particular coin. Indeed, it is easy to manufacture a coin, or to deform an existing one, in such a way that the sides are far from being equally likely to be facing up after the toss. It is also quite easy to toss the coin in such a way that the random assumption is not met (though it takes a good deal of practice). Ordinarily, however, using coins just picked out of a pocket and tossed in the usual manner, the random assumption is so close to describing actual outcomes when the tossing is repeated, that it is entirely reasonable.

Table 11.7 shows the joint distribution of two variates (outcomes of two tosses) using the random assumption that permits us to convert the proportions, 0.5, into probabilities, 0.5. Note again that the individual prob-

Table 11.7 Joint distribution of two random tosses of a coin

Second toss	First toss Head	Tail	
Tail	0.25	0.25	0.50
Head	0.25	0.25	0.50
	0.50	0.50	1.00

abilities, p and q, appear as the marginals in this bivariate distribution and that the cell probabilities are products of these marginal figures because the tosses are independent of each other.

11.3   ANOTHER WAY TO PRESENT THE DISTRIBUTION
OF RANDOM VARIATES

The distribution of a dichotomous random variate does not need to be presented in the form of a table as we have done so far. It can be presented in somewhat shorter form provided that certain conventions are understood. Actually, any representation will do, as long as it conveys the necessary information. It is, therefore, appropriate to seek a representation that is useful to a particular purpose. This practice is quite common in mathematics and has led to numerous major advances in many different fields. Indeed, learning how to represent a concept effectively is one of the great problems in all scholarship. In the case of a distribution, particularly the distribution of an attribute, a very simple and effective way to represent a distribution is to identify each proportion by a different letter. The particular letter that is used can then stand for a particular category of the variable. Using this convention, it is unnecessary to use *two* columns for a distribution, one identifying categories, the other frequencies or proportions. All of the necessary information can be contained in one column or row. For example, in the case of an all-or-none attribute we have written the distribution in tabular form where the columns are as follows:

X	Proportion
1	p
0	q
Total	1

Actually, these two columns are redundant. The proportion p occurs only in the row labeled "1" and q occurs only in the row labeled "0." We can just let p stand for the probability of occurrence of a "1" and q stand for the probability of occurrence of a "0." Using this convention we can write the distribution as

$$\text{The distribution of } X \text{ is } p + q = 1$$

or just

$$F = F(X) = p + q = 1$$

where the symbol F stands for "the distribution of X." As long as we always use p to stand for $X = 1$ and q to stand for $X = 0$, there is no confusion. (Although we shall not consider extensions here, this representation can easily be extended to manifold classifications. With three categories, for example, we might write $F = p + q + v = 1$, where v stands for the probability of observing the third category.)

Of course, there is no point at all in introducing a different way of doing something unless it is useful. A table, for instance, is useful in summarizing a distribution. This new way to represent a distribution is very useful in the study of random sampling. The reason is very simple. Because random variates are *independent* of each other, the cell probabilities in bivariate tables are products of the marginal probabilities. It turns out that this act of finding cell probabilities as products of marginal probabilities is precisely equivalent to *squaring* the new representation of the distribution. That is, the joint distribution of two random observations of X may be represented as

$$F(X_1) \cdot F(X_2) = F^2 = (p + q)^2 = 1$$

This fact is quite important. It can be extended to any number of random variates presented in a multivariate or joint form. For instance, the joint distribution of five random variates of a dichotomous variable can be written as

$$F^5 = (p + q)^5 = 1$$

and the distribution of 100 random variates as

$$F^{100} = (p + q)^{100} = 1$$

In other words, the joint distribution of the observations in a sample of size n may be written as the elementary distribution of a single observation raised to the nth power. It must be remembered, of course, that this result applies only when the individual variates are *all independent* of each other.

Let us consider in detail just how the joint distribution of two random variates is representable as a square of the elementary distribution. Consider the joint distribution:

$$
\begin{aligned}
F(X_1) \cdot F(X_2) &= (p + q)^2 \\
&= (p + q)(p + q) \\
&= p^2 + pq + qp + q^2
\end{aligned}
$$

Now look back at Table 11.5, which is the basic table of the joint distribution of the observations X_1 and X_2. The four cell values in that table are precisely the four terms in this equation. Furthermore, each term in the equation identifies precisely in what cell it belongs. Thus, $p^2 = p \cdot p$ is the probability that X had the value "1" on both observations, which is to say that it belongs in cell$_{12}$ of the table. The same reasoning may be applied to each other term in the equation. Thus, pq indicates cell$_{22}$ because $X = 1$ on the first observation and $X = 0$ on the second.

This result applies to all sample sizes. It is always the case that the various terms of the expansion of

$$(p + q)^n$$

are cell probabilities in a multivariate distribution of n random (and independent) variates. This fact permits us to identify many sampling distributions.

11.4 THE BINOMIAL EXPANSION

We have seen that $(p + q)^2$ contains four terms corresponding to the four cells in a bivariate table. In a similar way, $(p + q)^3$ contains eight terms that correspond to the eight cells in a $2 \times 2 \times 2$ table, $(p + q)^4$ contains 16 terms that correspond to the 16 cells in a $2 \times 2 \times 2 \times 2$ table, etc. Each time we add a new variate (add a new observation to our sample) we double the number of terms or cells. We soon build up an extraordinarily cumbersome structure of terms. With a sample of only $n = 100$ we would have $2^{100} = 1,267,650,600,228,229,401,496,703,205,376$ terms, which is a very large number. Fortunately this rate of expansion is not necessary. Many of these terms are identical except for the order in which the p's and q's occur. In the sample of size $n = 2$ we have

$$(p + q)^2 = p^2 + pq + qp + q^2 = 1$$

Notice that pq and qp are the same except for the order in which p and q appear; that is, $pq = qp$ and each term represents the same overall sample since, in each case, the sample consists of one observation of $X = 1$ and one observation of $X = 0$. In sampling, we ordinarily do not care *when* (that is, on which draw) a given outcome occurs but only *how many times* it occurs. When all that we are interested in is the number of times that each event occurs we may write $(p + q)^n$ in a much shorter form. This form is called the *binomial expansion*. For example, for a sample of size two we write

$$F(X_1) \cdot F(X_2) = (p + q)^2 = 1$$
(long form) $$= p^2 + pq + qp + q^2 = 1$$
(short form) $$= p^2 + 2pq + q^2 = 1 \qquad \text{(binomial)}$$

In the binomial expansion the terms no longer refer to individual cells in the bivariate or multivariate table. Instead they represent the probability of getting a certain *number* of observations of one kind in the sample. In a sample of size $n = 2$, for example, what are the chances that there is exactly one observation in which $X = 1$? This question is answered by examining the terms of the binomial expansion (the short form). We seek the term that contains p just once. This term is the second one, or $2pq$. Therefore, the probability that we are seeking is $2pq$.

We can apply this result to the example we gave earlier. We were sampling from a population that was 60 percent male. What is the probability of getting exactly one male in a sample of two persons from this population? The probability is $2pq = 2(0.6)(0.4) = 0.48$. Look back at Table 11.6, which shows the joint distribution of these two observations. There are two cells in this table that imply one male and one female in the sample. The probabilities in these cells are 0.24 and 0.24. The probability of being in *either one or the other* cell is, therefore, $0.24 + 0.24 = 0.48$, which is our result. (This principle is sometimes referred to as the *law of addition* of probabilities.)

Let us now consider the general formula for the binomial expansion. Remember, this expansion gives the probability of getting a certain number of observations of one kind in a sample of n random variates. It is customary to call observations of one kind "successes" and observations of the other kind "failures." That is, instead of talking about the number of times that $X = 1$, we talk about the number of successes in the sample. The category called a success is the category referred to by p. We symbolize the number of successes in the sample by the letter r. In these terms, the binomial expansion gives us the probability of getting r successes in n trials. The general term of the binomial is

$$P(r) = \binom{n}{r} p^r q^{n-r}$$

In this formula $\binom{n}{r}$ is called the binomial coefficient or "the number of combinations of n things taken r at a time." It identifies the number of terms in the long form of the expansion of $(p + q)^n$ that contain the same number of p's.

The binomial coefficient is shorthand for

$$\binom{n}{r} = \frac{n!}{r!(n-r)!}$$

where the sign "!" is called the factorial sign and means the product of the number immediately in front of it times each succeeding smaller integer down to the integer "1." Thus, $6! = 6 \times 5 \times 4 \times 3 \times 2 \times 1 = 720$. In general,

$$n! = n(n-1)(n-2) \ldots (3)(2)(1)$$

and

$$r! = r(r-1)(r-2) \ldots (3)(2)(1)$$

by convention,

$$0! = 1$$

One other technical comment is important. In the general formula we use $P(r)$ to refer to the probability of getting r successes in n trials. The four symbols here (that is, P, the two parentheses, and r) all combine to form a phrase. They do not signify an arithmetic operation. Unfortunately, these same symbols are sometimes used to indicate multiplication. It is conventional to specify probabilities in this manner, however. In this text you should always read P followed by a set of parentheses with something inside as "the probability that such and such is true." For example, $P\{X = 1\} = p$ should be read "the probability that $X = 1$ is equal to p." Note that braces are used here. They have the same meaning as the parentheses.

Now let us consider some specific examples of binomial probabilities. Suppose that we want to know the probability of drawing exactly *four* males in a random sample of *six* observations from the population in which 60 percent of all individuals are male. We compute this probability directly from the binomial formula:

$$P\{r = 4\} = \frac{6!}{4!\,2!}\,(0.6)^4(0.4)^2$$

$$= \frac{(6)(5)(4)(3)(2)(1)}{(4)(3)(2)(1)(2)(1)}\,(0.6)^4(0.4)^2$$

$$= \frac{720}{48}\,(0.1296)(0.16)$$

$$= 0.311$$

We can shorten these computations considerably by what is called canceling. Notice that the numerator and denominator of $\binom{n}{r}$ both contain many of the same factors. In this example, they both contain $(4)(3)(2)(1)$. These factors may be canceled, in which case our computations will look more like this:

$$P\{r = 4\} = \frac{(6)(5)(4)(3)(2)(1)}{(4)(3)(2)(1)(2)(1)}\,(0.1296)(0.16)$$

$$= \frac{30}{2}\,(0.1296)(0.16)$$

$$= 0.311$$

It is always sensible to cancel wherever possible in computational routines involving factorials. Otherwise the numbers get very large.

As another example, let us find the probability of getting exactly five heads in ten tosses of a fair coin. In this case $n = 10$ and $r = 5$. We have

$$P\{r = 5 | n = 10\} = \frac{(10)(9)(8)(7)(6)(5!)}{(5)(4)(3)(2)(1)(5!)} (0.5)^5 (0.5)^5$$

$$= \frac{(9)(40)(7)}{(1)} (0.0009765)$$

$$= 0.246$$

Notice here that we have written out the left-hand side of the equation more fully. The vertical line "|" is a symbol used to indicate that whatever comes after is given or already known. In other words, we read this expression as "the probability that $r = 5$ in a sample of ten observations" or "the probability that $r = 5$ given that $n = 10$." Unless it is clear from the context, it is important to add this "given" because the probability that $r = 5$ depends upon how large the sample is as well as upon the value of p.

Let us consider one final example. We are at a card table, using an ordinary deck of cards. We deal five cards to each of four persons, so there are 32 cards remaining in the deck. What is the probability that all of the cards dealt to one individual are spades? We begin by noting that a hand of five cards is a sample so $n = 5$. But now watch out!!! What is the probability that a given card will be a spade? For the first card, it is *prob* $= 13/52$. Now what is this probability for the second card dealt? *It is not the same number,* because we did *not* replace the first card before dealing the second. At the time that we deal the second card there are only 51 cards left in the deck. The probability of a spade on this second card is either $13/51$ or $12/51$, depending upon whether or not a spade was dealt the first time. Obviously, we are over our heads. We are outside the binomial system; the probabilities change from draw to draw. We can no longer think of the taking of successive observations as raising $(p + q)$ to successively higher powers. The proper answer to this problem, given the information contained in this book, is "I do not know!" The binomial can be used only when sampling with replacement and only when the random variates (observations) are independent of each other.

11.5   THE BINOMIAL AS A SAMPLING DISTRIBUTION

It is now time to return to the main theme of statistical inference. The basic problem is to estimate some parameter or to test an hypothesis about this parameter. Suppose that the parameter is the proportion of successes, p, in some population. In either case our procedure will involve taking a sample of observations and calculating an *estimator of p* from these observations. This estimator we call p_s. In any sample that we take we calculate p_s by counting the number of successes in the sample (r) and dividing the result by the sample size, n. That is,

$$p_s = \frac{r}{n}$$

To proceed further than this point in the analysis we need to know the sampling distribution of this estimator so that we can tell how much it fluctuates from sample to sample or how inaccurate it is. The sampling distribution is the distribution of the estimator in all possible random samples of the same size that could be drawn from the population. More precisely, it is the probability distribution of the n random variates that go to make up the sample, where this probability distribution itself has been summarized in some appropriate way. In particular, it is summarized to display the probability of occurrence of each possible sample proportion (each possible value of p_s).

A table of this sampling distribution will contain two columns, one identifying the *possible* values of p_s and the other identifying the probability of occurrence (given random sampling) of each of these possible values. We can write the possible values in one of two ways, either as fractions (r/n) or as decimals. Thus, the first column of our table may look like either of these lists (using $n = 8$ as an example).

As fractions	As decimals
p_s	p_s
8/8	1.000
7/8	0.875
6/8	0.750
.	.
.	.
$r/8$	.
.	.
.	.
1/8	0.125
0/8	0.000

Either of these columns is a listing of all of the possible different values of p_s that might occur in our sample (if $n = 8$).

The sampling distribution also identifies the probability that each of these possible sample values would actually occur in a given simple random sample. *These probabilities are precisely specified by the binomial expansion.* Table 11.8 shows the complete distribution for $n = 8$. In this table we have solved for the combinations directly since they depend only upon r and n.

Table 11.8 Binomial sampling distribution for $n = 8$

p_s	$P(p_s)$
1.000	(1) p^8q^0
0.875	(8) p^7q^1
0.750	(28) p^6q^2
0.625	(56) p^5q^3
0.500	(70) p^4q^4
0.375	(56) p^3q^5
0.250	(28) p^2q^6
0.125	(8) p^1q^7
0.000	(1) p^0q^8

We made $n = 8$ and the value of r is contained (implicitly) in the first column of the table. To reduce each probability to an actual number it is only necessary to specify the value of p (which, of course, also specifies the value of q). Table 11.9 shows two examples of these completely specified sampling distributions, one in which $p = 0.6$ and the other in which $p = 0.5$.

Read these distributions carefully. The third line in Example 1, for instance, says that the probability of getting a sample proportion of 0.750 from a population in which the actual proportion is 0.6 and the sample consists of eight observations is $P\{r/n = 0.750\} = 0.209$. That is, such a sample proportion would appear about one time in five from this population, assuming that all samples were simple random and of size $n = 8$.

Table 11.9 Specific examples of binomial distributions, $n = 8$

Example 1	$p = 0.6$	Example 2	$p = 0.5$
p_s	$P(p_s)$	p_s	$P(p_s)$
1.000	0.017	1.000	0.004
0.875	0.089	0.875	0.031
0.750	0.209	0.750	0.109
0.625	0.279	0.625	0.219
0.500	0.232	0.500	0.274
0.375	0.124	0.375	0.219
0.250	0.041	0.250	0.109
0.125	0.008	0.125	0.031
0.000	0.001	0.000	0.004
Total	1.000	Total	1.000

In this same way, the next to the last row in example 2 means that a sample proportion of 0.125 would occur only approximately 3 percent of the time if the true proportion were 0.5 and the sampling was simple random with $n = 8$.

11.6 USING THE SAMPLING DISTRIBUTION TO TEST AN HYPOTHESIS

It is one thing to know what a sampling distribution is and quite another to know how to use it. The problem of how to use a sampling distribution proves bothersome to many beginning students, primarily because it involves making decisions on the basis of "the odds" or the probabilities. We like to make decisions with certainty but in inference we can never be sure, except by being so vague that we include every possibility. As we learned in the preceding chapter we can draw inferences either to make estimates of parameters or to test hypotheses about them. In most areas of social science it is more common to test hypotheses than to make estimates. In this section we shall present the exact procedure for using a sampling distribution in hypothesis testing, leaving estimation as developed in Chapter 10. In particular, we shall discuss in detail how to test hypotheses about a single population proportion, p, using the binomial sampling distribution. Something of a compromise is involved here. Ordinarily, we do not test hypotheses about single proportions but rather about differences between proportions. However, it is more difficult to explain the derivation of the sampling distribution of a difference between proportions so we shall consider this more elementary case. The logical structure of the test applies to all sampling distributions, so no real generality is lost.

Types of Hypotheses

Generally speaking, social scientists test one of two types of hypothesis, which are called "two-tailed" and "one-tailed" hypotheses. The first kind is the hypothesis that the parameter p has a specific value. The hypothesis that we *test* is always called H_0 or the *null hypothesis*. We symbolize this first type of hypothesis as

$$H_0: p = p_0$$

(Note that this type is the one we discussed in the preceding chapter.) In this symbolization, as you know, p_0 stands for the specific value of p defined by the hypothesis. For example, we might test the hypothesis that a certain coin is a fair coin. Our hypothesis is that $p = 0.5$. This specific number,

0.5, is the value p_0, so we would say that our hypothesis is called $p_0 = 0.5$. In genetics a simple Mendelian pattern of dominant and recessive genes in the parents leads to the hypothesis that 25 percent of the offspring will manifest the recessive character. We might test this hypothesis, in which case we would say that H_0 is that $p_0 = 0.25$. The reason that this type of hypothesis is called "two-tailed" will be explained after we have defined the other type.

The second kind of hypothesis that is tested is that the parameter is in some interval, particularly, either the interval extending from a certain value on up, or from a certain value on down. Hypotheses of this type are symbolized as

$$H_0: p \leq p_0$$

or

$$H_0: p \geq p_0$$

The symbol "$\leq$" should be read "less than or equal to" and the symbol "$\geq$" should be read "greater than or equal to." In a study of politics, for example, we might hypothesize that there are at least 50 percent Republicans in a given county. We would think in terms of 50 percent because this percent is sufficient to guarantee winning an election. This hypothesis is that $p \geq 0.5$. Another example of the use of one-tailed hypotheses arises in industrial work. Machines break down occasionally and must be repaired. Time consumed in repairing a machine is called "down time." Down time is expensive both because the repairs cost money and also because no product is forthcoming when the machine is down. Often the question as to whether or not to replace a given machine will hinge upon whether or not the possible replacement definitely has a smaller proportion of down time to total operating time. Suppose, for example, that by long experience with the machine already in use we know that it is down 10 percent of the time. We want to replace it only if we can be sure that the new machine will be down less than 10 percent of the time. Accordingly, we test the hypothesis that the new machine will *not* be down less than 10 percent. In other words, the hypothesis actually tested is

$$H_0: p \geq 0.1 \text{ on the new machine}$$

If we reject this hypothesis then we will replace the old machine with the new. On the other hand, if we fail to reject the hypothesis then we will keep the old machine.

Hypotheses are called two-tailed or one-tailed according to where those sample results which would lead to the rejection of the hypothesis are located. We look at the deviation between p_s (the evidence we have) and p_0

(the hypothesis). As we know, the greater the deviation between these two numbers, the more inclined we are to *reject* the hypothesis. Where are the large deviations to be found? To answer this question we want to look at all of the *possible* sample outcomes and see which ones involve large deviations from the hypothesis.

Consider, first, the *hypothesis that p is equal to some specific value, p_0.* Let us identify all of the possible values of p_s. Clearly, p_s can range only between 0 and 1, so all of its possible values fall in an interval extending from 0 and 1. (See Figure 11.1.)

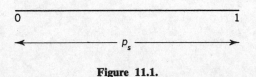

Figure 11.1.

Now let us locate the hypothesis, p_0, in this interval and consider where relatively large discrepancies between p_s and p_0 might occur. Suppose, in particular, that p_0 is at the point indicated by the arrow in Figure 11.2.

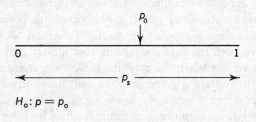

Figure 11.2.

Look at the possible values of p_s. It is clear that relatively large deviations from p_0 occur either down in the vicinity of $p_s = 0$ or up in the vicinity of $p_s = 1$. Visually, we have Figure 11.3, where the shaded area represents

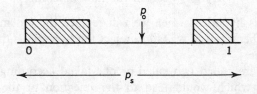

Figure 11.3.

those values of p_s that are quite far from p_0. The extreme values of p_s are called its tails. The fact that large deviations occur *both* near 0 and near 1 is to say that they occur in both tails of the possible values. We would be inclined to reject the hypothesis if p_s were too small or if it were too large. Hence we use the term "two-tailed" to describe this type of hypothesis.

Now consider *hypotheses of the second type*. We shall illustrate the structure for the hypothesis that p is equal to *or* greater than a given value, p_0. Let us go through the same three steps. First, we identify all of the possible values of p_s, as in Figure 11.4. As before, these values range from 0

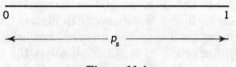

Figure 11.4.

to 1. Second, we locate the position of the hypothesis within this interval. The hypothesis is that p itself is inside an interval, as indicated in Figure 11.5. Finally, we locate those values of p_s for which a large deviation

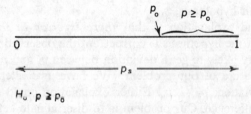

Figure 11.5.

exists between p_s and p_0. Such large discrepancies exist in the vicinity of $p_s = 0$, but *not* near $p_s = 1$ because and p_s near 1 is actually inside the interval specified by H_0. Therefore, no deviation at all exists there. Visually we have the situation shown in Figure 11.6, where, again, the shaded area

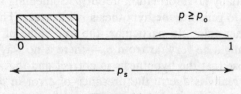

Figure 11.6.

represents the more deviant values of p_s relative of p_0. Since all of these extreme values are in one tail of the possible values of p_s we call an hypothesis of this type a "one-tailed" hypothesis. Of course, we illustrated this hypothesis with a "greater than" interval. It could also have the form of a "less than or equal to" interval, in which case the extreme values of p_s would be near 1 because the hypothesized values of p would extend from 0 to p_0.

When to Reject an Hypothesis

In Chapter 10 we reviewed the general procedure for rejecting or failing to reject an hypothesis. In this section we shall discuss this procedure from a slightly different perspective to deepen our knowledge of it. The basic decision as to whether or not to reject H_0 involves the deviation between p_s (the sample estimate of the parameter) and p_0 (the hypothesis about the parameter). In effect, in reaching a decision here we are attempting *to explain* just *why* the difference between sample evidence and hypothesis occurred. There are two possible explanations of the deviation.

1. The first explanation is that *the hypothesis is wrong*. If so, then we certainly should reject the hypothesis. Clearly, if the hypothesis actually is wrong then it is very likely that we will get a deviation between our sample value, p_s, and our hypothesis, p_0.

2. The second explanation is that *there is error in the observations*. Clearly, again, if the hypothesis is correct but the observations are in error, we would be very likely to get a deviation between p_s and p_0.

Notice the nature of our problem: We have two alternative explanations of the deviation, $p_s - p_0$. Either explanation could account for the existence of a difference. Our problem is to discriminate between these two possibilities. Of course, we cannot make this discrimination just on the basis that a difference exists because both explanations imply that a difference would exist. Therefore, we need some other criterion to use as a basis for inferring which explanation is correct.

Let us consider each explanation to see if we can find some way to discriminate between them. First, suppose that the hypothesis is wrong. In this case p has some value other than p_0. If the hypothesis is wrong, then we really have essentially no information about p. Something about the reasoning that we used to generate the hypothesis is incorrect. The true value of p might be any other value. In particular, the true value of p might be quite close to p_0 or it might be very far from p_0—there is no way to tell.

Second, suppose that the hypothesis is correct and that the deviation between p_s and p_0 really is due to the presence of error in p_s. In Chapter 10 we identified the two types of sampling error that might be present: bias and random error. Suppose that the error that is present is a bias. Now we are stuck. We do not know how large the bias is and have no way of finding out. Therefore, if bias is present, the deviation $p_s - p_0$ might be large or small. We cannot tell. Note the implication. There is no way to distinguish between an incorrect hypothesis and a bias in the sample. Whatever difference we observe, it could be due either to an incorrect hypothesis or to a bias, *unless we have already eliminated the possibility of sampling bias through care in selecting the sample.* Now you can see clearly just why it is so important to sample in such a way that sampling bias is eliminated. Only when we eliminate bias do we have any real hope of discriminating between the two basic explanations.

We can definitely eliminate sampling bias, of course, by taking a random sample. However, even in random sampling there remains another kind of error that might be the explanation of the deviation between sample evidence and hypothesis. We call this kind of error *random sampling error.* Let us suppose that the actual explanation of the deviation $p_s - p_0$ is that p_s is a random or chance fluctuation from p_0. What will the deviation be like if this explanation is true? We finally have a question to which we can give a definite answer. Although we cannot tell precisely what difference we will get in any particular sample, we can identify precisely what the *distribution* of deviations is. This distribution is the sampling distribution of p_s with p_0 as the parameter. In other words, the sampling distribution tells us what deviations to anticipate if it is true that the only element generating deviation between sample and hypothesis is random sampling error. Broadly speaking, we learn from a study of the sampling distribution that (1) we should anticipate a relatively small deviation if random sampling error accounts for the difference, and (2) the larger the sample the smaller the expected deviation.

Now let us summarize this discussion. First, suppose that we actually get a relatively small deviation between p_s and p_0, using random sampling. We are left in considerable doubt as to its explanation. The deviation could be due to random sampling error. It could also be due to some flaw in the line of reasoning that led to H_0; that is, H_0 might be wrong. (Note that we assume random sampling, so sampling bias is no problem.) Second, suppose that we actually get a large deviation between p_s and p_0. Such a large deviation could easily arise if our hypothesis is incorrect but it would be very unlikely to arise just from random sampling fluctuation in p_s. In this situation, then, we can discriminate between the two possible explanations. We can be quite sure, when a large difference exists, that the hypothesis is wrong. That is, we are in a position to reject our hypothesis.

With a large deviation, then, we reject the hypothesis and with a small difference we remain in doubt. Actually, we can go a bit further in the case of a small difference. Since we definitely know that random sampling error is present in our sample we ordinarily conclude, tentatively, that it is the explanation of a small deviation. That is, we tentatively accept the hypothesis or we say that our sample evidence is certainly consistent with our hypothesis. This conclusion must be tentative, however, because there is always the possibility that the hypothesis is wrong but only to an extent that could not be detected in a sample of the size taken. At this point, you may wish to review Section 10.8 on The Power of a Test.

Identifying a Large Deviation Between p_s and p_0

The only remaining problem, and it is the key one, is to determine beforehand what is a large and what is a small deviation. The student who has followed our reasoning up to this point will already suspect the answer. The discrimination between the explanations depends entirely upon how unlikely it is that the deviation would arise as just a chance fluctuation. A "large" deviation, then, is one that is relatively unlikely to occur by chance. (We shall modify the details of this statement a bit in the next few paragraphs.) These likelihoods are, of course, described by the sampling distribution. Thus, the solution to the problem of when a deviation is large or small (that is, when to reject or to fail to reject H_0) lies in the careful study of the sampling distribution.

One of the first things that we learn from a study of the sampling distribution is that it is impossible to use the size of the deviation itself to identify a large deviation. The reason is straightforward: a deviation of a given size may be quite an ordinary random fluctuation in a sample of one size and be a very rare occurrence, indeed, in a sample of another size. The important idea is not how large the difference is but *how likely* the deviation is under the assumption that it is just a random sampling fluctuation.

It turns out, however, that when we shift to this likelihood we face precisely the opposite problem. The likelihood or probability of *any* particular sample outcome becomes smaller and smaller as the sample size increases. This statement even applies to the sample outcome that is precisely the same as the parameter. For example, consider the probability of getting exactly one-half heads and one-half tails in even numbers of tosses of a coin. For various sample sizes we have

$$P(p_s = 0.5 | n = 2) = 0.5$$
$$P(p_s = 0.5 | n = 4) = 0.375$$
$$P(p_s = 0.5 | n = 6) = 0.312$$
$$P(p_s = 0.5 | n = 8) = 0.274$$

Clearly, the probability of getting *this particular outcome* decreases substantially as the sample size increases. The student may easily confirm this fact for any other particular outcome among smaller samples. The implication of this fact is that *the probability of an individual outcome cannot be used effectively to distinguish between ordinary and rare sampling fluctuations.*

The major alternative possibility, and the one universally adopted by statisticians, is to *cumulate* the probabilities found in the sampling distribution. Before any cumulation can occur, of course, the different outcomes must be placed in an array. The array that proves most useful in distinguishing between large and small deviations is implied by this distinction itself. In particular, we arrange the sample outcomes according to the deviation between each one and the hypothesis. For a two-tailed hypothesis, for example, we form the difference $p_s - p_0$ for each possible sample outcome and then take the absolute value of this difference: $|p_s - p_0|$. These absolute values are then placed in an array from the largest one down to the smallest. The probabilities corresponding to the outcomes in this array are then cumulated in the usual manner.

This process can be illustrated by considering the sampling distribution of samples of size $n = 8$ from a population in which our hypothesis is that $p = 0.6$. (This sampling distribution was presented as example 1 in Table 11.9.) We form the array we want by finding $|p_s - p_0|$ for each possible outcome and then arraying them. Then we cumulate the corresponding probabilities. Table 11.10 shows the steps.

Table 11.10 A sampling distribution arrayed by deviation between p_s and p_0 $H_0{:}p = p_0 = 0.6$

p_s	$|p_s - p_0|$	$P(p_s)$	Cumulated $P(p_s)$
0.000	0.600	0.001	0.001
0.125	0.475	0.008	0.009
1.000	0.400	0.017	0.026
0.250	0.350	0.041	0.067
0.875	0.275	0.089	0.156
0.375	0.225	0.124	0.280
0.750	0.150	0.209	0.489
0.500	0.100	0.232	0.721
0.625	0.025	0.279	1.000

At first this table looks rather peculiar, since the various individual sample outcomes (p_s values) appear to be in disarray. Superficially, they are, but only superficially. The deviations, $|p_s - p_0|$, are in order. Notice that the probabilities, $P(p_s)$, are also in order—from the least likely to the most likely outcomes. In all sampling distributions found in elementary statistical analysis this pattern exists; the most deviant sample is also the least likely to occur is H_0 is true. Even the p_s values themselves are not in as much disorder as appears at first glance. What has happened is that the two tails of the distribution have been combined for the purpose of cumulating the probabilities. Within each tail the outcomes are in order. That is, 0.000 is above 0.125, which is above 0.250, and so on.

The last column in this table lists the cumulated probabilities. These cumulated probabilities are the basis upon which we reach a decision as to whether or not a given sample estimate shows a large or a small deviation from the hypothesis. Notice that an entry in this cumulated column tells us the probability of getting a sample estimator *as deviant or more deviant* than the indicated outcome. For example, we see the number 0.026 in the third row of this column. In this same row in the first column we see that the sample outcome associated with this probability is $p_s = 1.000$. Verbally, we say that a sample at least as deviant as $p_s = 1.000$ would occur by chance only 2.6 percent of the time in random samples of size $n = 8$ from a population in which $p = 0.6$.

Remember that our problem was to decide when a large deviation between p_s and p_0 exists. We can now *define a large deviation in terms of a small cumulated probability.* Just how small the cumulated probability must be for us to decide that the deviation is large is up to the researcher. This criterion probability is called α. As noted in the preceding chapter most social scientists use either $\alpha = 0.05$ or $\alpha = 0.01$. The criterion, α, is just the cumulated probability that is used as the cutting point between large and small deviations. Using Table 11.10 as an example, if we set $\alpha = 0.05$ we would classify three sample outcomes as involving large deviations. Therefore, we would *reject* the hypothesis that $p = 0.6$ if any of these outcomes actually occurred in our sample. These sample outcomes are $p_s = 0.000$, 0.125 and 1.000. The cumulated probability of these outcomes is $CumP = 0.026$, which is below our criterion, 0.050. On the other hand, if we included the next sample outcome in the array (namely, $p_s = 0.250$) the cumulated probability would rise to 0.067, which is more than 0.050. Therefore, this next outcome is *not* included in the rejection region.

We proceed in the same manner in testing a *one-tailed hypothesis,* except that we cumulate probabilities only in one tail since large deviations exist only in one tail. Suppose, for example, that the hypothesis being tested is $H_0: p \geq p_0 = 0.6$ or simply, $p \geq 0.6$. Now a large deviation can only arise when p_s is relatively small. Accordingly, ordering the outcomes by deviation involves only this tail. In particular, the entries in the first few rows of the cumulated sampling distribution would look like Table 11.11 ($n = 8$).

Table 11.11   Cumulated sampling distribution

p_s	$|p_s - p_0|$	$P(p_s)$	$CumP(p_s)$
0.000	0.600	0.001	0.001
0.125	0.475	0.008	0.009
0.250	0.350	0.041	0.050
.	.	.	.
.	.	.	.

Using $\alpha = 0.05$, the rejection region would now contain these three outcomes since their combined probability is exactly 0.05.

We now have a complete decision procedure. Remember that our original problem was to attempt to discriminate between two possible explanations of whatever deviation we observe between the sample estimator in a *random* sample and the hypothesis being tested. There are two possible explanations: (1) the hypothesis is wrong or (2) the deviation is a chance fluctuation due to sampling from a population in which the hypothesis is true. We saw that either explanation could be correct if the difference is small but that only the first explanation (that the hypothesis is wrong) is plausible if the difference is large. We have now defined large. A large difference is defined in terms of likelihood. When a sample outcome occurs such that *it or a more extreme outcome* would be very rare (no more than a preset α) then we reject the chance explanation and conclude that the hypothesis is wrong. Otherwise, we conclude that the sample evidence is consistent with our hypothesis.

11.7   THE SIGN TEST:
AN APPLICATION OF BINOMIAL SAMPLING THEORY

Our main objective in this chapter has been to provide a deeper understanding of how the statistician makes inferences. We have discussed the binomial sampling distribution primarily because it is the easiest sampling distribution to derive. It also has important applications, of course. One application that is particularly interesting in sociology is called the sign test, which is used when we study *change*. Suppose, for example, that we wish to find out whether or not working on a common project makes people like each other more. We establish the hypothesis that no *systematic* change occurs through joint participation. Let us define a success as a person who has become friendlier after working with another person. Whether or not our hypothesis is true we expect some people to change, so we expect some successes and some failures in our study. However, if our hypothesis is true that there is no *systematic* change then the probability of a success is the same as the probability of a failure. Using p as the proportion of successes (persons becoming friendlier) we have H_0: $p = 0.5$ and the problem reduces to a basic binomial situation. All we need do now would be to build some specific study around this hypothesis and thereby test it. Note that if we reject H_0 we can conclude that working together does produce a systematic change. With a little imagination this kind of test can be used in many situations in sociology.

11.8 WHERE WE STAND

In this chapter we have presented the basic argument of statistical inference. In drawing inferences from a sample to the population the statistician creates the sampling distribution. We illustrated this activity in the case of the binomial distribution—the most elementary of all sampling distributions because it is based upon an all-or-none attribute. We use the sampling distribution, once identified, either to estimate the parameter or to test some hypothesis about the parameter. In this chapter we concentrated upon the testing of hypotheses. We noted that the hypothesis may be either "one-tailed" or "two-tailed." In a one-tailed hypothesis the parameter is in a "less than or equal to" or a "greater than or equal to" interval. A two-tailed hypothesis is that the parameter has some specific value.

In either case we saw that the essential argument in testing an hypothesis is as follows:

1. When we take a sample, the sample estimator will almost always deviate to some extent from the hypothesis, H_0. There are three possible explanations for this deviation.
   (a) The hypothesis may be true, but the sample may be biased.
   (b) The hypothesis may be true, but the deviation may be a chance or random sampling fluctuation.
   (c) The hypothesis may be false or incorrect.
2. We distinguish among these three possible explanations by
   (a) Taking a random sample and, therefore, eliminating sampling bias. (Whenever the sampling is *not* random, or its equivalent, the possibility of bias exists as an explanation. Since we cannot then tell how much bias exists this possibility virtually eliminates the validity of a test—hence the importance of random sampling.)

(b) Noting the difference between the sample outcome and the hypothesis and interpreting this deviation as *large* or *small* on the basis of the sampling distribution.

(i) If the difference is small, then either of the explanations (b) or (c) may be correct. We fail to reject the hypothesis and say that our evidence is consistent with the hypothesis.

(ii) If the difference is large, then chance fluctuation is ruled out and the only remaining explanation is that the hypothesis is false.

A deviation between evidence and hypothesis is considered to be small whenever the probability of a deviation that large or larger is, itself, larger than a preset figure called α. Whenever the probability of a given deviation or a larger one is smaller than α we say that the deviation is large.

12

TESTS
OF THE HYPOTHESIS
OF ZERO ASSOCIATION

The typical hypothesis that the social scientist tests today is the hypothesis that two variables are independent of each other (that is, not associated) in some population. The bivariate distribution is a very fundamental building block in science because it is through the existence of relationships between variables that prediction and control (as well as understanding) are achieved. It is, therefore, quite important to know whether or not two variables are related to each other. If two variables are related, the researcher proceeds on to further analysis of them, perhaps in the form of multivariate analysis as outlined in Chapter 9, or perhaps in the form of further thought and theory building. If two variables are *not* related to each other, the researcher typically discards one or the other and passes on to more interesting patterns. Occasionally, of course, the lack of association between two variables will, itself, be theoretically interesting.

The problem of identifying whether or not two variables are independent of each other in a *population* is far from trivial. The social scientist essentially always analyzes a *sample* of observations. Sample information is subject to error, particularly to random sampling error. When the researcher looks at a bivariate table based on his sample he will almost certainly find some association in his figures; that is, the proportions in the various conditional distributions in the sample will virtually never be *exactly* equal to each other. The association or relationship that appears in the sample should be accounted for or explained. As we know from earlier discussions, there are two basic ways to explain the relationship that appears in the sample. First, it may be just a chance sampling fluctuation from a population in which there is no relationship. Second, it may reflect the fact that there is a relationship between the variables in the population. In this chapter we shall show how to discriminate between these two possibilities.

We have already discussed the way in which the statistician makes this kind of discrimination. Let us review the basic steps.

1. We develop an hypothesis concerning what exists in the population. We call this hypothesis H_0. (In this chapter we are concerned with the hypothesis that there is no association between two variables in the population.)

2. We select a level of significance, which we call α. This level of significance is the risk of error that we are willing to run of rejecting a true hypothesis. It is the fundamental criterion used in the test and refers, as we know, to a cumulated form of the sampling distribution.

3. We identify the appropriate sampling distribution using the information contained in our hypothesis, H_0. This sampling distribution tells us how samples would be distributed if chance fluctuation were the only explanation of the deviation between sample results and the hypothesis.

4. We arrange the possible sample outcomes (as found in the sampling distribution) in order from the most deviant outcome to the least deviant outcome, relative to H_0, and cumulate the probabilities.

5. Using these cumulated probabilities we agree to reject H_0 whenever any sample outcome whose cumulated probability is less than or equal to α occurs. If any other outcome occurs (in the particular sample we actually draw) we agree tentatively to accept H_0 or to treat the sample evidence as consistent with the hypothesis.

In this chapter we shall apply this procedure to test the hypothesis of zero association at each level of measurement; that is, among attributes, ordinal variables, and interval variables. Actually, we already presented two large sample tests of association in Chapter 10. In particular, we have shown how to test the hypothesis that two conditional proportions are equal and that two conditional means are equal. Given large enough samples, the sampling distributions in these tests will be normal. The problem of cumulating the most deviant outcomes into a rejection region is solved by considering outcomes in the tails of the normal curve. The relevant cumulated probabilities are available in the table of the normal curve. We shall continue here with a further consideration of this solution and then shall study other approaches to the problem of testing the hypothesis that there is no association between two variables.

12.1 THE CENTRAL LIMIT THEOREM

The key to solving any problem in statistical inference lies in identifying the sampling distribution of the sample estimator of the parameter being considered. We have illustrated how the mathematical statistician makes this identification in the case of the binomial distribution. This particular sampling distribution is quite easy to derive. In many cases, however, it is very difficult to derive the relevant sampling distribution. In some situations the proper distribution still has not been discovered.

Because the task of finding exact sampling distributions is so formidable in many instances, mathematical statisticians have attempted to find approximate solutions. These approximation procedures usually take one of two forms. On one hand, certain simplifying assumptions may be made as to the nature of the distribution of X or of both X and Y if the distribution is bivariate. The sampling distribution that is identified through the use of these assumptions will be only an approximation to the distribution that exists when the assumptions are not entirely met in the population studied. On the other hand, the statistic being used as an estimator may be studied carefully. Sometimes this study will reveal that a known sampling distribution is a close approximation to the exact distribution. Remember that the sampling distribution is built up by considering the distribution of the random variate, which is an observation of the variable in question. Remember also that this random variate has the same distribution as X does in the population, except that what is a proportion in the population becomes a probability in the random variate. Any particular sample, then, is a combination of n random variates. It is out of this n-dimensional multivariate distribution that the sampling distribution of any statistic may be generated.

Since any one random variate has the same distribution as the variable in the population, it is clear that the way that this variable is distributed in the population will have a great impact upon the nature of the sampling distribution. However, it has been found that *this impact diminishes as the sample size increases.* This finding is summarized in what is called the *central limit theorem,* which is a very fundamental law in theoretical statistics. The central limit theorem states that the sampling distribution of any mean will approach normality as the sample size increases, regardless of the form of the distribution of the variable in the population from which the samples are drawn, provided only that the population distribution has a finite mean and variance. Distributions in which the mean or variance is not finite are theoretically possible but seldom occur in practice. It is this central limit theorem that permits us to use the normal curve as the sampling distribution of a mean or a proportion or difference provided only that the sample is large enough.

There is, however, one important problem that arises when this theorem is used to identify sampling distributions. When the distribution of X in the population is unknown it is difficult to determine just how large n, the sample size, must be to be "large enough" for the central limit theorem to apply. For some distributions (such as the binomial distribution where p and q are both reasonably large) the normal curve is a good approximation even when the samples are relatively small. (In particular, the normal curve approximation is acceptable whenever both np and nq are greater than five. For example, if $n = 30$, the approximation is reasonably good for p in the range one sixth to five sixths.) For other distributions (such as highly skewed distributions, illustrated by a binomial in which either p or q is very small) the normal curve will be a good approximation to the true sampling distribution only in rather large samples. If $p = 0.001$, for example, a success occurs only one time in 1000 in the population. In this case an n of 5000 or more is required before the normal curve is a good approximation.

Mathematically, the central limit theorem is based on the idea that n, the sample size, can be made infinitely large (that is, larger than *any* arbitrarily large number). In the terminology of calculus, the sampling distribution is normal *in the limit*. This means that the *proof* of the theorem (that is, its mathematical derivation as distinct from experimental evidence in its favor) shows that it *must* be true when n is infinitely large. In short, the mathematical argument does not really help us to decide how large is large enough. In general, then, if we do not know the form of the distribution of the variable in the population, or at least something about this form, we cannot always tell whether or not to depend upon the central limit theorem.

Statisticians have developed two ways around this problem. One is to begin with the assumption that the distribution of Y in the population has some form that is known. Usually, it is assumed that Y, itself, is normally distributed. This approach leads to what may be called *parametric statistical inference* (meaning inference based upon assumptions about parameters or population distributions). The most elaborately developed system of inference using this approach is what is generally called *analysis of variance*. (The variance is one of the two parameters needed to describe a normal distribution precisely.) The other approach is to seek sampling distributions, either exact or approximate, that apply in particular situations and whose characteristics can be studied carefully in those situations. Tests developed using this approach are called *nonparametric tests* (or distribution-free tests) because of the absence of assumptions about the distribution of the variable in question. For the most part the tests to be presented in this chapter are of this latter type. Each test is a test of the hypothesis that two variables are independent of each other (that is, are *not* related to each other) in the population we are sampling. These tests are illustrative of various approaches to the problem of testing the hypothesis of zero association. Many other tests of this hypothesis have been developed but will not be presented here.

At this point it is important to understand a technical problem that is often a bit confusing to the beginning student. The hypothesis that two variables are independent of each other is equivalent to the hypothesis that there is *no relationship* between these variables. In Part II of this book we discussed various ways of measuring the amount of relationship using measures such as ϕ, γ, τ', d_{yx}, and r. At first glance, then, it would appear that the best way to test the hypothesis of independence would be to test the hypothesis that one or another of these measures is *zero*. Sometimes such tests are appropriate. We shall show, for example, how to test the hypothesis that the correlation coefficient is zero in a population. In many other situations, however, we do not proceed in this way, usually for one of two reasons. First, many measures of association or relationship contain some restricting assumption that we do *not* want to include in the test. For example, r is a measure of the *linear* relationship between variables not just relationship. Second, the sampling distribution of a particular measure of association may be unknown.

These considerations have led statisticians, in many instances, to develop special measures of the extent to which a sample outcome differs from the outcome expected under the null hypothesis of independence. The measures have been developed because their sampling distributions can be determined at least approximately. Thus, from the point of view of statistical inference, they are quite convenient. However, these measures usually have very unfortunate properties when they are interpreted as indications of the amount of association. This is where the confusion arises. We have one set of measures that we use when we want to talk about how much association or relationship there is in a table and another set of measures that we use when we want to decide whether the amount of association we have found in the sample deviates by more than chance from no association. The two sets of measures, in general, cannot be interchanged. Ideally, there should only be a single set but this ideal set is not in existence. Thus, you must be prepared to learn a double set and to keep them separate. One set, which you have already learned, measures the amount of association. The other set, which we shall present here, measures the deviation between a sample outcome and the outcome expected if the hypothesis of zero association is true.

12.2 THE CHI SQUARE TEST:
INDEPENDENCE BETWEEN TWO ATTRIBUTES

The simplest measure of the extent to which a sample table deviates from the table that would be expected given independence is called *chi square*, and is written χ^2. Unfortunately, the term chi square is used in two different senses. First, it is used for this measure of discrepancy. Second, it is the name of a sampling distribution. However, the measure called chi square proves to be approximately distributed according to the chi square distribution, so the two uses are quite closely related to each other. Let us consider, first, the measure of discrepancy called chi square.

Chi Square as a Measure of the Difference Between Observation and Expectation Given Independence

In Chapter 8 we showed how to calculate expected values in a contingency table assuming independence. We called these expected frequencies E_{ij} and showed that

$$E_{ij} = \frac{n_{i.}n_{.j}}{n}$$

where the numerator frequencies are the row and column totals and the denominator frequency is the grand total in the entire table. We then introduced the concept δ_{ij}, which is simply the difference between the observed frequency in a cell and this expected frequency. Symbolically,

$$\delta_{ij} = n_{ij} - E_{ij}$$

Finally, we showed how to combine these cell differences into a single measure of departure from independence called ϕ^2. The formula for this measure is

$$\phi^2 = \frac{1}{n} \sum \frac{\delta_{ij}^2}{E_{ij}}$$

where we sum over all cells. (To refresh your memory on these points study Tables 8.3 and 8.4 and the accompanying textual discussion.)

Since ϕ^2 is the sum of various quantities divided by n it is essentially an average of those quantities. That is, it expresses the deviation *per individual* in the sample. It turns out that a better way to study chance fluctuation involves computing the total deviation in the table rather than the deviation per individual. This measure of total deviation is called *chi square*. Symbolically, we have

$$\chi^2 = n\phi^2 = \sum \frac{\delta_{ij}^2}{E_{ij}}$$

where we sum over all cells.

Before turning to the sampling distribution of this measure let us consider an example of its computation. In a sample of Baptist and Methodist pastors, Johnson (1966) reports the following table (see Table 12.1)

Table 12.1   Political preference of Liberal, Neo-Orthodox, and Conservative pastors, Oregon

	Liberals	Neo-Orthodox	Conservatives	Total
Republican	30	9	150	189
Any other	39	18	38	95
Total	69	27	188	284

SOURCE: Johnson, 1966. Adapted from Table 4, p. 203.

Calculations for chi square

ROW	COLUMN	n_{ij}	E_{ij}	$(n_{ij} - E_{ij})$ δ_{ij}	δ_{ij}^2	δ_{ij}^2/E_{ij}
1	1	30	45.9	−15.9	252.81	5.51
1	2	9	18.0	− 9.0	81.00	4.50
1	3	150	125.1	24.9	620.01	4.96
2	1	39	23.1	15.9	252.81	10.94
2	2	18	9.0	9.0	81.00	9.00
2	3	38	62.9	−24.9	620.01	9.86
					Sum	$44.77 = \chi^2$

showing the relationship (if any) between political conservatism and religious conservatism. The computational procedure for chi square is very similar to that for ϕ^2, of course. As indicated in the table, the first step is to calculate the expected frequency for each cell. Next we subtract each expected frequency from the corresponding observed frequency and then square the result. At this point we have calculated δ^2_{ij} for each cell. Next, we divide each of these figures by E_{ij} and then sum these quotients. The result is *chi square*. To distinguish this calculated measure of deviation from the sampling distribution of the same name this measure is often called the *observed value of chi square*.

Chi Square as a Sampling Distribution

Various summary measures of discrepancy, such as the one just presented, are distributed in random samples approximately as what is called the chi square distribution. This statement applies, of course, only when the samples are from a population in which the variables are independent of each other. Actually, the chi square distribution is a family of distributions, which differ from each other in a systematic way. This family of sampling distributions is summarized in a chi square table. The complete table is presented as Table 4 in the Appendix. Each row in the table represents a different distribution. The element that determines precisely which chi square distribution applies in a given case is called the number of degrees of freedom (*d.f.*) in the contingency table. This concept is quite important in statistics and, therefore, is worth a brief digression.

The concept of degrees of freedom refers to the number of quantities that are free to vary, given that certain other quantities have already been identified. For example, consider the following general equation:

$$A + B = C$$

In this equation, as it stands, both A and B are free to vary, meaning that we can put any quantity in the place of A and any quantity in the place of B and legitimately call the sum of those two quantities C. Suppose that we specify the value of C beforehand; in particular, suppose that $C = 100$. Our equation reads

$$A + B = 100$$

In this equation, only one of the two quantities A and B is free to vary. For example, if we replace A with a specific quantity we immediately fix B also because $B = 100 - A$. Similarly, if we choose a number for B we also fix A because $A = 100 - B$. Only one of these two quantities is "free"; the other is fixed by that free quantity and the fact that the value of C has already been given. In this equation, then, there is *one degree of freedom*.

This idea can easily be generalized. Consider the equation,

$$A + B + C = 100$$

Here, any two of the quantities may vary but the third is then fixed. Suppose we freely choose A and B, for example. Then C is given because $C = 100 - A - B$. Notice that, in general, if the sum of a single column of numbers is given then that column contains one fewer degree of freedom than there are numbers.

In a general contingency table there are r rows and c columns. In computing the expected frequencies for the cells we assume that we already know the marginal totals; that is, the row and column sums. Given that we know these marginal frequencies, there are only a certain number of cell frequencies that are free to vary, since the rest can be computed by subtraction. In particular, the number of degrees of freedom in a contingency table is

$$d.f. = (r - 1)(c - 1)$$

In words, the degrees of freedom equal the cross product of one less than the *number of rows* (r) and one less than the *number of columns* (c). In Table 12.1, for example, there are two rows and three columns. This table, therefore, contains $(2-1)(3-1) = 2$ degrees of freedom. The student should confirm this fact by attempting to fix any two cell frequencies, not both in the same row or the same column, without at the same time fixing all of the others by subtraction. (It cannot be done.)

Let us consider the table of the chi square distribution. Degrees of freedom are listed down the left-hand side and the probability of obtaining a given chi square, or any larger chi square, is listed along the top. The cells of this table contain the values of chi square that correspond to the levels of probability listed along the top. Table 12.2 presents a portion of the chi square table and explains a typical entry. Notice that the chi square distribution is presented in the form of a table in just the opposite way as the normal distribution. In the normal distribution the cell values were areas (that is, probabilities) and the z scores were listed at the side. In the table of chi square, the probabilities are listed along the top margin and the values of chi square are listed in the cells. (Note that the listed values of chi square in its table correspond to the critical deviations discussed in connection with the normal curve in Chapter 10.) The reason for the arrangement in the chi square table is that we ordinarily use this table only when we are testing an hypothesis. In such tests we fix the basic probability level before we begin and call it α. Then, we ask: "Given α what is the corresponding value of chi square?" The table is constructed to answer this question. It is convenient to refer to the value of chi square in the table as the "table value of chi square" or as χ_α^2, since it is the chi square that corresponds to a given level of significance.

Remember that chi square is a sampling distribution. When we use a

Table 12.2   Part of the table of chi square

d.f.	$P = 0.05$	$P = 0.01$
1	3.841	6.635*
2	5.991	9.210
3	7.815	11.341
4	9.488	13.277
5	11.070	15.086
.	.	.
10	18.307	23.209
.	.	.
20	31.410	37.566

* If we get a chi square in our sample as large or larger than 6.635 with only one degree of freedom, then we have a sample table that would arise only one percent of the time or less if the variables were independent or not associated in the population.

sampling distribution we cumulate the probabilities of the individual outcomes from the most deviant to the least deviant, relative to the hypothesis. In the table of chi square these individual outcomes have already been cumulated. If the null hypothesis is true we anticipate relatively small deviations between what we observe and what we expect; that is, we anticipate relatively small values of chi square. Large values are quite unlikely to appear when sampling from such a population. When we get a large value, then, we are inclined to account for that occurrence on the grounds that H_0 is false rather than on the grounds that a chance fluctuation has occurred around a true H_0. The table of chi square tells us *how large* our *computed* chi square must be before we can reject H_0 at any given level of significance.

Using Chi Square to Test the Hypothesis of Zero Association

Let us now summarize the way in which we test the hypothesis that X and Y are independent, using both the computed value (symbolized by χ^2) and the theoretical distribution as tabled (whose values are symbolized by χ_α^2). The basic steps are

1. Select a level of significance, α.
2. Use α and the size of the contingency table (that is, its degrees of freedom, d.f.) to find the theoretical value of chi square, χ_α^2, from the table. This value is the critical deviation between evidence and hypothesis. It will be exceeded only α proportion of the time if H_0 is true.
3. Draw a random sample and calculate chi square from the observations. We now have χ^2.
4. Compare χ^2 with χ_α^2. If the computed value is equal to or larger than the theoretical value, reject H_0; otherwise, treat the evidence as consistent with the hypothesis, H_0.

For Table 12.1, for example, we would reject the hypothesis of independence at the .01 level of significance because our observed chi square (44.77) is larger than the table value (9.21).

Limitations on the Use of Chi Square as a Test of Independence

As we now know, chi square refers both to a number we calculate in a sample to measure the deviation between observation and expectation and to the variable in a particular sampling distribution. Unfortunately, these two meanings are not quite identical. The *exact* sampling distribution of the computed value is *not* the distribution that is called chi square. The chi square distribution is only a close approximation to that exact distribution. There are certain conditions, however, in which the approximation is *not* close. The user of this test, then, must be careful to avoid these situations.

A simple rule of thumb describes when it is safe to use the chi square table to test the hypothesis of independence. This rule states that: the chi square test may be used whenever all *expected* frequencies are at least five. (For a somewhat more complete statement, as well as some alternative rules of thumb, see Walker and Lev, 1953, p. 107. To see what to do when this condition is not met, see *Fisher's exact test,* which is described in the following section.)

In the event that the expected frequencies in a given table do not meet these criteria we cannot use the test on that particular table. One solution to this problem is to reduce the size of the table, either by combining some rows or some columns. Such a combination of rows was made, for example, in Table 12.1. In the original table political preferences were listed as

> Republican
> Democratic
> Both equally

We combined the latter two categories into a residual category ("Any other") because the expected frequencies for Neo-Orthodox ministers were less than five for these categories. If the general table has been reduced to a 2×2 table and there still is an expected frequency that is too small, special treatment is indicated. This special case will be considered in the next section on Fisher's exact test.

Two other limitations on chi square should be considered. First, chi square should be used only with two-tailed hypotheses. The two tails (represented by positive associations as well as by negative associations) are combined by the act of squaring the deviations, $n_{ij} - E_{ij}$. There is no easy way to separate these two tails. Second, chi square is best used when testing independence between attributes. Although it can be used to test independence at any level of measurement of the variables, it is usually the case that there are better tests to use when the variables are ordinal or interval. The reason is that the value of chi square is not affected by rearrangements of the rows or columns. These rows and columns can be presented in any order and the computed value of chi square will be the same. This property of interchangeability among categories applies only to attributes because the categories of both ordinal and interval variables must be arranged so as to display the order among them. The value of chi square is independent of this order, which means that the test uses all of the available information in the sample only in the case of attributes. In the case of ordinal and interval variables there is some information left over. It is available in the sample but not used in the test. The more appropriate tests of independence (to be described later in this chapter) take advantage of this extra information. (There are some special situations, such as when testing for a curvilinear departure from independence with ordinal information, in which chi square is the best available test, however.) One final point is important: Chi square is sensitive to grouping, so that if you divide the categories differently, you may get a different answer.

CHI SQUARE AND THE 2 × 2 TABLE

In the 2 × 2 table a slightly different formula is used to compute chi square because it gives a better approximation to the underlying distribution. This formula is

$$\chi^2 = \sum \frac{(|\delta_{ij}| - 0.5)^2}{E_{ij}}$$

where we sum over all cells. In this formula the vertical lines mean the absolute value of the δ_{ij} figures. The absolute value is, of course, the corresponding positive number. Thus, if δ_{ij} is already positive its absolute value is the same number. On the other hand, if δ_{ij} is negative its absolute value has the same digits but with the opposite sign. The formula, in general, tells us to subtract 0.5 from each absolute difference before squaring. This adjustment is called *Yate's correction.*

Because of the simplicity of a 2 × 2 table it is convenient to compute chi square from a formula that uses a different set of symbols. The four cell frequencies in the table are listed as *a, b, c,* and *d.* The entire body of the table can then be written

a	b	$a + b$
c	d	$c + d$

$$a + c \quad b + d \qquad n = a + b + c + d$$

Using this notation, we have

$$\chi^2 = \frac{n(ad - bc)^2}{(a + b)(c + d)(a + c)(b + d)}$$

or, using Yate's correction,

$$\chi^2 = \frac{n(|ad - bc| - n/2)^2}{(a + b)(c + d)(a + c)(b + d)}$$

Table 12.3 (p. 264) illustrates these computations.

One final note of caution about chi square is needed. Chi square is a measure of the total discrepancy between observation and expectation given independence. It is *not* a measure of the amount of association in a table, however. In a 2 × 2 table, as we have seen, ϕ^2 is a sensible measure of the amount of association and in larger tables C^2 is an adequate measure. The reason that chi square is *not* a measure of association is that its value de-

**Table 12.3   Organizational size and the division of labor
in small bureaucracies**

		Small agencies	Larger agencies	Total
	Advanced	13	38	51
Division of	Rudimentary	79	21	100
labor	Total	92	59	151

SOURCE: Blau, Heydebrand, and Stauffer, 1966, adapted
from Table 4.

Calculations for χ^2:

$$\chi^2 = \frac{151(13 \times 21 - 38 \times 79)^2}{(51)(100)(92)(59)}$$

$$= \frac{151(273 - 3002)^2}{(5100)(5428)}$$

$$= \frac{151(2729)^2}{27,682,800}$$

$$= 40.62$$

Using Yate's correction, the computation is

$$= \frac{151(2729 - 75.5)^2}{27,682,800}$$

$$= 38.41$$

pends in part upon how big a sample we have taken and also upon how
big a table (number of degrees of freedom) we construct. You must be
careful to avoid the mistake (made, unfortunately, by many people) of
thinking of chi square as a measure of association. The proper measures
are those we discussed in Chapter 8.

12.3   FISHER'S EXACT TEST

Earlier in this chapter we pointed out that the computed value of chi
square is only approximately distributed as chi square and that the approximation breaks down when the expected frequencies are very small. In the
case of tables with more than one degree of freedom, the proper procedure
to follow in this situation is to reduce the size of the table by combining
categories. The problem remains as to what to do when the expected fre-

quencies are too small in a 2×2 table, for this table cannot be reduced to a smaller one. This problem is solved by what is known as *Fisher's exact test*. This test is based on the exact sampling distribution of a 2×2 bivariate table when both sets of marginal frequencies are considered to be fixed or known in advance. Using the *a, b, c, d* designation for the cell frequencies (see the preceding section) we have, as the exact probability of getting any particular table given that X and Y are independent in the population,

$$P(a,b,c,d) = \frac{(a+b)!(c+d)!(a+c)!(b+d)!}{n!\,a!\,b!\,c!\,d!}$$

The left-hand side of this equation should be read "the probability of getting any particular set of cell frequencies in a 2×2 table if the variables are independent." The expression on the right-hand side, although it looks rather formidable, is basically just an arithmetic function of the four cell frequencies. This formula gives, for the 2×2 table, the same information that the binomial formula gives for the sampling distribution of a single dichotomous variable.

To perform a test using this formula we go through precisely the same procedure that we follow in developing any test. First, we select the level of significance, α. Next, we list all of the possible ways that the sample might come out. Third, we compute the probability of the sample occurring in each possible way (using the above formula). Fourth, we arrange the possible outcomes in order by the size of the deviation from H_0. Fifth, we cumulate the probabilities until we reach α, starting with the most deviant outcome. All outcomes in this extreme group form what is called the rejection region. Sixth, and last, we look at our sample and determine whether or not it falls into the rejection region. The following example will illustrate this procedure.

Let us suppose that in a sample of ten observations we found this distribution of X and Y:

$$X$$

2	4	6
3	1	4
5	5	10

Y labels the rows.

We note that the *expected* frequencies in the second row are both two $(4 \times 5/20 = 2)$, which means we are below the minimum required for the use of the chi square approximation. Therefore, we decide to use Fisher's exact test. The first step is to select α. We decide to use the conventional level of significance, namely, $\alpha = 0.05$. The second step is to list all of the possible ways that the sample might turn out. To do so, it is convenient to imagine the table without the cell frequencies:

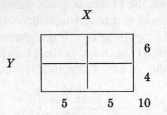

The marginal totals are given. To write down all of the possible outcomes is to write down all of the possible cell frequencies that could occur, given these marginals. In a 2 × 2 table, with the marginals given, there is only one remaining degree of freedom—which means that we need specify only one cell frequency in order to specify all four of them. In other words, it is sufficient to list all of the frequencies that could appear in any one cell, say the upper-left-hand cell, where the frequency is called a. The largest frequency that we could get in this cell is 5, since $a + c = 5$ and c cannot be negative. We could also get: a 4, a 3, a 2, and a 1 in this cell. These are other possible outcomes. Notice that we cannot get a 0 in this cell because then b would have to be 6, but $b + d = 5$, and d cannot be negative. In short, all of the possible outcomes are represented by the possible values of a. The list of outcomes is

$$a = 5$$
$$= 4$$
$$= 3$$
$$= 2$$
$$= 1$$

The next step is to compute the probability of getting each of these outcomes under the assumption that the variables are independent. To accomplish this objective, we construct each possible table and then use the formula.

5	1	6
0	4	4
5	5	10

$$P(a = 5) = \frac{6!\ 4!\ 5!\ 5!}{10!\ 5!\ 1!\ 0!\ 4!}$$

$$= \frac{6!\ 4!\ 5!\ 5!}{10!} \times \frac{1}{5!\ 1!\ 0!\ 4!}$$

$$= \frac{720 \times 24 \times 120 \times 120}{3,628,800} \times \frac{1}{120 \times 1 \times 1 \times 24}$$

$$= \frac{248,832,000}{3,628,800} \times \frac{1}{2880}$$

$$= 68.571 \frac{1}{2880}$$

$$= \frac{68.571}{2880}$$

$$= 0.024$$

4	2	6
1	3	4
5	5	10

$$P(a = 4) = \frac{6! \; 4! \; 5! \; 5!}{10!} \times \frac{1}{4! \; 2! \; 1! \; 3!}$$

$$= 68.571 \frac{1}{24 \times 2 \times 1 \times 6}$$

$$= \frac{68.571}{288}$$

$$= 0.238$$

3	3	6
2	2	4
5	5	10

$$P(a = 3) = \frac{6! \; 4! \; 5! \; 5!}{10!} \times \frac{1}{3! \; 3! \; 2! \; 2!}$$

$$= 68.571 \frac{1}{6 \times 6 \times 2 \times 2}$$

$$= \frac{68.571}{144}$$

$$= 0.476$$

2	4	6
3	1	4
5	5	10

$$P(a = 2) = \frac{6! \; 4! \; 5! \; 5!}{10!} \times \frac{1}{2! \; 4! \; 3! \; 1!}$$

$$= \frac{68.571}{2 \times 24 \times 6}$$

$$= \frac{68.571}{288}$$

$$= 0.238$$

1	5	6
4	0	4
5	5	10

$$P(a = 1) = 68.571 \frac{1}{1! \; 5! \; 4! \; 0!}$$

$$= \frac{68.571}{1 \times 120 \times 24 \times 1}$$

$$= \frac{68.571}{2880}$$

$$= 0.024$$

These computations·are not as difficult as they look since most of the elements remain the same from one table to the next. These constant figures are all of the marginal totals and the grand total. Hence, the computation is this ratio (68.571 for our illustration) times the function of the cell frequencies. We may summarize these results as follows:

a	$P(a)$
5	0.024
4	0.238
3	0.476
2	0.238
1	0.024

The next step is to arrange these outcomes in order by deviation from H_0 and then cumulate the probabilities. If H_0 is true (that is, if the variables are independent) then we would expect a to equal 3 (that is, $E_{11} = 3$). Using that information, we proceed as follows:

a	$P(a)$	$CumP(a)$
5	0.024	
1	0.024	0.048
4	0.238	
2	0.238	0.524
3	0.476	1.000

Notice that when two outcomes are equally deviant we do not cumulate until we are through the set of "tied" outcomes. The reason is that we cannot tell which outcome should be listed first and, hence, must treat them as a pair.

Now we compare the cumulated probabilities with α and identify the rejection region. In this case the largest cumulated probability that is below $\alpha = 0.05$ is 0.048, a cumulation over the outcomes $a = 5$ and $a = 1$. Therefore, we agree to reject our hypothesis whenever our sample result is either of these outcomes. Otherwise, we will treat the sample evidence as consistent with the hypothesis.

The final step is to look back at our original table. We note that in it, $a = 2$. We see that this outcome is not in the rejection region and so our conclusion is to accept (tentatively) H_0. Remember, of course, that we may have failed to reject H_0 only because our sample was too small to detect whatever relationship between X and Y existed. On the other hand, had we been able to reject H_0, the sample size would have been entirely adequate. That is, we can reject just as positively with a sample of ten as with a sample of 1000 but with a very small sample we must be much more tentative in accepting H_0.

12.4 THE KOLMOGOROV–SMIRNOV TEST: INDEPENDENCE BETWEEN A DICHOTOMY AND AN ORDINAL VARIABLE

In Chapter 3 we discussed the basic properties of an ordinal variable and emphasized the importance of *cumulation*. Since the categories of an ordinal variable are in order, it is meaningful to consider the number of objects that are less than or equal to a given value. Cumulation, of course, may also be performed on the proportions that are derived from the frequencies. We then have the proportion of objects that are less than or equal to a given value. The set of cumulated proportions is the basic summary of the distribution of one ordinal variable. Now consider a bivariate table consisting of an ordinal variable (Y) cross-classified with a dichotomy (X). Each *conditional* distribution of Y may be summarized by its cumulated proportions. These conditional distributions may now be compared with each other. If the cumulated conditional distributions are identical, there is no relationship between the variables. To the extent that the cumulated distributions differ, however, the variables are related. This idea provides us with a basic way both to measure the extent to which the distributions differ and also to test the significance of whatever difference we find in a sample. The method was developed by the statisticians whose names identify the test.

In Chapter 3 we used a lower-case letter, f, to stand for the frequency in a category and an upper-case letter, F, to stand for the cumulated frequency up to and including the category. In the same spirit, we will let p_s stand for the proportion of cases in a category and P_s stand for the cumulated proportion. We have

$$p_s = f/n$$
$$P_s = F/n$$

We also need to indicate which conditional distribution we are representing. Since there are only two categories of X there will be only two conditional distributions of Y. It is convenient to refer to these using the subscripts "1" and "2." Thus, P_{s_1} is the column of cumulated proportions in the conditional distribution specified by X_1 and P_{s_2} is the corresponding column in which X_2 is given.

In general, we compare the P_{s_1} values with the corresponding P_{s_2}

values to determine whether or not the variables are related. Of course, several individual comparisons are possible. We must summarize these individual comparisons into a single number so that we can seek the sampling distribution of that number. In this case, a sensible summary number is the largest difference that we can find. This difference is called D and is defined as

$$D_s = \text{maximum } |P_{s_1} - P_{s_2}|$$

where the vertical straight lines refer, as before, to the absolute value of the difference. D_s is our measure of the extent to which the two conditional distributions of Y differ.

Two variables are independent if the conditional distributions of one, given the other, are identical. In other words, the hypothesis that X and Y are independent in some population is equivalent to the hypothesis that $D = 0$ in that population. In short, we test the hypothesis:

$$H_0: D = 0$$

Now consider sampling from this population. In any given sample we can find the maximum difference, which we call D_s. D_s will not be zero (usually), even when we are sampling from a population in which D is zero. Random sampling fluctuations will produce some discrepancies between the two conditional distributions in any one sample. The problem is to identify the sampling distribution of D_s under the assumption that H_0 is true. Once this sampling distribution is identified we can develop a rejection region that will consist of those D_s values that are so large that they could not reasonably have arisen on a chance basis. It turns out that this sampling distribution can be represented by a simple criterion, provided only that each conditional distribution is represented by at least 40 observations in the sample. In particular, H_0 should be rejected whenever D_s is equal to or larger than

$$1.22 \sqrt{\frac{n_1 + n_2}{n_1 n_2}} \qquad \text{when } \alpha = 0.10$$

$$1.36 \sqrt{\frac{n_1 + n_2}{n_1 n_2}} \qquad \text{when } \alpha = 0.05$$

$$1.63 \sqrt{\frac{n_1 + n_2}{n_1 n_2}} \qquad \text{when } \alpha = 0.01$$

$$1.95 \sqrt{\frac{n_1 + n_2}{n_1 n_2}} \qquad \text{when } \alpha = 0.001$$

Table 12.4 Alienation by cultural origin

			Background	
	MEXICAN		ANGLO-AMERICAN	
Alienation	f	p_{s_1}	f	p_{s_2}
4 (high)	6	0.07	8	0.05
3	25	0.31	30	0.20
2	20	0.25	50	0.34
1	14	0.17	25	0.17
0	16	0.20	36	0.24
Total	81	1.00	149	1.00

SOURCE: Adapted from Zurcher, Meadow, and Zurcher, 1965.

In these formulas, n_1 is the number of observations in the X_1 conditional distribution and n_2 in the X_2 conditional; $n_1 + n_2 = n$.

A recent study of alienation provides an illustration of the use of this test. The basic data are presented in Table 12.4. To perform the test we first decide on our level of significance. This time, for the sake of variety, let us choose the 0.10 level. (Remember that this choice is up to the researcher.) The next step is to cumulate the sample proportions and note the difference between them at each level of alienation. We develop a worksheet that would have approximately the form of Table 12.5

Table 12.5 Worksheet for test alienation

Alienation	P_{s_1}	P_{s_2}	$\lvert P_{s_1} - P_{s_2} \rvert$
4	1.00	1.00	0.00
3	0.93	0.95	0.02
2	0.62	0.75	0.13 = max = D_s
1	0.37	0.41	0.04
0	0.20	0.24	0.04

From these figures we can immediately locate $D_s = 0.13$ by inspection, since it is the largest of the absolute differences. Now we determine the significance of this sample value by using the formula listed earlier. With $\alpha = 0.10$, D_s must be at least

$$1.22 \sqrt{\frac{81 + 149}{(81)(149)}} = 1.22(0.138) = 0.168$$

before we can reject H_0. Since our sample value is less than this figure we treat the data as consistent with the hypothesis. This tentative acceptance means either that alienation and cultural origin actually are independent of each other in the population from which this sample was drawn or that the sample was too small to detect whatever difference there was in the population. (In the original study the authors used a more elaborate classification scheme and a different test. They found a significant difference, apparently because Mexican nationals differ from Mexican Americans. We combined these two groups for this illustrative analysis. This fact clearly illustrates why accepting H_0 must be only tentative, at best.) (For small-sample procedures in connection with this test see Siegel, 1956, or Blalock, 1960.)

12.5 THE RANDOMIZATION TEST:
INDEPENDENCE BETWEEN A DICHOTOMY
AND AN INTERVAL VARIABLE

This test is appropriate whenever the dependent variable is an interval variable and the independent variable is a dichotomy. In this situation we already know how to make a test of the significance of the difference between the conditional means, provided that the sample is large enough. In particular, we use the normal curve as an approximation to the underlying sampling distribution of the difference. What we need is a procedure that will apply to small samples. In traditional statistics this problem is solved by the *t-test*. Many years ago a statistician who worked for an English brewery discovered the exact sampling distribution of a difference between means, provided that the variable involved is itself normally distributed. In writing his paper on this test he called himself "Student" because he preferred to remain anonymous—and the test ever since has been known as Student's t-test. It is, in a sense, the classic example of a *parametric* statistical test. The sampling distribution involved is derived from an assumption about the form of the population distribution.

There has been a tendency to avoid this test in sociology because of the unwillingness of many researchers to make the necessary assumption about the distribution of Y, but for a long time there were no acceptable alternatives to the t-test. In recent years, however, an alternative test has been developed, which is very ingenious, which involves no assumptions about parameters, and which is every bit as effective as the t-test. Indeed, under fairly general conditions, the t-test proves to be a close approximation to this test. The nonparametric test that possesses these qualities is called the *randomization test*. It is one of the most elegant tests in all of statistics, for it is both extremely simple and very powerful. In discussing this test we shall be able, once again, to see just how a sampling distribution is created. The one problem presented by the test is that it is computationally cumbersome when the samples are large. In that case we fall back on the normal curve approximation.

The hypothesis to be tested is

$$H_0: \mu_1 = \mu_2$$

where μ_1 and μ_2 are the means of the two conditional distributions of Y. To build the test, however, we make the slightly stronger assumption that the distribution of Y is completely independent of X, which is to say that the two conditional distributions are identical. (The hypothesis, as such, only asserts that the means of these two distributions are equal.)

To develop the test we shall consider a very small sample. Suppose that we have observed eight individuals, of whom three were female and five were male. Sex is the independent variable, X. In addition, we noted the age of each person, which is our dependent variable, Y. The ages of the people in our sample are

Girls	Boys
13	17
10	14
8	21
	11
	12

We wish to test the hypothesis that the mean ages of boys and girls are the same in the population from which we drew the sample. We assume that the distribution of age is the same among boys and girls if H_0 is true. If the conditional distributions are identical, then the proportion of girls who are one particular age is identical to the proportion of boys who are that particular age. Under this condition, it is purely a matter of chance as to which sex occurred with which age in our sample. For example, the first girl listed was 13 and the first boy was 17. Under H_0, we would have been just as likely to have observed a girl who was 17 first and a boy who was 13. In other words, under H_0 whether a particular age occurs in the sample of girls or in the sample of boys is purely a random matter.

Using this idea, we may construct a sampling distribution by considering the ages to be fixed but the sex associated with each age observation to be a variable. Keeping the total number of girls the same as in the existing sample, we can consider all of the possible arrangements of the ages with respect to the two groups, boys and girls. For example, one arrangement would be for the three youngest observations all to be girls, another for the three oldest observations all to be girls, and so on. The formula that tells us the total number of arrangements we can get is the combinatorial formula we used in connection with the binomial expansion. Letting n stand for the size of the sample and n_1 for the number of girls in it we have

$$\text{Number of possible arrangements} = \binom{n}{n_i} = \binom{8}{3} = \frac{8!}{3!5!} = 56$$

Remember, in constructing a sampling distribution and using it to test hypotheses we first identify all of the possible ways that the sample could come out and find the probability associated with each of these ways if H_0 is true. Then we form an array of these outcomes, beginning with the one furthest from the expected outcome under H_0 and working in to the closest one to that expected under H_0. We cumulate the probabilities in this array until we reach our preselected α and consider all sample outcomes in the cumulated portion as the rejection region.

Table 12.6   Preliminary list for array

| Sample of Three Girls | | | Sample of Five Boys | | |
OBSERVATIONS	SUM	MEAN	SUM	MEAN	DIFFERENCE BETWEEN MEANS
8, 10, 11	29	9.7	77	15.4	−5.7
8, 10, 12	30	10.0	76	15.2	−5.2
8, 10, 13	31	10.3	75	15.0	−4.7
8, 10, 14	32	10.7	74	14.8	−4.1
.					
8, 11, 12	31	10.3	75	15.0	−4.7
8, 11, 13	32	10.7	74	14.8	−4.1
.					
.					
10, 17, 21	48	16.0	58	11.6	4.4
.					
11, 17, 21	49	16.3	57	11.4	4.9
.					
.					
12, 17, 21	50	16.7	56	11.2	5.5
13, 14, 21	48	16.0	58	11.6	4.4
13, 17, 21	51	17.0	55	11.0	6.0
14, 17, 21	52	17.3	54	10.8	6.5

In this example, we have identified 56 possible ways that our sample might have come out. We note that each of these ways is *equally likely* if H_0 is true. Accordingly, we form an array beginning with the most remote outcomes. Since H_0 is that $\mu_1 = \mu_2$, the most remote outcomes will have the largest (absolute) value for $D_s = |\bar{X}_1 - \bar{X}_2|$. It is best to form the array in two steps. First, we form a preliminary list of all of the outcomes which we believe to be extreme, remembering to include both tails. Note that we only need list those ages appearing in the smaller sample because the sum of the observations in the other sample can then be determined by subtraction (using the total for all observations). Our preliminary list might look something like Table 12.6.

We started this preliminary list with the smallest three age observations in the sample of girls. Then we took the next higher observation and substituted it for the last of the three listed, continuing in this way until we ran out of observations (the last few in this series are not listed but are represented by dots). At this point, we increased the middle observation by one observation and repeated the process. We continued until we had listed the largest three ages in the sample of girls at the bottom of the chart. If we had listed all of the intervening cases, we would have had 56 rows in this listing. However, we omitted many of the rows with smaller differences. All of the relatively extreme outcomes have been listed.

Once the preliminary list has been constructed the job of creating the sampling distribution and the rejection region is almost complete. We now make a second list, which is an array of the outcomes, beginning with the largest absolute difference between the means, as in Table 12.7.

The final step is to use the cumulated probability column in relation to α to identify those outcomes that would lead to rejection of H_0. For example, if $\alpha = 0.05$, then only the first two outcomes in the list would be in the rejection region, whereas if $\alpha = 0.10$, the first five outcomes would be in the rejection region.

Table 12.7 Array of outcomes

| | *Array of Outcomes for Girls* | | | |
$\|D_s\|$	SMALL TAIL	LARGE TAIL	PROBABILITY	CUMULATED PROBABILITY
6.5		14, 17, 21	0.018	0.018
6.0		13, 17, 21	0.018	0.036
5.7	8, 10, 11		0.018	0.054
5.5		12, 17, 21	0.018	0.072
5.2	8, 10, 12		0.018	0.090
4.9		11, 17, 21	0.018	0.108

Look back at the sample with which we started. In this sample, the girls' ages were 8, 10, and 13. We do not find this sample in either the 0.05 or the 0.10 rejection region so we tentatively accept H_0 and state that the difference we observed between the girls' and the boys' ages *could* be due to chance. (Obviously, we must once again be conscious of the fact that to say it *could* be due to chance is not the same as saying that it *is* due to chance.)

This procedure is followed in every application of the randomization test. First, we list the relatively more extreme outcomes and then make an array of them from the most extreme down, to find the rejection region. We can tell at once how many outcomes will be in the rejection region by forming the product

$$\alpha \binom{n}{n_1} = \text{number of outcomes in the rejection region}$$

The desired number of outcomes is the largest whole number that is equal to or smaller than this number. In our example, with $\alpha = 0.05$, we have $(0.05)(56) = 2.8$, so there are two outcomes in the rejection region—as we had already discovered. Making this preliminary calculation will aid materially in shortening the labor of constructing the appropriate tables since we need only list a few more outcomes than will be in the rejection region in our preliminary listing. (We list a few more just to be sure that we have not missed any.)

Finally, note that this procedure would be rather tedious, to say the least, if we had a relatively large number of observations. With a sample of 30 girls and 50 boys there would be $\binom{80}{30}$ possible outcomes, which is a number somewhat larger than

$$32,000,000,000,000,000,000,000,000$$

Even writing down only 5 percent of these outcomes would be considered onerous by all but the most compulsive researchers. Fortunately, when the samples get this large the normal curve approximation can be used.

12.6   TESTING THE SIGNIFICANCE OF TAU: INDEPENDENCE BETWEEN TWO ORDINAL VARIABLES

When both variables are ordinal we may test whether or not they are independent of each other by testing the hypothesis, $H_0: \tau = 0$. When dealing with more than ten observations the sampling distribution of T (the sample estimator of τ) will be approximately normal when H_0 is true. The mean or expected value of T will be 0 in this case and the standard deviation of T will be

$$\sigma_T = \sqrt{\frac{2(2n + 5)}{9n(n - 1)}}$$

Using the normal curve theory that we developed in Chapter 10 we know that any observed T equal to or larger than, in absolute value, $z_\alpha(\sigma_T)$ will lead us to reject the hypothesis that $\tau = 0$. (The symbol z_α refers to that z score in the normal curve table that corresponds to the level of significance, α.)

As an example, suppose that we have taken a sample of 100 individuals and calculated T for these observations. We found that $T = 0.17$ and we want to know if this value is large enough to permit us to reject H_0: $\tau = 0$. We decide to use the 0.05 level of significance. The z score corresponding to this level is $z_{0.05} = 1.96$. Next, we calculate σ_T:

$$\sigma_T = \frac{2(2 \times 100 + 5)}{9 \times 100(100 - 1)} = \frac{410}{89,100} = 0.004615 = 0.068$$

Multiplying $z_{0.05}$ and σ_T together we have, as the critical deviation from the hypothesis,

$$z_{0.05}(\sigma_T) = 1.96(0.068) = 0.133$$

Finally, we note that our observed T is larger than the critical deviation so we reject H_0. In other words, we conclude that the variables are related to each other in this population.

12.7 TESTING THE SIGNIFICANCE OF r_{yx}: INDEPENDENCE BETWEEN TWO INTERVAL VARIABLES

We shall conclude this chapter with a brief discussion of the procedure to follow when testing the hypothesis that $\rho_{yx} = 0$, where ρ_{yx} (read "rho yx") refers to the correlation coefficient in the population from which we draw our sample. The correlation that we calculate in our sample we call r_{yx}. (To refresh your memory about correlation and regression you may wish to review Chapter 7 at this point.) The tests to be presented here are examples of *parametric statistical tests* because they are derived from assumptions about the distribution of Y in the population as well as assumptions about the nature of the sampling process. In particular, we must assume the joint distribution of X and Y is a bivariate normal distribution, which means that the conditional distributions of Y given particular values of X are normal and that they all have equal variances. You will remember this latter assumption as the assumption of homoscedasticity.

An extensive discussion of the rationale behind these tests lies well beyond the scope of this book. Basically, each test involves a ratio. These ratios, in turn, involve a sampling distribution, which is called the F distribution. Table 3 in the Appendix is a description of this distribution. Although the theory that leads up to the tests is quite complicated the tests themselves are quite simple. Note that we have used the word "tests" rather than "test," because three related tests are ordinarily performed when studying correlation. Before describing these tests let us see how to read the F table.

The entries in the body of the table of the F distribution are critical deviations in that any ratio calculated from the sample that is larger than the table entry leads to the rejection of H_0. In this respect the table is constructed in the same way as the table of chi square. The important thing to note about the F distribution, however, is that it involves *two* degrees of freedom figures rather than one, as in chi square. These degrees of freedom we call df_1 and df_2. The values of df_1 are written at the top of the columns of the table and the values of df_2 are written to the left of the rows. In each test it is important to know not only the form of the test itself, but also how to calculate the degrees of freedom.

H_0: $\rho_{yx} = 0$

The first test that we ordinarily make in connection with correlation is a test of the hypothesis that there is no linear correlation or that $\rho_{yx} = 0$. We test this hypothesis by calculating r_{yx} in our sample and then finding the F ratio

$$F = \frac{r^2(n - 2)}{(1 - r^2)}$$

where $df_1 = 1$ and $df_2 = n - 2$. In this formula we omitted the subscripts on r for the sake of clarity; these subscripts are always assumed to be y and x. If this calculated value of F is equal to or larger than the table value for the given level of significance than we reject H_0 and conclude that the variables are related to each other linearly.

H_0: $\eta_{yx} = 0$

The second test that we make is a test of the hypothesis that there is no curvilinear relationship between Y and X or that the correlation ratio, η_{yx}, equals zero. We test this hypothesis by calculating E_{yx} from our sample data. (Note that η_{yx} is the value of the correlation ratio in the population and E_{yx} its estimate in the sample. Review the final sections of Chapter 8 for a further discussion of E_{yx}. In Chapter 8 we presented E_{yx} as a measure of relationship between an attribute and an interval variable. Here we use it to describe the curvilinear relationship between two variables. To calculate it in this situation use class intervals of X as categories.)

The F ratio that tests this hypothesis is

$$F = \frac{E^2(df_2)}{(1 - E^2)(df_1)}$$

where $df_1 = k - 1$ and $df_2 = n - k$. The symbol k in this formula refers to the number of class intervals we used to categorize X. Again, if this calculated value of F exceeds the corresponding table value we reject the hypothesis of zero curvilinear relationship.

H_0: $\eta_{yx}^2 - \rho_{yx}^2 = 0$

The third, and last, test that we make is a test of the hypothesis that the relationship between X and Y is *linear*. It is linear if the amount of linear relationship in the population (ρ_{yx}^2) is the same as the amount of curvilinear relationship there (η_{yx}^2). In other words, if $\eta_{yx}^2 - \rho_{yx}^2 = 0$ the relationship is linear. The appropriate F ratio for testing this hypothesis is

$$F = \frac{(E^2 - r^2)\, df_2}{(1 - E^2)\, df_1}$$

where $df_1 = k - 2$ and $df_2 = n - k$. If this calculated F is larger than the corresponding table value we conclude that the relationship between X and Y is *not* linear.

To illustrate the use of these tests consider some data from the 1960 Census referring to census tracts in Birmingham, Ala. In working with tracts in other cities we have noted what seems to be a tendency for tracts that have very few people on them (X) also to have relatively few owner-occupied homes on them. We measure relative owner occupancy by the percent of all housing units that are owner-occupied, which is our dependent variable, Y. To see whether or not the apparent pattern is just a chance fluctuation we decide to test the hypothesis that $\rho_{xy} = 0$ in the city of Birmingham. Accordingly, we analyze the 106 tracts in this city (and its immediate environs) and get the following results:

$$n = 106$$
$$r_{yx}^2 = 0.019$$
$$E_{yx}^2 = 0.117 \qquad \text{where } k = 5$$

We have not shown the computations because we explained how to make them in earlier chapters.

Our first new step is to test the hypothesis that $\rho_{yx} = 0$. We do this by setting up the first F ratio and then comparing it with the corresponding table value. We have

$$F = \frac{0.019(104)}{0.981} = \frac{1.976}{0.981} = 2.01$$

$$df_1 = 1$$
$$df_2 = 104$$
$$F_{0.05} = 3.94 = \text{the critical deviation}$$

To find the table value of F, that is, $F_{0.05}$ above, we first selected α to be 0.05 and then used the degrees of freedom to locate the correct figure in the table. In particular, we looked down the first column (because $df_1 = 1$) and in the row labeled $df_2 = 104$. In the table in the Appendix, of course, this row is missing, so we interpolate between the nearest adjacent rows. The nearest figures are

df_2	$F_{0.05}$
60	4.00
120	3.92

To interpolate we used the formula for linear interpolation. In particular, since 104 is 27 percent of the distance from 120 to 60, the F we want is 27 percent of the distance between 3.92 and 4.00, or is $3.92 + 0.27(0.08) = 3.94$.

Having found the table value we compare it with the observed or computed value and note that the computed value is the smaller. Therefore, we fail to reject H_0 and conclude that our evidence is consistent with the hypothesis that there is no linear relationship between tract population (X) and percent housing units that are owner-occupied (Y).

However, this test alone is really insufficient because it tests only for *linear* relationship. Accordingly, we turn next to the question of whether or not there is any curvilinear relationship and we test the hypothesis that $\eta_{yx}^2 = 0$. We have

$$F = \frac{0.117(101)}{0.883(4)} = \frac{11.817}{3.532} = 3.35$$

$$df_1 = 4$$
$$df_2 = 101$$
$$F_{0.05} = 2.47$$

Comparing F and $F_{0.05}$ we note that in this case the computed value is the larger (3.35 versus 2.47). We therefore reject the hypothesis that there is no curvilinear relationship and conclude that X and Y are related in a curvilinear manner.

At this point it is tempting to stop. Our tests seem to show that there is no linear relationship but some curvilinear relationship. It is very easy to infer (incorrectly) from this evidence that η^2 and ρ^2 must, therefore, differ from each other, without performing that test. Unfortunately, many researchers make this kind of inference even though it is incorrect. The problem again involves the correct interpretation of failing to reject the hypothesis that $\rho_{yx}{}^2 = 0$. Our evidence shows that $\rho_{yx}{}^2$ *could* be zero but that does not mean that it *is* zero. It could also be some other number, presumably a relatively small number somewhere in the vicinity of zero. We know, however, that $\eta_{yx}{}^2$ is *not* zero, but it could also be a relatively small number. In particular, it is perfectly possible that $\rho^2 = \eta^2$. To find out we must perform the third test.

Now we test the hypothesis, H_0: $\rho^2 = \eta^2$. We have

$$F = \frac{(0.117 - 0.019)(101)}{0.883(3)} = \frac{9.898}{2.649} = 3.74$$

$$df_1 = 3$$
$$df_2 = 101$$
$$F_{0.05} = 2.71$$

We see that the observed value is again larger than the table value so we reject H_0 and conclude that the difference between E^2 and r^2 (namely, $0.117 - 0.019 = 0.098$) is *not* just a chance fluctuation resulting from sampling in a population in which the regression is linear.

Our general conclusion is that there is some relationship between X and Y and that this relationship is curvilinear in form. The category means of Y reveal this fact rather clearly:

Size	Mean percent owner-occupied
0–1000	38.8
1000–2000	60.2
2000–3000	57.1
3000–4000	53.8
4000 or more	58.5

The various tests presented here represent just one of several possible approaches to the study of bivariate distributions of interval variables. It is also possible, for example, to approach the problem through a study of the regression of X on Y rather than through a study of their correlation. It turns out, for instance, that ρ will be zero if and only if the slope of the regression line is also zero. Thus, we may test the hypothesis that there is no linear relationship between X and Y either by testing

$$H_0: \beta = 0$$

or by testing

$$H_0: \rho = 0$$

One final comment is in order concerning the nature of this particular test. In making it, we used all of the census tracts from Birmingham rather than just a sample of them—but our test theory seems to depend upon having a sample of observations. Should the test be used when we have all of the existing data rather than just a sample? There is some disagreement among statisticians as to how to handle this question. If you have followed the reasoning in this book, however, the test is basically appropriate even though the observations can only be considered to be a sample from some rather hypothetical population, such as the population of tracts that *might exist* in Birmingham, given the same procedures for creating them. You will remember that we distinguished between two types of error that arise in observations: random error and bias. We noted that random error, fundamentally, is error that tends to disappear as the number of observations increases, whereas sampling bias is error that remains even if we assemble a great many observations. The critical fact concerning our evidence from Birmingham, then, is that we assembled 106 sets of observations. In any set of $n = 106$ observations there is considerable room for random variation (relative to all observations that might have occurred). Therefore, it is reasonable to make the test even though we are dealing with all of the existing data.

12.8   WHERE WE STAND

We have now completed our discussion of various tests of independence. Our objective has been to give you an insight into the nature of statistical inference in general, and hypothesis testing in particular. We have not attempted to provide an exhaustive set of available tests to use. At each level of measurement a great many excellent tests have been proposed in the statistical literature, both for general independence and for the equality of specific parameters in the conditional distributions. The tests we have discussed are but examples of this variety. We have tried to stress the basic structure of the testing procedure, using as our basic hypothesis that two variables are independent of each other. If this hypothesis is true, then some summary description of each relevant conditional distribution will be the same for all distributions. Once we have settled upon a single measure of the difference between the conditional distributions *in our sample* we proceed to identify the sampling distribution of this measure, assuming that the hypothesis of independence is true. We then use the sampling distribution to construct a rejection region—a region containing sample outcomes that are so unlikely under H_0 that we will conclude that H_0 is false if we should actually get one of these outcomes in our sample. Our next step is to take the sample and see if its summary measure falls into the rejection region. This elementary inferential structure is repeated again and again in the numerous tests that are available.

We noted that tests of the general hypothesis of independence branch into two major types, *parametric* tests and *nonparametric* tests. The parametric tests have been most elaborately developed for testing under experimental conditions. They are generally subsumed under the heading *analysis of variance* and make extensive use of the F distribution, which is one of the basic sampling distributions in statistics.

13

ON SOME USES
OF STATISTICAL
ANALYSIS

A survey of elementary statistical procedures is incomplete without some general discussion of how those procedures may properly be used in the analysis of social science data. Accordingly, we shall conclude this book with a presentation of some of the problems that confront the researcher in the course of creative work and how statistics may be brought to bear upon these problems. Throughout this book we have stressed the importance, when analyzing data, of following a basic procedure, which consists of three steps:

1. *Summarize* the relevant information.

2. *Compare* the summary with some standard or with a comparable summary obtained elsewhere.

3. *Explain* the results of the comparison by (a) listing possible explanations and (b) testing to see which is the most reasonable, often by eliminating alternatives as unreasonable.

In statistics the fundamental entity that is studied is a distribution. The distribution, in turn, tells us something about objects and events and the characteristics that they possess. The idea of a distribution really arises out of the comparison of these objects or events. One object is tall whereas another is short; one is square, another round. One person handles administrative work so that most colleagues are satisfied whereas another is always confronted with complaints. One student does well in school, another does badly and drops out. It is such simple comparisons as these that give rise to the concept of a distribution. The distribution describes the variation found in a characteristic within a population.

When we find that a characteristic varies from object to object or event to event we usually next ask why or how this variation occurs. To answer

this question we introduce other information and show how the characteristic is related to it. This other information is brought into the picture because it is relevant to one or another of the possible explanations that we
have created or borrowed from the works of others. It is at this point that
a major branching occurs in scientific analysis with respect to explanations.
One major branch in the list of possible explanations leads back to the
researcher and the particular methods that he used to make his observations. The other major branch leads out into the world of related variables
and how they are related to the variable in question. The kind of explanation that leads back to the researcher is often referred to as an *artifact*
of the research process. We say that the researcher did something that
made the variation he found artificial in some sense. The kind of explanation that leads out into the world of related variables is often called *theory*.
A great deal of statistical analysis is concerned with the attempt to make a
sensible discrimination between these broad classes of explanation. The
logical procedure that is used is to attempt to rule out, through statistical
analysis, those explanations that fall under the classification of artifacts. If
all such explanations can be ruled out, then a theoretical explanation is
clearly in order. The statistician, at this point, does not create a theory but
rather provides a means of discriminating between statements that are
theoretically useful and statements that are largely artifacts. Once it has
been determined that a theoretical explanation is sensible, statistics may
also be used to discriminate between theories—a process that is called
theory testing. Although this type of discrimination is becoming more com
mon, it is still true that the bulk of statistical work is concerned with the
attempt to separate artifactual results from what may be called theoretically
relevant results.

13.1   RELIABILITY AND VALIDITY
THROUGH STATISTICAL ANALYSIS

If we find that two observations differ from each other on some characteristic, one explanation is that they differ because the observing process
is unreliable; that is, that the measuring instrument being used generates
variable results. A rubber ruler is an unreliable measure of distance. The
test of reliability clearly is to use the measuring instrument more than once
to measure the same object. When the same object is repeatedly measured,
it is clear that any variation is the result of changes in the measuring instrument. (In practice, of course, we must be careful at this point, particu
larly in the social sciences. The object measured may change between the
first and second measurement, perhaps even directly as a result of the first

measurement having been made. The researcher who is testing reliability must take care to keep such possible shifts under control or absent.) The statistical tool that is used in studying reliability is the concept of association or relationship between variables. A measurement is made on each of several objects. This series of measurements is called X. Then another measurement is made on each of the same objects, using the same procedure. This series is called Y. Now, the bivariate distribution of X and Y is examined. If the measuring procedure is reliable, this bivariate distribution should display a very high correlation between X and Y, which is to say that there should be little variation between the two series or around the *line of regression*.

The basic argument is this: lack of reliability is one obvious possible explanation of variation among a set of observations. If the method of making those observations has been checked for reliability with the result that repeated observations do correlate highly, this possible artifactual explanation has been ruled out. If reliability has not been checked or has been checked but with poor results, lack of reliability in the instrument remains as a possible explanation of variability.

Let us explore the statistical side of reliability a bit further. Often when we refer to the *same* measuring instrument we do not mean literally the same question or the same interviewer or the same judge, but rather a comparable question or comparable interviewer or comparable judge. For instance, we might have four different people rank order a series of houses with respect to upkeep to see whether or not people can rank them reliably. Suppose that we find that the reliability in any one measurement is lower than we consider acceptable. What can be done? One solution is to *take the average* of the several measurements. Such an average is often called an index or a scale. It may be a mean or some other combination of the various measures (such as the majority opinion). In any case it is a combination of several individual measurements. The presumption is that this average measurement is more reliable than the individual measurements. This assumption is also based upon a statistical argument. It is an application of sampling theory. If the variability of a given measurement procedure is σ, the variability of the average of several measurements using the same procedure is $\sigma/\sqrt{n}$, provided that the variation is random. In other words, the mean of several measurements *is* more reliable provided that the lack of reliability in the individual measurements is randomly distributed. Notice, however, that the reliability only increases as the square root of n (where n is the number of measurements). This rate of increase is rather slow. To reduce the error by one half you must take four times as many measurements.

At this point it might seem that we should always use multiple measurements, if possible. However, there are limitations on the use of indices and scales, and statistical concepts elucidate these limitations also. One limitation involves *bias*. If one or more of the individual items to be combined generates biased measurements then this bias will be built into the combination. A measurement may be biased and still correlate highly to unbiased measurements. The only way to study possible biases is to examine the *regression lines* in the bivariate distributions of the measurements. If two series of measurements literally are the same except for random error, the regression $Y = a + bX$ should be $Y = 0 + 1X$. Any departure from this pattern suggests the possibility of bias. Once again, the only safe procedure is to attempt to eliminate bias through care in conducting the research.

Consider the indexing problem just a bit further. In our discussion about repeated measurement increasing reliability we assumed that each measurement was subject to the same variability, σ. As long as several measurements are equally subject to error and this error is random, it is sensible to combine those measurements into an index or scale because the combination will be more reliable than any of the component measurements. Now suppose that the variability or reliability of the individual components varies. Is it still sensible to combine them? (We can sense, intuitively, for example, that if we have two measures of time—one from a modern wristwatch and the other from an old-fashioned water clock—we are better off using the wristwatch's measurements alone rather than an average of the two, because we assume that the wristwatch is a much more reliable instrument.) Again, an elementary statistical formula provides the answer. Consider two instruments. Let us call the error variance of the first instrument σ_1^2 and of the second, σ_2^2. (Such error variances are analogous to variation around a regression line, which we have called $\sigma_{X.Y}^2$ or the standard error of estimate.) In general, the error variance of the mean of these numbers will be

$$\sigma_{\bar{X}}^2 = \frac{1}{2}\left(\frac{\sigma_1^2}{2} + \frac{\sigma_2^2}{2}\right)$$

$$= \frac{\sigma_1^2 + \sigma_2^2}{4}$$

(Notice that in this formula we have assumed that the *errors* in the two instruments are independent of each other.) An examination of this formula shows that whenever the error variance of the second instrument is more than three times the error variance of the first instrument, it is better to use the first instrument alone rather than a combination of the two. In short, it is certainly *not* always the case than an index is more reliable than its best component. This thought should be kept in mind when considering the use of indexes rather than individual measurements.

Let us now turn to the question of *validity*. Just as elementary statistical analysis enables us to test reliability and also to think more sensibly about it, so this analysis is also useful when studying validity. Observation is often somewhat indirect, even in the case of very simple variables. When we ask a person how old he or she is, we claim to be measuring age, that is, years since birth. We have not actually observed how many years have passed since the person was born, however. Instead, we trust an indirect method of measurement. This indirectness creates the possibility that we are not measuring what we really want to measure; that is, that our measurement is invalid. This general methodological problem can be effectively and sensibly studied through the statistical concept of *bias*. Bias, of course, can arise in any one of several different ways. In this book we have concentrated upon sampling bias, that is, bias associated with the procedure used to gather the observations. In the same spirit, we could also discuss measurement bias (bias resulting from using poor instruments) or reporting bias (bias resulting from how the researcher reports his findings), to mention just two of many alternatives. The important point here, however, is that any procedure is *invalid* to the extent that it produces error that will *not* disappear even though we may take many, many observations. As we know, the statistician calls such errors biases. In one sense, the statistician does not deal with bias because he does his best to sample in such a way that sampling bias is eliminated. Other forms of bias are usually considered to be problems in general scientific method rather than statistical problems as such. When a more direct observational process is available against which we can compare our indirect one, statistical analysis comes into the picture again in the study of measurement bias. The basic way to demonstrate validity is to compare the measurements using the indirect instrument with measurements using an instrument of known validity. Once again, this comparison is properly summarized in the form of a measure of the amount of association or relationship between the two series of measurements.

Notice that both validity and reliability are properties of a single series of measurements. That is, they are properties of univariate distributions. In each case, however, we make a decision with respect to whether or not the measure we are using is reliable (or valid) *by introducing a second variable and examining a bivariate distribution*. By introducing the correct second variable we can answer our question as to reliability or validity. This property is a rather general characteristic of statistical analysis and inference. To explain, or account for, a distribution containing a given number of variables we generally consider a table containing at least one more variable. For example, in Part II we discussed how to decide whether or not the relationship between two variables was direct (possibly causal) or indirect (possibly spurious). We based this decision on the outcome of a distribution of three variables; that is, on the result of adding one extra variable to the analysis. The same principle applies to sampling as discussed in Part III. In sampling theory, each observation is treated as a random variate and these random variates are assembled until we have enough to make a discrimination between a chance explanation of deviation from our hypothesis and the explanation that our hypothesis is wrong.

To some extent, at least, it is possible to work this path in the other direction. If we can test the reliability of a set of observations by taking two measurements using the same instrument and noting the correlation between the two series, then it is clear that one possible explanation of any correlation is that it arises because the two variables measure the same thing. (We also considered this point in Chapter 9.) Given that two variables are related, we can proceed in either of two directions. First, we can add a variable to the analysis to see whether the added variable is that which both original variables measure. Second, we can attempt to reduce the two variables to the single one implicit in both. This latter approach, which involves attempting to analyze data by reducing the number of variables, involves systems of analysis such as *factor analysis, item analysis, scale analysis,* and other kinds of dimensional analyses. The approach is based, essentially, upon the same arguments as are used when we increase the number of variables. In this case we said that if Z accounts for the relationship between X and Y then the partial association between X and Y (with Z constant) will be zero. But suppose that Z is unknown, that is, suppose that all of the information that we have is contained in the correlation between X and Y. We can make an inference about Z by identifying some combination of X and Y such that, if this combination is held constant, there will be no remaining correlation between X and Y. If we can discover such Z's, even though they are measurable only in terms of X and Y, we can accomplish much the same purpose as is accomplished through partial analysis. The study of techniques such as factor analysis lies well beyond the scope of this text, but the central idea in this type of analysis is contained in this attempt to explain a given distribution by considering a distribution with one more variable in it—in this case a hypothetical variable.

13.2 STATISTICAL ANALYSIS AND THE CONTROL OF EXTRANEOUS VARIATION

Let us reconsider another aspect of this general method of analysis, namely, how we account for or explain the existence of a bivariate relationship. As noted before, the basic procedure is to introduce a third variable and see whether or not the relationship disappears when that third variable is held constant. We refer to this procedure as *controlling* the influence of a third variable. As we know, if the relationship drops to zero when the third variable is controlled, we explain the relationship as being due to the variation in the third variable. If the relationship stays the same when the third variable is controlled, we say that the relationship is perhaps causal or direct—at least it is not mediated by the particular third variable that we have studied. (Remember, of course, that a third possibility is that the independent and control variables interact. For simplicity's sake we shall ignore the possibility of interaction in this discussion.)

The principal difficulty with this approach to the explanation of a given relationship is that it controls other variables only one at a time. Applied directly, it proves to be a slow and cumbersome procedure when many potential control variables exist, as is normally the case. For a great many years statisticians and others concerned with scientific inference have sought ways to control variables more than one (or just a few) at a time. Several different approaches to this problem have been developed, which fall into one or another of four main categories. It is important that the beginning student gain at least a brief familiarity with each of these approaches.

Analyzing Joint Distributions of Many Variables at Once

This idea is the most direct extension of the basic system of analysis. If we learn something about the relationship between X and Y by including in our analysis a single extra variable, Z, then why not also include several extra variables simultaneously? Would we not learn that much more? The general answer is "Yes." This approach is sensible under many conditions. It is quite common today to see studies in which three, four, or even more, variables have been held constant at once. On the other hand, there are limits to how far this process can, or should, be carried. The basic problems are technical in nature. It is virtually impossible to analyze a large number of variables at once without making some simplifying assumptions. These assumptions usually involve either interaction (in which case the typical assumption is that interaction does not exist) or the regression between pairs of variables (in which case the typical assumption is that the regression is linear). When both assumptions are made, the analysis of several variables at once is called *multiple correlation analysis* or *multiple-partial correlation analysis*. These procedures are discussed in more advanced texts. If they are used in an article or book you are reading, remember that they really involve no new analytic ideas but just many repetitions of the ideas that we have discussed. It is such repetition that makes caution appropriate at some point. When dealing with a few variables we can check fairly carefully and completely as to whether or not the assumptions we make are plausible. When dealing with many variables, say, 25 or even 100, this process of checking becomes almost impossible. Furthermore, the assumption that linearity and no interaction apply universally becomes less plausible as the total number of variables increases. When these assumptions are not met in the data, errors in interpretation are easily made.

Analyzing a Joint Distribution in a Very Narrowly Defined Population

It will be remembered that the definition of the population specifies categories of one or more variables that are held constant for the purposes of the study. A survey taken among United States' citizens, for example, holds nationality constant *at one value.* A survey taken among Lutherans holds religion constant, again at one of its many possible values or in one of its possible categories. Given this fact, it would appear that we could hold a great many variables constant at once, just by defining the population very narrowly. For example, if we decide to conduct a study of married, male citizens of the United States, who are Protestant, between the ages of 35 and 40, and with only two children ever born, we will have held quite a variety of variables constant.

Two elements (both very misleading) make this approach to the problem quite appealing to the naive person. The first is the direct one of apparently gaining control over many variables at once. The second is that, if one defines the population sufficiently narrowly, it will be quite small in number and may be entirely enumerated rather than sampled. Since it can be enumerated, there is no apparent reason for worrying about sampling fluctuation. Hence, it would appear that the whole problem of statistical inference can be avoided and the results simply reported. These advantages appear to be almost overwhelming.

Unfortunately, however, both supposed advantages are more apparent than real. In practice, the principal outcome of this approach to the problem is the collection of highly specific findings whose generalizability cannot be determined without more general studies. Under some conditions such very specific findings prove useful but only rather rarely, unless they are compared with other specific findings. The dilemma in this kind of research is easily stated. In effect, we are looking at a *single partial table,* which is only one of a great many that we might have looked at had we chosen to define the population differently. Whatever we find in this particular table, we have no way of telling whether it is specific to that table or general in the set of partial tables. We cannot distinguish between interaction and indirect effects, for example. Furthermore, we have no way of telling which variables held constant in the definition of the population have an impact upon our results and which do not.

The sampling problem is a bit more subtle but is essentially similar. (See also the final paragraph in Section 12.7.) In effect we have taken a sample from a single cluster. The fact that only a few objects happen to exist in this cluster does not make those objects any more representative of the objects that *might* exist in the cluster than are a few coins lying on the floor representative of the total set of possible outcomes of tossing coins. The researcher who engages in this kind of research may argue in reply that he has no interest whatever in objects that "might" exist but only in those that *do* exist. So be it. He is then, in effect, just reporting an observation or a specific series of observations. (Note that a single observation can be interpreted as the most narrowly defined population of all.) As soon as this researcher makes any interpretative statement about his observations, however, he must confront their very special nature. The problem of possible coincidence (that is, random fluctuation as the explanation of the observations) will plague him because he will have no basis upon which to judge whether or not it is present other than through appropriate statistical tests. In short, a chance outcome does not change its character just because we choose to be concerned with no other outcomes.

Analyzing Matched Samples

A third approach to the problem of controlling the effects of several variables at once involves assembling what are called *matched samples*. Consider the relationship between X and Y. Remember that this relationship exists when the conditional distribution of Y given X_1 is different than the conditional distribution of Y given X_2. Ordinarily, we observe this relationship in a random sample. In such a sample the observations in one conditional distribution have been selected independently of the observations in the other conditional distribution. It is not necessary that we proceed in this manner, however. Instead, we can choose a random sample under one of the conditions and then purposely select a sample under the other condition that matches the random sample with respect to one or more other variables. For example, if a person who is 36 years old appears in the original random sample, then we select a person who is 36 years old for the second sample. If matching on age is done for each and every individual in the original sample, then age cannot account for any differences we find between the two conditional distributions because age is distributed in exactly the same way in the two conditions. In this way we achieve control over whatever variables we include in the matching process.

The technique of matching successfully solves the problem of achieving control over several variables at once. It avoids the error of fractioning the general population into innumerable subpopulations and at the same time restricts the variability of those variables whose effects the researcher wishes to eliminate. Matching while selecting the samples is essentially similar to standardizing tables when analyzing data that have already been assembled. The principal difficulty encountered in attempting to match samples is technical in nature. It is often very time-consuming to achieve a sensible match. Furthermore, many potential observations must be discarded because they do not match. Finding the right subjects for the matched sample may be very difficult. Nevertheless, the method has been used with considerable success in a variety of research situations.

There are many ways of matching two samples, ranging from finding individuals who match on each and every characteristic being controlled to assembling a matched sample in which the distributions of these characteristics are the same as in the original sample. One simple and effective way to match samples is to use the very same subjects over again. The individuals in the sample are then matched with themselves. Studies that use the same sample more than once are becoming more common throughout social science. In sociology they are referred to as *panel studies*.

From a statistical point of view it is very important to know whether or not matching has occurred because the statistical tests that are appropriate for comparing conditional distributions are different when the samples themselves are matched. *Essentially all of the tests introduced in this book are for independent samples.* (One exception is the sign test discussed in Section 11.7.) Tests for independent samples are far too conservative when extensive matching has occurred. This point can be illustrated by considering the elementary large-sample test of the significance of the difference between two means. It will be recalled that the sampling distribution in this test is the normal distribution and that we, therefore, make use of the standard error of the difference. For independent samples we presented the basic formula

$$\sigma_D{}^2 = \sigma_{\bar{X}_1}{}^2 + \sigma_{\bar{X}_2}{}^2$$

which says that the error variance of the difference between two means is the sum of the respective error variances of these means. When the samples are related to each other through matching, however, this error variance becomes smaller because a third term is introduced:

$$\sigma_D{}^2 = \sigma_{\bar{X}_1}{}^2 + \sigma_{\bar{X}_2}{}^2 - 2r_{12}\sigma_{\bar{X}_1}\sigma_{\bar{X}_2}$$

where r_{12} (indicated by the arrow) stands for the amount of relatedness that has been introduced through matching. Whenever r_{12} is positive (which will essentially always be the case when we match samples) the effect of matching is to reduce the role of chance variation, which, in turn, makes it easier to identify population differences between means.

Control Through Randomization or Random Assignment

There is a final method of achieving control over several variables at once that deserves careful consideration. It is a different way of using probability theory in research. In this book, for instance, we have discussed probability theory only as an aid to making inferences from samples to populations. The key idea here is the *selection* of individuals in a random manner so that each individual has the same chance of appearing in the sample as each other individual. This use is called *random selection*.

The other way of using probability theory is called *randomization* or *random assignment*. This use involves assigning individuals to categories of the independent variable (usually called "treatments") in a random manner and then observing what happens to them; that is, then observing the dependent variable at some later time. Random assignment controls other variables by breaking up any relationships they might have to the independent variable. Thus, if the conditional distributions of the dependent variable differ, the researcher argues that the difference *is due to* the treatments. We shall see just how other variables are controlled by this process by considering an example.

In recent years there have been many studies of what are called "teaching machines." The elementary idea in this method of teaching is to break up what is being taught into very elementary units and to teach these units *one* at a time. The student stays on a unit until he learns it and then passes on to the next unit. (The method is associated with teaching by machine because machines can be programmed to tell when a student has learned each unit.) In ordinary classroom teaching, of course, the student is confronted with several new things at once. Elementary statistics is one of the subjects that have been programmed for the newer style of teaching. We might well be interested in determining whether or not students learn more by using this new method than by the old one. Accordingly, we design a study in which X, the independent variable, is teaching method. X has two categories: (1) the use of a traditional textbook and (2) the use of a programmed textbook involving the study of just one thing at a time. We decide to study a sample of students who are using each method in order to determine which one is better.

There are two quite different ways in which we might proceed from this point. First, we may proceed in the general manner described earlier in this book, in which case we would search for classes whose students have been exposed to each kind of textbook. Having drawn a random sample of these students we would give them a test to see how much statistics each one knows (Y). Then we would classify them according to the type of text each used and see whether or not the two conditional distributions of scores differ. In other words, we would try to find out whether or not the scores of students using the programmed text were higher than the scores of students using the traditional text (on the average). Whatever the outcome of this direct bivariate analysis, we would immediately be confronted with the possibility that the difference we found was not due to the textbook but rather to some selective factor acting on which students used which text. We know, for example, that performance in a statistics course depends quite heavily on how much prior mathematical preparation the student has had (Z). It might well be that those students using the text that involved higher scores had had more mathematical preparation. That is, whatever differences we found might be due to differences in preparation rather than to differences in the textbooks.

We know how to handle this problem in the case of an identifiable variable such as mathematical preparation. We would form a set of partial tables holding preparation constant and see if the relationship continued to exist. This technique was discussed in Chapter 9. We can use this method to study any particular alternative explanation *that we can identify* and on which we have the relevant observations. Of course, there always remains the possibility that the selective factor that really accounts for the observed difference is unknown to us and, therefore, beyond our ability to control through partial analysis.

Now consider a second, and quite different, approach to the same problem. Let us take a group of students who have enrolled in an elementary statistics course in a large university—so that there are many such students. Now let us divide these students *in a random manner* into two classes. We agree to use the ordinary text in one class and the programmed text in the other. We wait until the end of the semester or quarter and then give the test on knowledge of statistics (which measures our dependent variable). Once again we compare the conditional distributions of scores and note whatever difference occurs. Let us say that the scores are higher for the old style of textbook. What has happened to possible alternative explanations?

We must be very careful in answering this question because the answer is not really very obvious. First, consider a variable that is located in the individual student, such as his prior mathematical preparation. By distributing students randomly to the two classes *we also distributed this prior preparation randomly. Therefore, any effect upon knowledge that is due to prior mathematical preparation now appears as random error.* If we test the hypothesis of no association and reject it we assert that the difference we find is *not* due to random variation. Notice that with this design, however, this statement is equivalent to saying that the difference is not due to prior mathematical preparation. Stating the case quite differently but with precisely the same meaning, we can argue in the following way. Given this design we cannot account for any real (that is, nonrandom) difference we find on the grounds that some unknown or known selective factor was operating on which students used which text. The reason is clear—there can be no such selective factor *because we controlled the selection* and made sure that it was random. Therefore, variables that are located in the individual students cannot represent alternative explanations of the outcome.

Second, consider a variable *not* carried by the student. For example, consider the argument that the teacher in the class in which students received higher scores was a superior teacher. This alternative explanation cannot be handled in the same way as the first one. In the design we have presented we would have to handle it in the ordinary way discussed in this book. Had we thought of this possible explanation before starting the study we might have used the same teacher in both classes or we might have matched the teachers. In general, however, there will be many alternative explanations that are *not* eliminated by any particular system of random assignment. With reference to such alternatives we proceed *via* the analysis of partial tables. In short, through random assignment we can achieve control over some alternative sources of variation (including some we may not be able to identify precisely) but we cannot achieve this control over all alternative sources. We gain control over those alternatives specifically located in or carried by the objects that are randomly assigned.

Various other problems can arise in connection with randomization or random assignment techniques. It is not our intention here to review these problems in any systematic manner, but two of them will be mentioned briefly just to give you an idea of the range of problems that must be considered in the design of research studies. First, since we assign the individuals to the categories *before* we observe the values of the dependent variable we ordinarily make the individuals aware that they are being studied. This awareness, in turn, may affect the results. (It is a well-known fact, called the Hawthorne effect, that industrial workers increase their productivity when they know that they are being studied by a research team regardless of how they are treated.) There are various ways in which this problem may be at least partially solved but it illustrates the fact that randomization itself may bring new alternative explanations into the picture even as it eliminates others. Second, since we cannot randomly assign individuals in many social situations (we cannot randomly assign religion to individuals, for example) there is often a certain contrived character to studies using this technique. To what extent the results are affected by the arrangements is often very difficult to determine.

In general, the random assignment of objects before "treating" them may be and often is a very effective way of eliminating the confounding effects of many alternative explanations at once. In the social sciences, however, the researcher must be careful that he is not introducing a new set of alternative explanations through the very act of prior random assignment. If he does introduce this new set he may actually gain relatively little through the use of this design.

13.3 SEQUENTIAL SAMPLING

In the preceding section we discussed the third step in statistical analysis, namely, explaining or accounting for the results of comparisons. We have noted several times that this process involves adding a new variable to the analysis and then basing our explanation on whatever effect this addition has on our basic table. We also stressed earlier that sampling theory is based on the idea that each observation is a random variate and that by adding new random variates (that is, taking more observations) we achieve greater control over *chance* fluctuation as a possible alternative explanation of our findings. Thus, there is a close parallel between the analysis of joint distributions of variables in populations and the analysis of joint distributions of random variates. The perceptive student will have recognized that we have not treated these two problems in *just* the same way, however. In particular, in analyzing variables, we generally begin with a univariate distribution, then shift to a bivariate distribution, then control for a third variable by considering the distribution of three variables, and so on. On the other hand, in studying random variates we ordinarily select a rather large sample all at once and study it as a whole. In effect, then, we take a large number of random variates at once. By working up from a small number of variables to a larger number we may easily miss one or more important ones, but by working first with a very large number of random variates (sample observations) we may easily include many more than are needed to reach a decision about ruling out chance.

Actually, it is possible to reverse both procedures. In studying variables we may start with a large number and work down to a smaller number by eliminating those that are unimportant. Similarly, in studying sampling fluctuation or random error we may start with a small number of random variates and work up to more and more, until we have enough to make a decision. This sampling model is called *sequential sampling*. In it the researcher draws one object and observes it. (He is now studying the sampling distribution of one random variate.) He either decides that this observation is sufficient and reaches a definite decision (either to accept H_0 or to reject H_0) or he decides to take a second observation, which is called the decision to continue sampling. If he continues sampling, he draws another object and observes it. (He is now studying the sampling distribution of two random variates.) Again he proceeds in the above manner, deciding either that he has enough information to make a decision or that he needs more information and should continue sampling. He continues in this way until he finally reaches a definite decision and so stops sampling.

Sequential sampling has been used extensively in practical applications of statistical reasoning because it generally leads to a definite decision with a smaller sample than is required when sampling a fixed number of observations. The fact that sequential sampling may be much less costly than other types is one reason for its adoption. However, sequential sampling is also employed just because it is a sensible way to reach a decision. We have already seen that in the study of variables we ordinarily proceed in this way. It is also interesting to note that in reading the literature or selecting among possible research projects, we tend to proceed in this manner. We read an article on a subject and make a decision. We may decide that we now know enough about the subject and stop—or we may decide that we need more information and so read another article. We might want to know whether or not a given finding has been well substantiated by others or would be worth our own research attention so we read a report of one man's research, then decide to stop or to continue reading, and so on.

We shall not discuss sequential sampling further in this book. Our purpose here is to point out another way in which the principles of statistical inference may be useful. The basic steps in inference are: *summarize, compare, list possible explanations,* and *test to see which one applies.* These steps may be used in a variety of ways: in sampling, in study, and in the analysis of how variables are related to each other in populations. Sequential sampling is one among these many rather exciting ways of using these principles.

13.4 THE SCIENTIFIC USE OF STATISTICAL ANALYSIS: A NOTE ON TESTING THE HYPOTHESIS OF ZERO ASSOCIATION

At the present time, in social science, the standard way in which statistical inference is used is through the test of the hypothesis of zero association; that is, through testing the hypothesis that there is no difference between two (or more) conditional distributions. Because testing this hypothesis has become so common it is important for you to understand clearly just what it tells us and when it is best used. To gain an understanding of these points let us consider how the scientist becomes interested in a bivariate distribution in the first place, for it turns out that the analysis that should be made will depend upon the nature of that interest.

At the bivariate level there are three fundamental options. First, the researcher may be interested in Y and want to account for its variation, however that variation arises. In this option the researcher acquires an interest in X (a particular independent variable) only to the extent that it actually aids him in accounting for the variation in Y. If any one particular X is not noticeably useful in this way, the researcher just passes on to another one that is more useful. Second, the researcher may be interested in testing a theory. To do so, he deduces from the theory some statement about the relationship between X and Y. He then uses a sample of observations to test this statement and, therefore, to test his theory. Third, the researcher may be interested in the relationship between X and Y because he presumes that they are both measures of some third variable in which he is really interested. In the next few paragraphs we shall consider the role of the hypothesis of zero association in each of these three research situations.

The Problem Is to Discover What Variables Account for the Variation in a Particular Dependent Variable, Y

In a very real sense, this problem is the typical one to which statistical analysis is addressed in social science. To solve it with respect to any particular X, it is appropriate to establish and test the hypothesis that X and Y are independent. In testing this hypothesis we agree to pass on to another X in the event that the one we are now testing yields a tentative acceptance of the hypothesis of independence. By the same token, we agree further to analyze this particular X whenever the hypothesis of independence must be rejected. In other words, we stop and study only when we are sure that the difference we note in our sample cannot reasonably be just a chance fluctuation. Were we to stop and study under other conditions we would risk wasting a great deal of time attempting to account for or understand relationships that really do not exist.

Research of this type is often called *exploratory* research, though that term can be quite misleading. It is exploratory in the sense that we are looking for variables that tend to account for variation in Y. On the other hand, we usually have some sensible notions beforehand as to where such variables may be found. Thus, it is proper to call the research exploratory, provided that this expression does *not* mean "prior to serious thought and study." Indeed, it is usually inappropriate to conduct a search or an exploration without very careful prior planning. In scientific work, prior planning and thought means that the researcher has developed a rationale for looking at a certain type of independent variable. In social science such a rationale is sometimes mistakenly referred to as a theory or as the true hypothesis to be tested. It is preferable to think of this rationale as a statement of where it is sensible to explore, that is, to look for important independent variables.

The difficulty with viewing the rationale as a set of the real or true hypotheses to be tested is easily explained. In statistical theory we test precisely the hypothesis that we test. This statement may sound very obvious to the beginning student but it is surprising how often it is ignored or misunderstood. If we test the hypothesis that two variables are independent, then that is the hypothesis that has been tested. *No other hypothesis has been tested.* There is an unfortunate tendency in talking about statistical testing to refer to a hunch or a plausible argument to the effect that X is related to Y as an hypothesis. When such a hunch or argument is in existence it is sometimes called the real hypothesis that we want to test. Using this approach we might say (and many persons do say) that we test the null hypothesis of no association only hoping to reject it so that we can accept our "real" hypothesis. This line of reasoning is very misleading; indeed, it is simply incorrect.

It is important to understand just why this approach is not correct. The reason is that in order to *test* any statement by examining evidence there must be *at least one way* that the evidence could turn out that would lead us *definitely to reject the statement.* (Otherwise, no matter how the evidence comes out we will accept the statement anyway, in which case we obviously have not tested anything.) For example, in testing the hypothesis H_0 (whatever that hypothesis may be), we develop the sampling distribution in order to generate *a rejection region,* that is, a region such that if our sample estimator occurs in it we will definitely reject our hypothesis.

Now let us apply this criterion to the attempt to test some other hypothesis, say H', by actually testing the hypothesis of no association, say H_0. In this situation, H' will be the hypothesis that X and Y are related to each other in some way. We test H_0 by establishing one set of sample outcomes where we will reject it and another where we will accept it tentatively or fail to reject it. Suppose, first, that we reject H_0. Now we can feel quite confident that H' is correct because we are quite sure that the statement that X and Y are independent is false. Suppose, second, that we accept H_0 tentatively. Does this imply that we can definitely reject H'? Not at all. As we pointed out repeatedly in Part III, to fail to reject H_0 does not mean necessarily that H_0 is correct. It means either that H_0 is correct *or* that we do not have sufficient evidence to distinguish between H_0 and whatever hypothesis is actually true. Notice the implication with respect to H'. If we test H_0 *there is no outcome that will lead us definitely to reject H'.* Therefore, by the elementary criterion of a test we have *not tested H'.*

In other words, we should test the hypothesis that two variables are independent of each other in some population only when that hypothesis is the precise one that we want to test. We should be very careful to remember that we have *not* tested any other hypothesis either directly or indirectly when we make this test. The role of the hunch or the plausible argument was only to guide us to a type of variable in which there is some reasonable likelihood that a nonchance explanation is sensible should we reject the null hypothesis. In making this test in exploratory research (which is where it is most useful) we agree beforehand that the only effects worth considering are those that can clearly be distinguished from random fluctuations.

This application of statistical reasoning is very similar to that used in *search* situations. When a person is searching for something he intends to look in many places and to stop only when he is really sure that he has found what he is looking for. When the object of the search is easily identified there is no problem of inference. The searcher just looks in each place, notes whether the object is there or not, and if it is not, passes on to the next place. In many situations, however, we cannot directly observe the object (at least without going to a great deal of trouble and expense) so we attempt to infer whether or not it is present on the basis of indirect evidence. For example, in searching for oil we begin with surface indications and form some idea on the basis of them that oil is probably below the ground before we go to the trouble of setting up a rig and drilling. The sensible way to conduct such a search is to assume that the object sought is *not* in the place we are now looking and to reject this hypothesis only when positive evidence shows that it is there. In scientific exploration we are in essentially this position. Each independent variable is going to be examined to see whether or not it contributes to the explanation of the dependent variable. We establish the hypothesis of zero association in each case because we do not expect any one particular variable to be the one we are looking for. We will change our minds, that is, decide it is the one we seek, only if we can definitely reject this hypothesis.

The Problem is to Test a Particular Theory

This research situation arises when the researcher wants to test a theory. To do so he derives a statement about the relationship between X and Y and tests this statement against empirical (sample) evidence. The statement derived from the theory becomes H_0 and the researcher agrees to reject this statement (and hence his theory) only if the deviation between the sample evidence and the theoretical statement is large enough to rule out chance as a plausible explanation. (To reject a theory, of course, does not mean its total rejection. It may only mean that some modification in the theory is necessary. Thus, it might be more realistic to say that the theory has failed to meet the test and must be modified.)

Notice that this research situation differs very substantially from the exploratory situation described above. In the exploratory situation we keep the same dependent variable throughout and shift from one independent variable to the next to find the best one or the best subset. In the theory-test situation we keep the same theory and shift from one specific derivation from it to another specific derivation in order to find whether or not it meets *all* relevant tests. The second derivation (or test) may not even involve the same two variables at all. Thus, the researcher's interest in a given pair of variables may be only temporary.

Obviously, in testing a theory it is *not, in general,* appropriate to test the hypothesis that the relevant variables are independent of each other unless the derivation from the theory leads us to expect that they actually will be independent. Otherwise, we commit the error of using one hypothesis to test another hypothesis, which, as we have seen, cannot be done correctly.

The problem remains as to how we can test a theory which implies that a relationship exists between X and Y by examining a sample of observations of X and Y. There are two major kinds of solution to this problem. One involves a more or less direct test of the theory itself. The other involves testing a theory against alternative theories. We shall consider the direct test first.

First, we should note that if the theory does no more than imply the existence of a relationship it *cannot* be tested, because no sample evidence could be assembled that would rule out the possibility of a relationship existing. (It is very difficult to imagine a theory that would permit only such a general deduction, anyway.) If the theory implies the direction of the association, a sensible and proper test can be made. In particular, we can test the hypothesis that the relationship is *not in the opposite* direction to that specified by the theory. For example, if the theory implies that P_1 is greater than P_2 we can test the hypothesis that $P_1 - P_2 \geq 0$, which is to say, we test the hypothesis that the difference is not less than zero. This test is a one-tailed test. If we reject this hypothesis, we can positively assert that P_1 is less than P_2 and, hence, that our theory is wrong (at least in the sense that it needs modification). This test is rarely if ever used in social science research, primarily because we actually rarely test theory in this direct sense but instead engage in exploratory research. (It should be noted that there is an exploratory situation in which a one-tailed test is also appropriate but the exploratory test is not set up in the same way as the theory test.) We mention it only to demonstrate that a definite rejection region can be established if a direct test is desired.

The other kind of solution involves a slightly different interpretation of what it means to test a theory. In particular, when we test a theory we usually mean that we wish to compare the explanatory power of that theory with the explanatory power of some other theory that involves the same dependent variables. This approach yields a second hypothesis that can be used to test a theory. Namely, we can agree to accept a theory only when it is clearly superior to other competitive theories. With this approach, we test the null hypothesis that the theory is no better than its competitors and accept the theory only when it is demonstrably superior. (In effect, we are *exploring* among theories to seek out and find the best one.) It is a bit difficult to illustrate this test with a bivariate distribution, but it can be done if the student will accept a certain oversimplification. Suppose that theories A and B imply that a different independent variable will account for some of the variation in Y. Let us say that theory A implies that X_a will be predictive and that theory B implies that X_b will be predictive. Let r_a stand for the relationship between X_a and Y and r_b be the relationship between X_b and Y. We can now test the null hypothesis

$$H_0: \rho_a = \rho_b$$

and agree to accept either theory only when this hypothesis can be rejected. (The procedure for testing a rather complicated hypothesis such as this one has not been presented in this book. We introduce it here only to illustrate this kind of solution to the problem of testing a theory.) In most areas of science, this hypothesis is the ordinary one that is tested when testing a theory. A theory is only considered acceptable when it is demonstrably superior to its competitors. It continues to be considered acceptable (despite the fact that it possesses known limitations) until some researcher creates a new theory whose superiority can clearly be demonstrated.

What is most important for the elementary student to recognize is that the problem of testing a theory through the use of statistical procedures involves a somewhat different approach than does the problem of accounting for the variation in a given dependent variable. The null hypothesis that is ordinarily tested, namely, that two variables are independent, is very useful in the latter kind of research but not in the former kind. It is more sensible to test other types of hypotheses when engaging in the testing of a theory. Properly constructed, these other hypotheses will also be null hypotheses but not the particular null hypothesis that the two variables are independent in some population.

Before closing this discussion of theory testing, it should be noted that there is a mixed situation that arises quite often in actual research. In this situation we know (either from prior evidence or through a compelling theory) that two variables are related but wish to explore whether or not the relationship is causal. As we know, the study of this problem involves more than two variables and, hence, is somewhat outside the scope of this discussion. However, in this situation randomization is often used to change control variables into random variation (see Section 13.2, the discussion of control through randomization). In this case we test the null hypothesis that the relationship is *not* causal (or direct) and assert that it is causal only if we can reject this null hypothesis. In other words, we assert that the relationship is causal only if the treatments produce more variation between the conditional distributions than could be accounted for on a chance basis—knowing that the random variation contains that variation due to control variables whose effects have been randomized.

The Problem Is to Determine Whether X and Y Both Measure the Same Thing

Before closing this section, it is appropriate to consider, briefly, the third situation in which the researcher often finds himself. In this situation he wants to know whether X and Y are both measures of the same thing. The typical way in which this situation arises is when the researcher wishes to use both variables in the construction of an index or scale of some presumably common element in them. Usually, under these conditions, it is not too relevant to test the hypothesis that the two variables are independent of each other. The reason for this conclusion is very different from that presented in the section on theory testing. The reason is just this: variables that have relatively *little* in common may well show up as not independent of each other in a reasonably large sample. Such variables should not, ordinarily, be combined into a single index because the common element that they share is too submerged in other elements that they do not share. In other words, the criterion that two variables belong in the same index is usually a much higher degree of association than that required to reject the null hypothesis. In Section 13.1 we presented one alternative approach to the solution of the problem of deciding when to make an index. There are others. Broadly speaking, the problem in index construction is how far below a perfect correlation of one we allow the relationship to be before we refuse to combine the variables. It is in this sense that the hypothesis of zero association is not very useful in making this decision.

13.5 WHERE WE STAND

In this, the final chapter of the book, we have presented some problems that are often encountered in actual research operations or in conceptualizing those operations. We have shown how statistical procedures may be brought to bear upon these problems. Statistical analysis is often misunderstood because of the great array of numeric information or data that can be processed by it. It is tempting to visualize statistics merely as a vehicle for summarizing such information. Actually, of course, it is much more than that. It is a way of thinking about data and descriptions of data that permits intelligent use to be made of those data. The fundamental ideas of statistical inference are well worth understanding regardless of whether or not they are ever applied in actual research. What is most useful about elementary statistics is the insight it gives as to how to handle uncertainty— uncertainty either in the sampling sense or in the sense of how to interpret a relationship. We have shown, in this chapter, that the elementary process of inference is the same in these two situations. The student who has mastered this process is in a position to solve various problems, many of which do not superficially appear to be of a statistical nature. We are all called upon frequently to make decisions in the face of uncertainty about the consequences of the decision. What you have learned in this book are the elementary ideas that have been worked out during the past few centuries about how man can intelligently cope with uncertainty. We cannot eliminate uncertainty but we can control it. Statistical analysis, at its most general level, shows how this control can be achieved.

BIBLIOGRAPHY
AND REFERENCES

ADLER, I., *Probability and Statistics for Everyman*. New York: The John Day Co., 1963.

ANDERSON, R. L., AND T. A. BANCROFT, *Statistical Theory in Research*. New York: McGraw-Hill Book Co., Inc., 1952.

ANDERSON, T. R., AND J. H. PARKER, *The Participation of Teachers in School and Professional Affairs*. Iowa City, Iowa: Iowa Urban Community Research Center, 1964.

BAGGALEY, A. R., *Intermediate Correlational Methods*. New York: John Wiley and Sons, Inc., 1964.

BERELSON, B. R., P. F. LAZARSFELD, AND W. N. McPHEE, *Voting*. Chicago: The University of Chicago Press, 1954.

BLALOCK, H. M., *Social Statistics*. New York: McGraw-Hill Book Co., Inc., 1960.

———, *Causal Inferences in Non-Experimental Research*. Chapel Hill: University of North Carolina Press, 1964.

———, "Theory Building and the Statistical Concept of Interaction," *American Sociological Review*, vol. 30, pp. 374–380, 1965.

BLAU, P. M., *Dynamics of Bureaucracy*. Chicago: The University of Chicago Press, 1955.

———, W. W. HEYDEBRAND, AND R. T. STAUFFER, "The Structure of Small Bureaucracies," *American Sociological Review*, vol. 31, pp. 179–191, 1966.

CAMILLERI, S. F., "Theory, Probability, and Induction," *American Sociological Review*, vol. 27, pp. 170–177, 1962.

CENTERS, R., "Marital Selection and Occupational Strata," *American Journal of Sociology*, vol. 54, pp. 530–535, 1949.

CLARK, K. B., AND M. P. CLARK, "Racial Identification and Preference in Negro Children." In G. E. Swanson, T. M. Newcomb, and E. L. Hartley, eds., *Readings in Social Psychology*. New York: Holt, Rinehart and Winston, Inc., 1952.

COCHRAN, W. G., *Sampling Techniques*. New York: John Wiley and Sons, Inc., 1953.

COSTNER, H. L., "Criteria for Measures of Association," *American Sociological Review*, vol. 30, pp. 341–353, 1965.

———, AND ROBERT K. LEIK, "Deductions from Axiomatic Theory," *American Sociological Review*, vol. 29, pp. 819–835, 1964.

DEMING, W. E., *Some Theory of Sampling*. New York: John Wiley and Sons, Inc., 1950.

DUNCAN, O. D., R. P. CUZZORT, AND B. DUNCAN, *Statistical Geography: Problems in Analyzing Areal Data*. New York: The Free Press, 1961.

EDWARDS, A. L., *Statistical Methods for the Behavioral Sciences*. New York: Holt, Rinehart and Winston, Inc., 1955.

————, *Expected Values of Discrete Random Variables and Elementary Statistics*. New York: John Wiley and Sons, Inc., 1964.

EZEKIEL, M., AND K. A. FOX, *Methods of Correlation and Regression Analysis, Linear and Curvilinear* (3d ed.). New York: John Wiley and Sons, Inc., 1959.

FARIS, R. E. L., AND H. W. DUNHAM, *Mental Disorders in Urban Areas*. Chicago: The University of Chicago Press, 1939.

FEDERIGHI, E., "The Use of Chi-Square in Small Samples," *American Sociological Review*, vol. 15, pp. 777–779, 1950.

FINNEY, D. J., "The Fisher–Yates Test of Significance in 2x2 Contingency Tables," *Biometrica*, vol. 35, New Statistical Table no. 7, 1948.

FISHER, R. A., *Statistical Methods for Research Workers* (12th ed.). Edinburgh: Oliver and Boyd, 1954.

FRANCIS, R. C., *The Rhetoric of Science: A Methodological Discussion of the Two-by-Two Table*. Minneapolis, Minn.: The University of Minnesota Press, 1961.

FREUND, J. E., *Modern Elementary Statistics*. Englewood Cliffs, N.J.: Prentice-Hall, 1952.

GOODMAN, L. A., AND W. H. KRUSKAL, "Measures of Association for Cross-Classifications," *Journal of the American Statistical Association*, vol. 49, pp. 732–764, 1954. *See also* vol. 54, pp. 123–163, 1959, and vol. 58, pp. 310–364, 1963.

GORDEN, R. L., "Interaction between Attitude and the Definition of the Situation in the Expression of Opinion," *American Sociological Review*, vol. 17, pp. 50–58, 1952.

HAGOOD, M. J., AND D. O. PRICE, *Statistics for Sociologists* (2d ed.). New York: Holt, Rinehart and Winston, Inc., 1952.

HAWLEY, A. H., *The Changing Shape of Metropolitan America*. New York: The Free Press, 1956.

HENRY, A. F., AND J. F. SHORT, *Suicide and Homicide*. New York: The Free Press, 1954.

HODGES, J. L., AND E. L. LEHMANN, *Basic Concepts of Probability and Statistics*. San Francisco: Holden-Day, Inc., 1964.

HOEL, P. G., *Elementary Statistics*. New York: John Wiley and Sons, Inc., 1960.

HYMAN, H. H., *Survey Design and Analysis*. New York: The Free Press, 1955.

JOHNSON, B., "Theology and Party Preference Among Protestant Clergymen," *American Sociological Review*, vol. 31, pp. 200–208, 1966.

KAPLAN, B., "A Study of Rorschach Responses in Four Cultures," *Papers of the Peabody Museum*. Cambridge, Mass., vol. 44, no. 2, 1954.

KATZ, E., AND P. F. LAZARSFELD, *Personal Influence*. New York: The Free Press, 1955.

KENDALL, M. G., *Rank Correlation Methods* (2d ed.). London: Griffin, 1955.

KISH, L., "Some Statistical Problems in Research Design," *American Sociological Review*, vol. 24, pp. 328–338, 1959.

———, *Survey Sampling*. New York: John Wiley and Sons, Inc., 1965.

LABOWITZ, S. I., "Methods for Control with Small Sample Size," *American Sociological Review*, vol. 30, pp. 243–249, 1965.

LATSCHA, R., "Tests of Significance in a 2x2 Contingency Table: Extension of Finney's Table," *Biometrica*, vol. 40, New Statistical Table no. 17, 1953.

LAZARSFELD, P. F., and P. L. KENDALL, "Problems in Survey Analysis," 1950, in R. K. Merton and P. F. Lazarsfeld, eds., *Continuities in Social Research: Studies in the Scope and Method of the American Soldier*. New York: The Free Press, 1950.

MARSH, C. P., AND A. L. COLEMAN, "Group Influences and Agricultural Innovations: Some Tentative Findings and Hypotheses," *American Journal of Sociology*, vol. 61, pp. 588–594, 1956.

McCOLLOUGH, C., AND L. VANATTA, *Statistical Concepts: A Program for Self-Instruction*. New York: McGraw-Hill Book Co., Inc., 1963.

McGINNIS, R., "Randomization and Inference in Sociological Research," *American Sociological Review*, vol. 23, pp. 408–414, 1958.

McNEMAR, Q., *Psychological Statistics* (3d ed.). New York: John Wiley and Sons, Inc., 1962.

MENZEL, H., "Comment on Robinson's 'Ecological Correlations and the Behavior of Individuals,'" *American Sociological Review*, vol. 15, p. 674, 1950.

MOOD, A. M., AND F. A. GRAYBILL, *Introduction to the Theory of Statistics* (2d ed.). New York: McGraw-Hill Book Co., Inc., 1963.

MUELLER, J. H., AND K. F. SCHUESSLER, *Statistical Reasoning in Sociology*. Boston: Houghton Mifflin, 1961.

National Health Survey, U.S. Dept. of Health, Education and Welfare, Public Health Service. Washington, D.C.: U.S. Government Printing Office, 1962.

POLK, K., H. M. BLALOCK, AND W. S. ROBINSON, "Asymmetric Causal Models: A Three-Way Discussion," *American Sociological Review*, vol. 27, pp. 539–547, 1962.

ROBINSON, W. S., "Ecological Correlations and the Behavior of Individuals," *American Sociological Review*, vol. 15, pp. 351–357, 1950.

ROGOFF, N., *Occupational Mobility*. New York: The Free Press, 1953.

ROSSI, P. H., *Why Families Move*. New York: The Free Press, 1955.

SCHROEDER, W. W., AND J. A. BEEGLE, "Suicide: An Instance of High Rural Rates," *Rural Sociology*, vol. 18, pp. 45–52, 1953.

SELVIN, H., "A Critique of Tests of Significance in Survey Research," *American Sociological Review*, vol. 22, pp. 519–527, 1957.

SEWELL, W. H., AND J. M. ARMER, "Neighborhood Context and College Plans," *American Sociological Review*, vol. 31, pp. 159–168, 1966.

SHAW, C. L., AND H. D. McKAY, *Social Factors in Juvenile Delinquency*. Washington, D.C.: U.S. Government Printing Office, 1931.

SHEWHART, W. A., *Statistical Method from the Viewpoint of Quality Control.* Washington, D.C.: Graduate School of the Department of Agriculture, 1949.

SIEGEL, S., *Nonparametric Statistics for the Behavioral Sciences.* New York: McGraw-Hill Book Co., Inc., 1956.

SNEDECOR, G. W., *Statistical Methods* (6th ed.). Ames, Iowa: Iowa State College Press, 1967.

SOGGE, T. M., "Industrial Classes in the United States, 1870–1950," *Journal of the American Statistical Association,* vol. 49, pp. 251–253, 1954.

SOMERS, R. H., "A New Asymmetric Measure of Association for Ordinal Variables," *American Sociological Review,* vol. 27, pp. 799–811, 1962.

STOUFFER, S. A., AND OTHERS, *Measurement and Prediction.* Princeton, N.J.: Princeton University Press, 1950.

THIBAUT, J., "An Experimental Study of the Cohesiveness of Underprivileged Groups," in D. Cartwright, and A. Zander, eds., *Group Dynamics.* New York: Harper and Row, 1953.

U.S. BUREAU OF THE CENSUS, "U.S. Census of Population," *Special Report PE 58.* Washington, D.C.: U.S. Government Printing Office, 1950.

U.S. BUREAU OF THE CENSUS, "U.S. Census of Population," *General Population Characteristics, U.S. Summary;* Final Report PC(1)–1B. Washington, D.C.: U.S. Government Printing Office, 1960.

U.S. BUREAU OF THE CENSUS, "U.S. Census of Population and Housing," *Census Tracts;* Final Report PHC(1)–17. Washington, D.C.: U.S. Government Printing Office, 1960.

U.S. BUREAU OF THE CENSUS, *Current Population Reports,* Series P-60, No. 51, "Income in 1965 of Families and Persons in the United States." Washington, D.C.: U.S. Government Printing Office, 1967.

WALKER, H. M., AND J. LEV, *Statistical Inference.* New York: Holt, Rinehart and Winston, Inc., 1953.

WALSH, J. E., *Handbook of Nonparametric Statistics.* Princeton, N.J.: D. Van Nostrand Co., Inc., 1962.

———, *Handbook of Nonparametric Statistics, II.* Princeton, N.J.: D. Van Nostrand Co., Inc., 1965.

The World Almanac. New York: New York World Telegram, 1963.

YULE, G. U., AND M. G. KENDALL, *An Introduction to the Theory of Statistics* (14th ed.). New York: Hafner, 1950.

ZEISEL, H., *Say It with Figures* (4th ed.). New York: Harper and Row, 1957.

ZETTERBERG, H. L., "Cohesiveness as a Unitary Concept" (unpublished manuscript, 1952).

———, *On Theory and Verification in Sociology* (3d enlarged ed.). Totowa, N.J.: The Bedminster Press, 1965.

ZURCHER, L. A., JR., A. MEADOW, AND S. L. ZURCHER, "Value Orientation, Role Conflict, and Alienation from Work: A Cross-Cultural Study," *American Sociological Review,* vol. 30, pp. 539–548, 1965.

APPENDIX

Table 1. Table of Square Roots

Number	Square Root	Number	Square Root	Number	Square Root
1	1.0000	47	6.8557	93	9.6437
2	1.4142	48	6.9282	94	9.6954
3	1.7321	49	7.0000	95	9.7468
4	2.0000	50	7.0711	96	9.7980
5	2.2361	51	7.1414	97	9.8489
6	2.4495	52	7.2111	98	9.8995
7	2.6458	53	7.2801	99	9.9499
8	2.8284	54	7.3485	100	10.0000
9	3.0000	55	7.4162	101	10.0499
10	3.1623	56	7.4833	102	10.0995
11	3.3166	57	7.5498	103	10.1489
12	3.4641	58	7.6158	104	10.1980
13	3.6056	59	7.6811	105	10.2470
14	3.7417	60	7.7460	106	10.2956
15	3.8730	61	7.8102	107	10.3441
16	4.0000	62	7.8740	108	10.3923
17	4.1231	63	7.9373	109	10.4403
18	4.2426	64	8.0000	110	10.4881
19	4.3589	65	8.0623	111	10.5357
20	4.4721	66	8.1240	112	10.5830
21	4.5826	67	8.1854	113	10.6301
22	4.6904	68	8.2462	114	10.6771
23	4.7958	69	8.3066	115	10.7238
24	4.8990	70	8.3666	116	10.7703
25	5.0000	71	8.4261	117	10.8167
26	5.0990	72	8.4853	118	10.8628
27	5.1962	73	8.5440	119	10.9087
28	5.2915	74	8.6023	120	10.9545
29	5.3852	75	8.6603	121	11.0000
30	5.4772	76	8.7178	122	11.0454
31	5.5678	77	8.7750	123	11.0905
32	5.6569	78	8.8318	124	11.1355
33	5.7446	79	8.8882	125	11.1803
34	5.8310	80	8.9443	126	11.2250
35	5.9161	81	9.0000	127	11.2694
36	6.0000	82	9.0554	128	11.3137
37	6.0828	83	9.1104	129	11.3578
38	6.1644	84	9.1652	130	11.4018
39	6.2450	85	9.2195	131	11.4455
40	6.3246	86	9.2736	132	11.4891
41	6.4031	87	9.3274	133	11.5326
42	6.4807	88	9.3808	134	11.5758
43	6.5574	89	9.4340	135	11.6190
44	6.6332	90	9.4868	136	11.6619
45	6.7082	91	9.5394	137	11.7047
46	6.7823	92	9.5917	138	11.7473

From Siegel, *Nonparametric Statistics for the Behavioral Sciences.* Abridged by permission from Sorenson, *Statistics for Students of Psychology and Education* (New York: McGraw-Hill Book Co., 1936).

Table 1. Table of Square Roots (*Continued*)

Number	Square Root	Number	Square Root	Number	Square Root
139	11.7898	187	13.6748	235	15.3297
140	11.8322	188	13.7113	236	15.3623
141	11.8743	189	13.7477	237	15.3948
142	11.9164	190	13.7840	238	15.4272
143	11.9583	191	13.8203	239	15.4596
144	12.0000	192	13.8564	240	15.4919
145	12.0416	193	13.8924	241	15.5242
146	12.0830	194	13.9284	242	15.5563
147	12.1244	195	13.9642	243	15.5885
148	12.1655	196	14.0000	244	15.6205
149	12.2066	197	14.0357	245	15.6525
150	12.2474	198	14.0712	246	15.6844
151	12.2882	199	14.1067	247	15.7162
152	12.3288	200	14.1421	248	15.7480
153	12.3693	201	14.1774	249	15.7797
154	12.4097	202	14.2127	250	15.8114
155	12.4499	203	14.2478	251	15.8430
156	12.4900	204	14.2829	252	15.8745
157	12.5300	205	14.3178	253	15.9060
158	12.5698	206	14.3527	254	15.9374
159	12.6095	207	14.3875	255	15.9687
160	12.6491	208	14.4222	256	16.0000
161	12.6886	209	14.4568	257	16.0312
162	12.7279	210	14.4914	258	16.0624
163	12.7671	211	14.5258	259	16.0935
164	12.8062	212	14.5602	260	16.1245
165	12.8452	213	14.5945	261	16.1555
166	12.8841	214	14.6287	262	16.1864
167	12.9228	215	14.6629	263	16.2173
168	12.9615	216	14.6969	264	16.2481
169	13.0000	217	14.7309	265	16.2788
170	13.0384	218	14.7648	266	16.3095
171	13.0767	219	14.7986	267	16.3401
172	13.1149	220	14.8324	268	16.3707
173	13.1529	221	14.8661	269	16.4012
174	13.1909	222	14.8997	270	16.4317
175	13.2288	223	14.9332	271	16.4621
176	13.2665	224	14.9666	272	16.4924
177	13.3041	225	15.0000	273	16.5227
178	13.3417	226	15.0333	274	16.5529
179	13.3791	227	15.0665	275	16.5831
180	13.4164	228	15.0997	276	16.6132
181	13.4536	229	15.1327	277	16.6433
182	13.4907	230	15.1658	278	16.6733
183	13.5277	231	15.1987	279	16.7033
184	13.5647	232	15.2315	280	16.7332
185	13.6015	233	15.2643	281	16.7631
186	13.6382	234	15.2971	282	16.7929

Table 1. Table of Square Roots (*Continued*)

Number	Square Root	Number	Square Root	Number	Square Root
283	16.8226	331	18.1934	379	19.4679
284	16.8523	332	18.2209	**380**	19.4936
285	16.8819	333	18.2483	381	19.5192
286	16.9115	334	18.2757	382	19.5448
287	16.9411	335	18.3030	383	19.5704
288	16.9706	336	18.3303	384	19.5959
289	17.0000	337	18.3576	385	19.6214
290	17.0294	338	18.3848	386	19.6469
291	17.0587	339	18.4120	387	19.6723
292	17.0880	**340**	18.4391	388	19.6977
293	17.1172	341	18.4662	389	19.7231
294	17.1464	342	18.4932	**390**	19.7484
295	17.1756	343	18.5203	391	19.7737
296	17.2047	344	18.5472	392	19.7990
297	17.2337	345	18.5742	393	19.8242
298	17.2627	346	18.6011	394	19.8494
299	17.2916	347	18.6279	395	19.8746
300	17.3205	348	18.6548	396	19.8997
301	17.3494	349	18.6815	397	19.9249
302	17.3781	**350**	18.7083	398	19.9499
303	17.4069	351	18.7350	399	19.9750
304	17.4356	352	18.7617	**400**	20.0000
305	17.4642	353	18.7883	401	20.0250
306	17.4929	354	18.8149	402	20.0499
307	17.5214	355	18.8414	403	20.0749
308	17.5499	356	18.8680	404	20.0998
309	17.5784	357	18.8944	405	20.1246
310	17.6068	358	18.9209	406	20.1494
311	17.6352	359	18.9473	407	20.1742
312	17.6635	**360**	18.9737	408	20.1990
313	17.6918	361	19.0000	409	20.2237
314	17.7200	362	19.0263	**410**	20.2485
315	17.7482	363	19.0526	411	20.2731
316	17.7764	364	19.0788	412	20.2978
317	17.8045	365	19.1050	413	20.3224
318	17.8326	366	19.1311	414	20.3470
319	17.8606	367	19.1572	415	20.3715
320	17.8885	368	19.1833	416	20.3961
321	17.9165	369	19.2094	417	20.4206
322	17.9444	**370**	19.2354	418	20.4450
323	17.9722	371	19.2614	419	20.4695
324	18.0000	372	19.2873	**420**	20.4939
325	18.0278	373	19.3132	421	20.5183
326	18.0555	374	19.3391	422	20.5426
327	18.0831	375	19.3649	423	20.5670
328	18.1108	376	19.3907	424	20.5913
329	18.1384	377	19.4165	425	20.6155
330	18.1659	378	19.4422	426	20.6398

Table 1. Table of Square Roots (*Continued*)

Number	Square Root	Number	Square Root	Number	Square Root
427	20.6640	475	21.7945	523	22.8692
428	20.6882	476	21.8174	524	22.8910
429	20.7123	477	21.8403	525	22.9129
430	20.7364	478	21.8632	526	22.9347
431	20.7605	479	21.8861	527	22.9565
432	20.7846	**480**	21.9089	528	22.9783
433	20.8087	481	21.9317	529	23.0000
434	20.8327	482	21.9545	**530**	23.0217
435	20.8567	483	21.9773	531	23.0434
436	20.8806	484	22.0000	532	23.0651
437	20.9045	485	22.0227	533	23.0868
438	20.9284	486	22.0454	534	23.1084
439	20.9523	487	22.0681	535	23.1301
440	20.9762	488	22.0907	536	23.1517
441	21.0000	489	22.1133	537	23.1733
442	21.0238	**490**	22.1359	538	23.1948
443	21.0476	491	22.1585	539	23.2164
444	21.0713	492	22.1811	**540**	23.2379
445	21.0950	493	22.2036	541	23.2594
446	21.1187	494	22.2261	542	23.2809
447	21.1424	495	22.2486	543	23.3024
448	21.1660	496	22.2711	544	23.3238
449	21.1896	497	22.2935	545	23.3452
450	21.2132	498	22.3159	546	23.3666
451	21.2368	499	22.3383	547	23.3880
452	21.2603	**500**	22.3607	548	23.4094
453	21.2838	501	22.3830	549	23.4307
454	21.3073	502	22.4054	**550**	23.4521
455	21.3307	503	22.4277	551	23.4734
456	21.3542	504	22.4499	552	23.4947
457	21.3776	505	22.4722	553	23.5160
458	21.4009	506	22.4944	554	23.5372
459	21.4243	507	22.5167	555	23.5584
460	21.4476	508	22.5389	556	23.5797
461	21.4709	509	22.5610	557	23.6008
462	21.4942	**510**	22.5832	558	23.6220
463	21.5174	511	22.6053	559	23.6432
464	21.5407	512	22.6274	**560**	23.6643
465	21.5639	513	22.6495	561	23.6854
466	21.5870	514	22.6716	562	23.7065
467	21.6102	515	22.6936	563	23.7276
468	21.6333	516	22.7156	564	23.7487
469	21.6564	517	22.7376	565	23.7697
470	21.6795	518	22.7596	566	23.7908
471	21.7025	519	22.7816	567	23.8118
472	21.7256	**520**	22.8035	568	23.8328
473	21.7486	521	22.8254	569	23.8537
474	21.7715	522	22.8473	**570**	23.8747

Table 1. Table of Square Roots (*Continued*)

Number	Square Root	Number	Square Root	Number	Square Root
571	23.8956	619	24.8797	667	25.8263
572	23.9165	**620**	24.8998	668	25.8457
573	23.9374	621	24.9199	669	25.8650
574	23.9583	622	24.9399	**670**	25.8844
575	23.9792	623	24.9600	671	25.9037
576	24.0000	624	24.9800	672	25.9230
577	24.0208	625	25.0000	673	25.9422
578	24.0416	626	25.0200	674	25.9615
579	24.0624	627	25.0400	675	25.9808
580	24.0832	628	25.0599	676	26.0000
581	24.1039	629	25.0799	677	26.0192
582	24.1247	**630**	25.0998	678	26.0384
583	24.1454	631	25.1197	679	26.0576
584	24.1661	632	25.1396	**680**	26.0768
585	24.1868	633	25.1595	681	26.0960
586	24.2074	634	25.1794	682	26.1151
587	24.2281	635	25.1992	683	26.1343
588	24.2487	636	25.2190	684	26.1534
589	24.2693	637	25.2389	685	26.1725
590	24.2899	638	25.2587	686	26.1916
591	24.3105	639	25.2784	687	26.2107
592	24.3311	**640**	25.2982	688	26.2298
593	24.3516	641	25.3180	689	26.2488
594	24.3721	642	25.3377	**690**	26.2679
595	24.3926	643	25.3574	691	26.2869
596	24.4131	644	25.3772	692	26.3059
597	24.4336	645	25.3969	693	26.3249
598	24.4540	646	25.4165	694	26.3439
599	24.4745	647	25.4362	695	26.3629
600	24.4949	648	25.4558	696	26.3818
601	24.5153	649	25.4755	697	26.4008
602	24.5357	**650**	25.4951	698	26.4197
603	24.5561	651	25.5147	699	26.4386
604	24.5764	652	25.5343	**700**	26.4575
605	24.5967	653	25.5539	701	26.4764
606	24.6171	654	25.5734	702	26.4953
607	24.6374	655	25.5930	703	26.5141
608	24.6577	656	25.6125	704	26.5330
609	24.6779	657	25.6320	705	26.5518
610	24.6982	658	25.6515	706	26.5707
611	24.7184	659	25.6710	707	26.5895
612	24.7385	**660**	25.6905	708	26.6083
613	24.7588	661	25.7099	709	26.6271
614	24.7790	662	25.7294	**710**	26.6458
615	24.7992	663	25.7488	711	26.6646
616	24.8193	664	25.7682	712	26.6833
617	24.8395	665	25.7876	713	26.7021
618	24.8596	666	25.8070	**714**	26.7208

Table 1.   Table of Square Roots (*Continued*)

Number	Square Root	Number	Square Root	Number	Square Root
715	26.7395	763	27.6225	811	28.4781
716	26.7582	764	27.6405	812	28.4956
717	26.7769	765	27.6586	813	28.5132
718	26.7955	766	27.6767	814	28.5307
719	26.8142	767	27.6948	815	28.5482
720	26.8328	768	27.7128	816	28.5657
721	26.8514	769	27.7308	817	28.5832
722	26.8701	770	27.7489	818	28.6007
723	26.8887	771	27.7669	819	28.6082
724	26.9072	772	27.7849	820	28.6356
725	26.9258	773	27.8029	821	28.6531
726	26.9444	774	27.8209	822	28.6705
727	26.9629	775	27.8388	823	28.6880
728	26.9815	776	27.8568	824	28.7054
729	27.0000	777	27.8747	825	28.7228
730	27.0185	778	27.8927	826	28.7402
731	27.0370	779	27.9106	827	28.7576
732	27.0555	780	27.9285	828	28.7750
733	27.0740	781	27.9464	829	28.7924
734	27.0924	782	27.9643	830	28.8097
735	27.1109	783	27.9821	831	28.8271
736	27.1293	784	28.0000	832	28.8444
737	27.1477	785	28.0179	833	28.8617
738	27.1662	786	28.0357	834	28.8791
739	27.1846	787	28.0535	835	28.8964
740	27.2029	788	28.0713	836	28.9137
741	27.2213	789	28.0891	837	28.9310
742	27.2397	790	28.1069	838	28.9482
743	27.2580	791	28.1247	839	28.9655
744	27.2764	792	28.1425	840	28.9828
745	27.2947	793	28.1603	841	29.0000
746	27.3130	794	28.1780	842	29.0172
747	27.3313	795	28.1957	843	29.0345
748	27.3496	796	28.2135	844	29.0517
749	27.3679	797	28.2312	845	29.0689
750	27.3861	798	28.2489	846	29.0861
751	27.4044	799	28.2666	847	29.1033
752	27.4226	800	28.2843	848	29.1204
753	27.4408	801	28.3019	849	29.1376
754	27.4591	802	28.3196	850	29.1548
755	27.4773	803	28.3373	851	29.1719
756	27.4955	804	28.3549	852	29.1890
757	27.5136	805	28.3725	853	29.2062
758	27.5318	806	28.3901	854	29.2233
759	27.5500	807	28.4077	855	29.2404
760	27.5681	808	28.4253	856	29.2575
761	27.5862	809	28.4429	857	29.2746
762	27.6043	810	28.4605	858	29.2916

Table 1. Table of Square Roots (*Continued*)

Number	Square Root	Number	Square Root	Number	Square Root
859	29.3087	907	30.1164	955	30.9031
860	29.3258	908	30.1330	956	30.9192
861	29.3428	909	30.1496	957	30.9354
862	29.3598	910	30.1662	958	30.9516
863	29.3769	911	30.1828	959	30.9677
864	29.3939	912	30.1993	960	30.9839
865	29.4109	913	30.2159	961	31.0000
866	29.4279	914	30.2324	962	31.0161
867	29.4449	915	30.2490	963	31.0322
868	29.4618	916	30.2655	964	31.0483
869	29.4788	917	30.2820	965	31.0644
870	29.4958	918	30.2985	966	31.0805
871	29.5127	919	30.3150	967	31.0966
872	29.5296	920	30.3315	968	31.1127
873	29.5466	921	30.3480	969	31.1288
874	29.5635	922	30.3645	970	31.1448
875	29.5804	923	30.3809	971	31.1609
876	29.5973	924	30.3974	972	31.1769
877	29.6142	925	30.4138	973	31.1929
878	29.6311	926	30.4302	974	31.2090
879	29.6479	927	30.4467	975	31.2250
880	29.6648	928	30.4631	976	31.2410
881	29.6816	929	30.4795	977	31.2570
882	29.6985	930	30.4959	978	31.2730
883	29.7153	931	30.5123	979	31.2890
884	29.7321	932	30.5287	980	31.3050
885	29.7489	933	30.5450	981	31.3209
886	29.7658	934	30.5614	982	31.3369
887	29.7825	935	30.5778	983	31.3528
888	29.7993	936	30.5941	984	31.3688
889	29.8161	937	30.6105	985	31.3847
890	29.8329	938	30.6268	986	31.4006
891	29.8496	939	30.6431	987	31.4166
892	29.8664	940	30.6594	988	31.4325
893	29.8831	941	30.6757	989	31.4484
894	29.8998	942	30.6920	990	31.4643
895	29.9166	943	30.7083	991	31.4802
896	29.9333	944	30.7246	992	31.4960
897	29.9500	945	30.7409	993	31.5119
898	29.9666	946	30.7571	994	31.5278
899	29.9833	947	30.7734	995	31.5436
900	30.0000	948	30.7896	996	31.5595
901	30.0167	949	30.8058	997	31.5753
902	30.0333	950	30.8221	998	31.5911
903	30.0500	951	30.8383	999	31.6070
904	30.0666	952	30.8545	1000	31.6228
905	30.0832	953	30.8707		
906	30.0998	954	30.8869		

Table 2. Probabilities That Given Values of z Will Be Exceeded

The probabilities shown are for the upper tail.

z	0	1	2	3	4	5	6	7	8	9
0.0	.5000	.4960	.4920	.4880	.4840	.4801	.4761	.4721	.4681	.4641
0.1	.4602	.4562	.4522	.4483	.4443	.4404	.4364	.4325	.4286	.4247
0.2	.4207	.4168	.4129	.4090	.4052	.4013	.3974	.3936	.3897	.3859
0.3	.3821	.3783	.3745	.3707	.3669	.3632	.3594	.3557	.3520	.3483
0.4	.3446	.3409	.3372	.3336	.3300	.3264	.3228	.3192	.3156	.3121
0.5	.3085	.3050	.3015	.2981	.2946	.2912	.2877	.2843	.2810	.2776
0.6	.2743	.2709	.2676	.2643	.2611	.2578	.2546	.2514	.2483	.2451
0.7	.2420	.2389	.2358	.2327	.2296	.2266	.2236	.2206	.2177	.2148
0.8	.2119	.2090	.2061	.2033	.2005	.1977	.1949	.1922	.1894	.1867
0.9	.1841	.1814	.1788	.1762	.1736	.1711	.1685	.1660	.1635	.1611
1.0	.1587	.1562	.1539	.1515	.1492	.1469	.1446	.1423	.1401	.1379
1.1	.1357	.1335	.1314	.1292	.1271	.1251	.1230	.1210	.1190	.1170
1.2	.1151	.1131	.1112	.1093	.1075	.1056	.1038	.1020	.1003	.0985
1.3	.0968	.0951	.0934	.0918	.0901	.0885	.0869	.0853	.0838	.0823
1.4	.0808	.0793	.0778	.0764	.0749	.0735	.0721	.0708	.0694	.0681
1.5	.0668	.0655	.0643	.0630	.0618	.0606	.0594	.0582	.0571	.0559
1.6	.0548	.0537	.0526	.0516	.0505	.0495	.0485	.0475	.0465	.0455
1.7	.0446	.0436	.0427	.0418	.0409	.0401	.0392	.0384	.0375	.0367
1.8	.0359	.0351	.0344	.0336	.0329	.0322	.0314	.0307	.0301	.0294
1.9	.0287	.0281	.0274	.0268	.0262	.0256	.0250	.0244	.0239	.0233
2.0	.0228	.0222	.0217	.0212	.0207	.0202	.0197	.0192	.0188	.0183
2.1	.0179	.0174	.0170	.0166	.0162	.0158	.0154	.0150	.0146	.0143
2.2	.0139	.0136	.0132	.0129	.0125	.0122	.0119	.0116	.0113	.0110
2.3	.0107	.0104	.0102	.0099	.0096	.0094	.0091	.0089	.0087	.0084
2.4	.0082	.0080	.0078	.0075	.0073	.0071	.0069	.0068	.0066	.0064
2.5	.0062	.0060	.0059	.0057	.0055	.0054	.0052	.0051	.0049	.0048
2.6	.0047	.0045	.0044	.0043	.0041	.0040	.0039	.0038	.0037	.0036
2.7	.0035	.0034	.0033	.0032	.0031	.0030	.0029	.0028	.0027	.0026
2.8	.0026	.0025	.0024	.0023	.0023	.0022	.0021	.0021	.0020	.0019
2.9	.0019	.0018	.0018	.0017	.0016	.0016	.0015	.0015	.0014	.0014
3.0	.0013	.0013	.0013	.0012	.0012	.0011	.0011	.0011	.0010	.0010

SOURCE: Adapted from Wallis and Roberts, *Statistics, A New Approach* (New York: The Free Press, 1956), by permission of the authors and publishers. The digits heading the columns are additional digits for the values of z shown in the first column. Thus, the probability corresponding to z = 1.32 is found in the row in which "1.3" appears at the left and the column in which "2" appears at the top. The probability is 0.0934. For two-tailed probabilities take 2P. For the area to the left of the ordinate at z take 1 − P. For the area between the mean and z take 0.5 − P.

Table 3. Table of Selected Critical Deviations of F

A. $\alpha = 0.05$

df_2 \ df_1	1	2	4	6	12	∞
1	161.4	199.5	224.6	234.0	243.9	254.3
2	18.51	19.00	19.25	19.33	19.41	19.50
3	10.13	9.55	9.12	8.94	8.74	8.53
4	7.71	6.94	6.39	6.16	5.91	5.63
5	6.61	5.79	5.19	4.95	4.68	4.36
10	4.96	4.10	3.48	3.22	2.91	2.54
15	4.54	3.68	3.06	2.79	2.48	2.07
20	4.35	3.49	2.87	2.60	2.28	1.84
30	4.17	3.32	2.69	2.42	2.09	1.62
60	4.00	3.15	2.52	2.25	1.92	1.39
120	3.92	3.07	2.45	2.17	1.83	1.25
∞	3.84	2.99	2.37	2.09	1.75	1.00

B. $\alpha = 0.01$

df_2 \ df_1	1	2	4	6	12	∞
1	4052	4999	5625	5859	6106	6366
2	98.49	99.01	99.25	99.33	99.42	99.50
3	34.12	30.81	28.71	27.91	27.05	26.12
4	21.20	18.00	15.98	15.21	14.37	13.46
5	16.26	13.27	11.39	10.67	9.89	9.02
10	10.04	7.56	5.99	5.39	4.71	3.91
15	8.68	6.36	4.89	4.32	3.67	2.87
20	8.10	5.85	4.43	3.87	3.23	2.42
30	7.56	5.39	4.02	3.47	2.84	2.01
60	7.08	4.98	3.65	3.12	2.50	1.60
120	6.85	4.79	3.48	2.96	2.34	1.38
∞	6.64	4.60	3.32	2.80	2.18	1.00

SOURCE: Table 3 is abridged from Table V of Fisher & Yates, *Statistical Tables for Biological, Agricultural, and Medical Research*, published by Oliver and Boyd Ltd., Edinburgh, and by permission of the authors and publishers.

Table 4. Table of Critical Values of Chi Square

df	Probability under H_0 that $x^2 \geq$ chi square													
	.99	.98	.95	.90	.80	.70	.50	.30	.20	.10	.05	.02	.01	.001
1	.00016	.00063	.0039	.016	.064	.15	.46	1.07	1.64	2.71	3.84	5.41	6.64	10.83
2	.02	.04	.10	.21	.45	.71	1.39	2.41	3.22	4.60	5.99	7.82	9.21	13.82
3	.12	.18	.35	.58	1.00	1.42	2.37	3.66	4.64	6.25	7.82	9.84	11.34	16.27
4	.30	.43	.71	1.06	1.65	2.20	3.36	4.88	5.99	7.78	9.49	11.67	13.28	18.46
5	.55	.75	1.14	1.61	2.34	3.00	4.35	6.06	7.29	9.24	11.07	13.39	15.09	20.52
6	.87	1.13	1.64	2.20	3.07	3.83	5.35	7.23	8.56	10.64	12.59	15.03	16.81	22.46
7	1.24	1.56	2.17	2.83	3.82	4.67	6.35	8.38	9.80	12.02	14.07	16.62	18.48	24.32
8	1.65	2.03	2.73	3.49	4.59	5.53	7.34	9.52	11.03	13.36	15.51	18.17	20.09	26.12
9	2.09	2.53	3.32	4.17	5.38	6.39	8.34	10.66	12.24	14.68	16.92	19.68	21.67	27.88
10	2.56	3.06	3.94	4.86	6.18	7.27	9.34	11.78	13.44	15.99	18.31	21.16	23.21	29.59
11	3.05	3.61	4.58	5.58	6.99	8.15	10.34	12.90	14.63	17.28	19.68	22.62	24.72	31.26
12	3.57	4.18	5.23	6.30	7.81	9.03	11.34	14.01	15.81	18.55	21.03	24.05	26.22	32.91
13	4.11	4.76	5.89	7.04	8.63	9.93	12.34	15.12	16.98	19.81	22.36	25.47	27.69	34.53
14	4.66	5.37	6.57	7.79	9.47	10.82	13.34	16.22	18.15	21.06	23.68	26.87	29.14	36.12
15	5.23	5.98	7.26	8.55	10.31	11.72	14.34	17.32	19.31	22.31	25.00	28.26	30.58	37.70
16	5.81	6.61	7.96	9.31	11.15	12.62	15.34	18.42	20.46	23.54	26.30	29.63	32.00	39.29
17	6.41	7.26	8.67	10.08	12.00	13.53	16.34	19.51	21.62	24.77	27.59	31.00	33.41	40.75
18	7.02	7.91	9.39	10.86	12.86	14.44	17.34	20.60	22.76	25.99	28.87	32.35	34.80	42.31
19	7.63	8.57	10.12	11.65	13.72	15.35	18.34	21.69	23.90	27.20	30.14	33.69	36.19	43.82
20	8.26	9.24	10.85	12.44	14.58	16.27	19.34	22.78	25.04	28.41	31.41	35.02	37.57	45.32
21	8.90	9.92	11.59	13.24	15.44	17.18	20.34	23.86	26.17	29.62	32.67	36.34	38.93	46.80
22	9.54	10.60	12.34	14.04	16.31	18.10	21.24	24.94	27.30	30.81	33.92	37.66	40.29	48.27
23	10.20	11.29	13.09	14.85	17.19	19.02	22.34	26.02	28.43	32.01	35.17	38.97	41.64	49.73
24	10.86	11.99	13.85	15.66	18.06	19.94	23.34	27.10	29.55	33.20	36.42	40.27	42.98	51.18
25	11.52	12.70	14.61	16.47	18.94	20.87	24.34	28.17	30.68	34.38	37.65	41.57	44.31	52.62
26	12.20	13.41	15.38	17.29	19.82	21.79	25.34	29.25	31.80	35.56	38.88	42.86	45.64	54.05
27	12.88	14.12	16.15	18.11	20.70	22.72	26.34	30.32	32.91	36.74	40.11	44.14	46.96	55.48
28	13.56	14.85	16.93	18.94	21.59	23.65	27.34	31.39	34.03	37.92	41.34	45.42	48.28	56.89
29	14.26	15.57	17.71	19.77	22.48	24.58	28.34	32.46	35.14	39.09	42.56	46.69	49.59	58.30
30	14.95	16.31	18.49	20.60	23.36	25.51	29.34	33.53	36.25	40.26	43.77	47.96	50.89	59.70

SOURCE: Table 4 is abridged from Table IV of Fisher & Yates: *Statistical Tables for Biological, Agricultural, and Medical Research*, published by Oliver & Boyd, Ltd., Edinburgh, and by permission of authors and publishers.

Table 5. A Page of Random Digits

59 58 00 64 78	75 56 97 88 00	88 83 55 44 86	23 76 80 61 56	04 11 10 84 08
38 50 80 73 41	23 79 34 87 63	90 82 29 70 22	17 71 90 42 07	95 95 44 99 53
30 69 27 06 68	94 68 81 61 27	56 19 68 00 91	82 06 76 34 00	05 46 26 92 00
65 44 39 56 59	18 28 82 74 37	49 63 22 40 41	08 33 76 56 76	96 29 99 08 36
27 26 75 02 64	13 19 27 22 94	07 47 74 46 06	17 98 54 89 11	97 34 13 03 58
91 30 70 69 91	19 07 22 42 10	36 69 95 37 28	28 82 53 57 93	28 97 66 62 52
68 43 49 46 88	84 47 31 36 22	62 12 69 84 08	12 84 38 25 90	09 81 59 31 46
48 90 81 58 77	54 74 52 45 91	35 70 00 47 54	83 82 45 26 92	54 13 05 51 60
06 91 34 51 97	42 67 27 86 01	11 88 30 95 28	63 01 19 89 01	14 97 44 03 44
10 45 51 60 19	14 21 03 37 12	91 34 23 78 21	88 32 58 08 51	43 66 77 08 83
12 88 39 73 43	65 02 76 11 84	04 28 50 13 92	17 97 41 50 77	90 71 22 67 69
21 77 83 09 76	38 80 73 69 61	31 64 94 20 96	63 28 10 20 23	08 81 64 74 49
19 52 35 95 15	65 12 25 96 59	86 28 36 82 58	69 57 21 37 98	16 43 59 15 29
67 24 55 26 70	35 58 31 65 63	79 24 68 66 86	76 46 33 42 22	26 65 59 08 02
60 58 44 73 77	07 50 03 79 92	45 13 42 65 29	26 76 08 36 37	41 32 64 43 44
53 85 34 13 77	36 06 69 48 50	58 83 87 38 59	49 36 47 33 31	96 24 04 36 42
24 63 73 87 36	74 38 48 93 42	52 62 30 79 92	12 36 91 86 01	03 74 28 38 73
83 08 01 24 51	38 99 22 28 15	07 75 95 17 77	97 37 72 75 85	51 97 23 78 67
16 44 42 43 34	36 15 19 90 73	27 49 37 09 39	85 13 03 25 52	54 84 65 47 59
60 79 01 81 57	57 17 86 57 62	11 16 17 85 76	45 81 95 29 79	65 13 00 48 60
03 99 11 04 61	93 71 61 68 94	66 08 32 46 53	84 60 95 82 32	88 61 81 91 61
38 55 59 55 54	32 88 65 97 80	08 35 56 08 60	29 73 54 77 62	71 29 92 38 53
17 54 67 37 04	92 05 24 62 15	55 12 12 92 81	59 07 60 79 36	27 95 45 89 09
32 64 35 28 61	95 81 90 68 31	00 91 19 89 36	76 35 59 37 79	80 86 30 05 14
69 57 26 87 77	39 51 03 59 05	14 06 04 06 19	29 54 96 96 16	33 56 46 07 80
24 12 26 65 91	27 69 90 64 94	14 84 54 66 72	61 95 87 71 00	90 89 97 57 54
61 19 63 02 31	92 96 26 17 73	41 83 95 53 82	17 26 77 09 43	78 03 87 02 67
30 53 22 17 04	10 27 41 22 02	39 68 52 33 09	10 06 16 88 29	55 98 66 64 85
03 78 89 75 99	75 86 72 07 17	74 41 65 31 66	35 20 83 33 74	87 53 90 88 23
48 22 86 33 79	85 78 34 76 19	53 15 26 74 33	35 66 35 29 72	16 81 86 03 11
60 36 59 46 53	35 07 53 39 49	42 61 42 92 97	01 91 82 83 16	98 95 37 32 31
83 79 94 24 02	56 62 33 44 42	34 99 44 13 74	70 07 11 47 36	09 95 81 80 65
32 96 00 74 05	36 40 98 32 32	99 38 54 16 00	11 13 30 75 86	15 91 70 62 53
19 32 25 38 45	57 62 05 26 06	66 49 76 86 46	78 13 86 65 59	19 64 09 94 13
11 22 09 47 47	07 39 93 74 08	48 50 92 39 29	27 48 24 54 76	85 24 43 51 59
31 75 15 72 60	68 98 00 53 39	15 47 04 83 55	88 65 12 25 96	03 15 21 92 21
88 49 29 93 82	14 45 40 45 04	20 09 49 89 77	74 84 39 34 13	22 10 97 85 08
30 93 44 77 44	07 48 18 38 28	73 78 80 65 33	28 59 72 04 05	94 20 52 03 80
22 88 84 88 93	27 49 99 87 48	60 53 04 51 28	74 02 28 46 17	82 03 71 02 68
78 21 21 69 93	35 90 29 13 86	44 37 21 54 86	65 74 11 40 14	87 48 13 72 20

SOURCE: Blalock, *Social Statistics* (New York: McGraw-Hill Book Co., 1960), p. 439. Originally published in The RAND Corporation, *A Million Random Digits* (New York: The Free Press, 1955), pp. 1–3. Reproduced with permission of the author and publisher.

INDEX